THE THEATRE OMNIBUS

Books by P. G. Wodehouse

Fiction
The Adventures of Sally
Aunts Aren't Gentlemen
Bachelors Anonymous
Barmy in Wonderland
Big Money
Bill the Conqueror
Blandings Castle and Elsewhere
Carry On, Jeeves
The Clicking of Cuthbert
Cocktail Time
The Code of the Woosters
The Coming of Bill
Company for Henry
A Damsel in Distress
Do Butlers Burgle Banks
Doctor Sally
Eggs, Beans and Crumpets
A Few Quick Ones
French Leave
Frozen Assets
Full Moon
Galahad at Blandings
A Gentleman of Leisure
The Girl in Blue
The Girl on the Boat
The Gold Bat
The Head of Kay's
The Heart of a Goof
Heavy Weather
Ice in the Bedroom
If I Were You
Indiscretions of Archie
The Inimitable Jeeves
Jeeves and the Feudal Spirit
Jeeves in the Offing
Jill the Reckless
Joy in the Morning
Laughing Gas
Leave it to Psmith
The Little Nugget
Lord Emsworth and Others
Louder and Funnier
Love Among the Chickens
The Luck of the Bodkins
The Man Upstairs
The Man with Two Left Feet
The Mating Season
Meet Mr Mulliner
Mike and Psmith
Mike at Wrykyn
Money for Nothing
Money in the Bank
Mr Mulliner Speaking
Much Obliged, Jeeves
Mulliner Nights
Not George Washington
Nothing Serious
The Old Reliable
Pearls, Girls and Monty Bodkin
A Pelican at Blandings
Piccadilly Jim
Pigs Have Wings
Plum Pie
The Pothunters
A Prefect's Uncle
The Prince and Betty
Psmith, Journalist
Psmith in the City
Quick Service
Right Ho, Jeeves
Ring for Jeeves
Sam the Sudden
Service with a Smile
The Small Bachelor
Something Fishy
Something Fresh
Spring Fever
Stiff Upper Lip, Jeeves
Summer Lightning
Summer Moonshine
Sunset at Blandings
The Swoop
Tales of St Austin's
Thank You, Jeeves
Ukridge
Uncle Dynamite
Uncle Fred in the Springtime
Uneasy Money
Very Good, Jeeves
The White Feather
William Tell Told Again
Young Men in Spats

Omnibuses
The World of Blandings
The World of Jeeves
The World of Mr Mulliner
The World of Psmith
The World of Ukridge
The World of Uncle Fred
Wodehouse Nuggets
(edited by Richard Usborne)
The World of Wodehouse Clergy
Weekend Wodehouse

Paperback Omnibuses
The Golf Omnibus
The Aunts Omnibus
The Drones Omnibus
The Clergy Omnibus
The Hollywood Omnibus
The Mr Mulliner Omnibus
The Jeeves Omnibus 1
The Jeeves Omnibus 2
The Jeeves Omnibus 3
The Jeeves Omnibus 4
The Jeeves Omnibus 5

Poems
The Parrot and Other Poems

Autobiographical
Wodehouse on Wodehouse
(comprising Bring on the Girls, Over Seventy, Performing Flea)

Letters
Yours, Plum

THE THEATRE OMNIBUS

P. G. Wodehouse

HUTCHINSON
London

1 3 5 7 9 8 6 4 2

This edition first published in 1994 by
Hutchinson

Random House (UK) Ltd
20 Vauxhall Bridge Road, London SW1V 2SA

Random House, Australia (Pty) Ltd
20 Alfred Street, Milsons Point, Sydney, NSW 2061, Australia

Random House New Zealand Ltd
18 Poland Road, Glenfield, Auckland 10, New Zealand

Random House South Africa (Pty) Ltd
PO Box 337, Bergvlei, 2012, South Africa

A CIP catalogue record for this book is available from the British Library

ISBN: 0 09 1785197

Set in Ehrhardt by Pure Tech Corporation, Pondicherry, India
Printed and bound in Great Britain by Clays Ltd, St Ives plc

Contents

BY WAY OF INTRODUCTION . . .

The principle I always go on is to think of the characters in terms of actors in a play. I say to myself when I invent a good character for an early scene, 'If this were a musical comedy we should have to get somebody like Leslie Henson to play this part, and if he found that all he had was a scene in act one, he would walk out. How, therefore, can I twist the story so as to give him more to do, and keep him alive till the fall of the curtain?'

When you're doing a long story you have got to be most infernally careful of the values of your characters. I believe I told you once before that I classed all my characters as if they were living salaried actors, and I'm convinced that this is a rough but very good way of looking at them. The one thing actors, important actors, I mean, won't stand is being brought on to play a scene which is of no value to them in order that they may feed some less important character, and I believe this isn't vanity but is based on an instinctive knowledge of stagecraft. They kick because they know the balance isn't right.

P. G. Wodehouse in letters to his friend, Bill Townend.

BRING ON THE GIRLS

The Improbable Story of Our Life in Musical Comedy
(Jointly written with Guy Bolton)

The minor revisions which Guy Bolton made to *Bring On the Girls* shortly before he died in September 1979, four-and-a-half years after his old friend and contemporary 'Plum', have been included in this version.

1

1

THE scene is a smoke-filled room in a hotel in Boston or Philadelphia or New Haven or wherever else musical comedies are tried out in preparation for their New York opening. Tonight's performance of this new venture has revealed a dull spot in the second act, what is technically known as a bug, and a conference has been called to debate methods of ironing it out.

Various proposals are made. The comedian thinks that, if he were given another song there, all would be well. The baritone feels that it is more the place for a baritone solo. The author of the book. . . .

In an armchair in the corner there is sitting a man in shirt-sleeves, chewing an enormous (unlighted) cigar. He is fifty-five years old and for twenty-five of those years he has been an impresario of musical comedy. Lending to the discussion the authority of long experience and uttering the slogan which he probably learned at his mother's knee, he says, 'Bring on the girls!'

It is the panacea that never fails. It dates back, according to the great Bert Williams, to the days of ancient Egypt.

'When one of those Pharaohs died,' he used to explain to his partner Walker, 'they'd lay that ole Pharaoh out, and then, just to make sure, they'd bring in wine – finest wine in the country – and they'd put it beside him. Then they'd bring in rich food that smelled just beautiful an' put that on the other side of him. Then they'd bring on the girls, an' those girls would do the veil-dance. An' if that ole Pharaoh didn't sit right up and take notice then . . . brother, he was dead.'

The impresario has his way. The girls are brought on.

And how wonderful those girls always were. They did not spare themselves. You might get the impression that they were afflicted by some form of chorea, but the dullest eye could see that they were giving of their best. Actors might walk through their parts, singers save their voices, but the personnel of the ensemble never failed to go all out, full of pep, energy and the will to win. A hundred shows have been pushed by them over the thin line that divides the floperoo from the socko.

It is for this reason that Bolton (Guy) and Wodehouse (P. G.), looking back over their years of toil in the musical comedy salt-mines, raise their glasses and without hesitation or heel-taps drink this toast: To the Girls!

And they feel that the least they can do in gratitude for all their hard work is to honour them in the title of this book.

2

There was I and there were you three thousand miles apart:
Who'd have thought that we would ever have met at the start?
But it's plain to see 'twas meant to be in spite of every bar,
For I met you and you met me, you see, and here we are.

The above is the refrain (or 'burthen', as Jerry Kern always insisted on calling it) of a duet Carroll McComas and Harry Brown used to sing in the fourth of the series of Princess Theatre intimate musical comedies, *Oh, Lady, Lady*, the idea being that, having discovered that they were kindred souls, they were feeling how tragic it would have been if they had never met. The thought might apply with equal force to the authors of the play.

At the outset it would have seemed that conditions for an early meeting were just right. Wodehouse was born in Guildford, Surrey, England, and almost simultaneously Bolton was added to the strength of Broxbourne, Herts. As the crow flies, Guildford and Broxbourne are not much more than twenty miles apart, and it is quite possible that the two infants, destined to collaborate for forty years, may often have seen the same crow engaged in checking the distance. One would have said that it would have been a mere matter of weeks before they got together and started working on a show.

But it was not to be. Just as Wodehouse, who even then wanted to write musical comedy lyrics, heard that there was a baby over at Broxbourne who wanted to write musical comedy books and resolved to save his pocket money and look him up directly he had amassed enough for the fare, he was stunned by the news that the Bolton parents, who were American, were taking their issue back to New York. And at about the same time he had to return with his own parents to Hong Kong, where the elder, bread-winning Wodehouse won bread as a judge. Collaboration for the moment became, if not void, certainly null.

It remained null for a considerable number of years, during which Bolton ripened into an architect in New York and Wodehouse into a writer in London, and the odds against the two ever meeting were raised astronomically by the fact that the latter's principal means of support was the composition of a daily column, supposedly humorous, on the London *Globe*. It was a steady job – £3 a week, just like finding it – and in those days no Englishman ever dreamed of giving up a steady job. It seemed as though Fate had definitely arranged that the words 'Book and Lyrics by Guy Bolton and P. G. Wodehouse' should never appear on a theatre programme.

But what Fate had not allowed for was the latter's secret passion for America. From his earliest years America had been to this pie-faced young dreamer the land of romance, and came a day when he decided that he had got to see it, if only briefly. The *Globe* job carried with it a five weeks' holiday per annum, and in 1909 it suddenly struck Wodehouse, an able mathematician, that, allowing eight days for the voyage out and another eight days for the voyage back, he could manage nearly three weeks in sunny Manhattan. Packing a toothbrush and a couple of short stories, he set out.

A week after his arrival he had sold one of the stories to the *Cosmopolitan* and the other to *Collier's Weekly*, both on the same day and each for $300, and feeling that a good thing like this must certainly be pushed along – the London price at that time for a Wodehouse story was £7 10*s*. – he sent in his resignation to the *Globe* and settled down in Greenwich Village with a second-hand Monarch typewriter and plenty of paper.

It was not too difficult, he found, to make a living of a sort as a freelance writer in New York. He had hit the city at a time when magazines multiplied like rabbits there, and even if you failed to join the swells in George Horace Lorimer's *Saturday Evening Post*, there were plenty of other markets where you could pick up your $150 or $200 for a short story, and you could live an incredible time on $200 in those days. And if everything else failed, there was the Munsey group of more or less half-witted pulp-paper magazines, with Bob Davis, their editor, always ready to bury his head in his hands for a couple of minutes and come up with a plot, which he presented to you gratis, and bought, when worked into a story, for 50 of the best or sometimes even 75.

The gap between the future collaborators having thus shrunk to a few city blocks, their meeting could not be postponed much longer. For there was now a new link between them. Like the men in the Bab ballad who both knew Robinson, they both knew Jerome Kern. A few years before, Wodehouse had written some numbers with Jerry – then aged about eighteen – for a London production, while Bolton had just done a piece called *Ninety in the Shade* with Kern music, the first time Jerry had been entrusted with an extra score.

Wodehouse, moreover, had recently become dramatic critic for Frank Crowninshield's *Vanity Fair*, and in this capacity he attended the opening performance of *Very Good Eddie* – book by Bolton, music by Kern – the second of the 'intimate' musical comedies at the little Princess Theatre on 39th Street.

3

It was Elizabeth Marbury, dear, kindly, voluminous Bessie Marbury, who first thought of musical comedy on a miniature scale – musical comedy with not more than two sets, eight to twelve girls and an orchestra of eleven, a celeste to take the place of woodwind. It was one of those inspired ideas that used to come to her every hour, on the hour.

For Bessie was a brilliant woman, a dramatic agent who held the entire European market in her plump and capable hands. Her clients relied on her not only to sell their work but to help them write it. If their second act seemed to have blown a fuse, she would tell them what to do about it. She would even suggest plots and characters. She was a sort of female Bob Davis.

She and Ray Comstock were running the little Princess Theatre on 39th Street at that time and not making much of a go at it. It was difficult to get the right sort of show for a house of that size. The last thing tried there had been an evening of one-act plays, and it had been a painful failure.

It was then that Bessie got her inspiration. Midget musical comedy!

The venture would have to be economically planned. The Princess, seating only 299, could not afford as author and composer any of the men with big names – the Henry Blossoms, the Otto Harbachs, the Victor Herberts and the Ivan Carylls, who, being established, had large views on the sort of money for which they were prepared to work. What was needed was young fellows who were on their way up the ladder but still climbing the lower rungs.

Jerry Kern was the obvious choice for composer. A much less knowledgeable woman than Bessie Marbury could have spotted him as a coming champ. In those days managers were importing large, heavy Viennese operettas with large, heavy scores, and it was always the gay, tuneful interpolated Kern numbers that put them over. She signed up Jerry at once. The question then arose: Who was to do the book? Jerry suggested Guy.

Bessie not only looked like a very charming and benign elephant, she had an elephant's memory. She remembered *Ninety in the Shade*, she remembered a divorce comedy by Bolton, *The Rule of Three*, and she remembered having heard his name mentioned by Charles Hanson Towne, the editor of the *Smart Set*, who had published some Bolton short stories.

'Yes, I know Bolton's work. He shows promise.'

'And now,' said Jerry, 'you're going to promise him shows.'

Nobody Home was the first of the series. It was enough of a success to encourage the management to feel that they were on the right lines, and Bolton and Kern were commissioned to write another. With this one, *Very Good Eddie*, intimate musical comedy – later to be known as the 'Princess Shows' – became definitely a New York institution.

4

Very Good Eddie took its title from a catchphrase which Fred Stone had made popular in his ventriloquist act in the latest Montgomery and Stone extravaganza at Charles Dillingham's Globe. It was a farce-comedy which would have been strong enough to stand on its own feet without the help of music, the first of its kind to rely on situation and character laughs instead of the clowning and cross-talk with which the large-scale musicals filled in between the romantic scenes. It was, in fact, intimate. It had no star part, the interest being distributed among a number of characters played by Ernest Truex, Jack Hazzard, John Willard (who later wrote *The Cat and the Canary*), Ada Lewis, Alice Dovey, who had made a success in that classic musical comedy, *The Pink Lady*, and a promising young beginner named Oscar Shaw.

On the opening night Jerry Kern came over to where Bolton stood leaning on the back-rail, his face pale, his lips moving as if in prayer.

'How do you think it's going?' he asked.

Guy came out of his trance.

'I'm too numb to tell. There's a man in large spectacles over there in the tenth row who seems to be enjoying it.'

Jerry glanced in the direction indicated.

'Wodehouse,' he said.

'I suppose it is,' said Guy, 'but that's only to be expected on an opening night. The question is, what's it going to be like tomorrow?'

'What on earth are you talking about?'

'You said it's a good house.'

'I didn't. I said Woodhouse.'

(For the benefit of the uninitiated, that is the way it is pronounced.)

'Oh, you mean his *name* is Woodhouse?'

'That's right. Plum Woodhouse.'

A gentleman in the last row, down whose neck Jerry was breathing, turned.

'I've no doubt what you two are saying is a lot funnier than what's going on on the stage,' he said, 'but I can't follow the two plots at once.'

'Sorry,' said Guy, cringing. 'Actually what's going on on the stage is very funny indeed.'

'Sez you,' said the man in the last row morosely.

The team-mates withdrew to the balcony stairs and sat down on them. A decent five or six feet now separated them from the audience.

> Any old night is a wonderful night
> If you're there with a wonderful girl. . . .

sang Oscar Shaw.

'Lousy lyric,' said Kern.

A standee turned to them.

'Look,' he said, 'if you don't like this show, why don't you get out?'

The pair withdrew to the lobby. If you applied an eye to the crack of the folding doors, the stage could still be seen. The doorman, who had been using this vantage-point to watch the proceedings, obligingly made way for them. Guy squinted through the crack.

'What has Ada Lewis done to her face?' he muttered anxiously. 'She looks most peculiar.'

'That isn't her face,' said the doorman. 'She's walking on her hands. Saving her face for the last act.'

Guy eyed the honest fellow with displeasure.

'We should have come to you for some gags,' he said coldly.

'Why didn't you?' said the doorman. 'I'd have been glad to help out if I'd known the show was supposed to be funny.'

'How's it going?' asked Jerry.

'It seems to be going all right.'

'Ever hear the one about the English author feller that had a show on over here with Charlie Dillingham?' broke in the doorman in his charming, friendly way. Neither Guy nor Jerry had ever seen a man so patently resolved to be the life of the party. 'He was in London, see, on account he couldn't get over for the opening, and he cabled Charlie "How's it going?" And C. B. [Dillingham] cabled back "It's gone." See what I mean? This feller asked "How's it going?" and Charlie cabled back "It's gone!" Get it?'

Guy drew a deep breath.

'I get it,' he said. 'Very droll.'

'Most amusing,' said Jerry. 'I'm convulsed. What's happening in there? Have the customers rushed the stage yet?'

'Not yet. And that chap with the spectacles is laughing again.'

'Probably overheard that story of mine,' said the doorman.

The lights on the stage dimmed for the *Babes in the Wood* number.

> Give me your hand:
> You'll understand
> We're off to slumberland. . . .

sang Ernie Truex in a cracked voice.

'God!' said Jerry. 'You never know what words are going to sound like till you hear them with a first-night audience. Why don't you get Plum to do your lyrics?'

'Does he write lyrics?'

'He certainly does. I did half a dozen numbers with him for a thing in London called *The Beauty of Bath*. One of them – "Mister Chamberlain" – used to get ten encores every night. As a lyric writer he's the cat's pyjamas.'

'Rather a dated expression,' said Guy coldly.

The audience began to stream into the tiny lobby. The man with the spectacles came up to them.

'Oh, hullo, Jerry,' he said.

'Hello,' said Kern. 'This is Bolton. You two fellows ought to know each other.'

Guy and Plum shook hands.

'I hope you liked the show,' said Guy.

'Best thing I ever saw in my life.'

'I wonder,' said Guy, 'if you would mind stepping over behind that man with the crumpled shirt-front and the rumpled hair? He is the *Tribune* critic.'

They moved to where Heywood Broun was chatting with Alexander Woollcott.

'What did you think of our little entertainment, Mr Wodehouse?' asked Guy in a clear, carrying voice.

'Not bad,' said Plum.

After the final curtain Jerry took them to his apartment on West 68th Street. There they were joined by a group of English friends who were appearing at Dillingham's Globe Theatre in *Tonight's the Night*. Fay Compton was there, and Lawrie Grossmith and his brother George, also Lawrie's brother-in-law, Vernon Castle, with his wife and dancing partner, Irene. They were all eager for news of *Very Good Eddie*.

The two interested parties had decided they would wait up for the notices. They were glad to have company for part of the night. Jerry took his place at the piano, Fay stood beside it and sang. Two or three of the girls were working away in the kitchen making sandwiches.

Plum and Guy gravitated to a corner. 'Do you think *Eddie* got over?' said Guy.

'I think it's a smash. I was listening to the audience as they came out. The woman ahead of me said it was the cat's pyjamas.'

'Really?' said Guy, beaming. 'The cat's pyjamas – one of my favourite expressions. Very clever and original. By the way Jerry Kern used it about you.'

'Me?'

'Yes, as a writer. He says you write good lyrics. Have you done any over here?'

'Not yet. But only the other day I missed landing a big job by a hairbreadth. Somebody gave me an introduction to Lee Shubert, and I raced round to his office. "Good morning, Mr Shubert," I said. "I write lyrics. Can I do some for you?" "No," said Lee Shubert. Just imagine if he had said "Yes". It was as near as that.'

'Would you like to join Jerry and me?'

'I'd love it.'

'Then let's get together.'

The Bolton diary of this date has the following entry:

Eddie opened. Excellent reception. All say hit. To Kerns for supper. Talked with P. G. Wodehouse, apparently known as Plum. Never heard of him, but Jerry says he writes lyrics, so, being slightly tight, suggested we might team up. W. so overcome couldn't answer for a minute, then grabbed my hand and stammered out his thanks.

Turning to the Wodehouse diary, we find:

Went to opening of *Very Good Eddie*. Enjoyed it in spite of lamentable lyrics. Bolton, evidently conscious of this weakness, offered partnership. Tried to hold back and weigh the suggestion, but his eagerness so pathetic that consented. Mem: Am I too impulsive? Fight against this tendency.

2

1

EDDIE was an immediate success and not one of the Princess's 299 seats was ever empty, but neither Bolton nor Kern, drawing their infinitesimal royalties, was able as yet to feel that he had made any very noticeable impact on Broadway.

What they needed, to put them up among the Blossoms, the Harbachs, the Herberts and the Carylls, was an equally successful venture at one of those vast houses that could play, when full, to as much as $16,000 on the week – say, for instance, Erlanger's New Amsterdam.

Abraham Lincoln Erlanger was at that time the Czar of the New York Theatre, though beginning to be a little worried by the competition of the up-and-coming Shuberts. All the big managers – Ziegfeld, Dillingham, Savage, Belasco, Cohan and Harris and the rest of them – were Erlanger men, booking their plays in his theatres.

One morning Plum had a telephone call from Guy.

'I've got a job for us,' said Guy. 'Come on down and I'll tell you about it.'

Plum found his partner looking awed, as if he had recently passed through some great spiritual experience.

'It's a Viennese operetta,' he said.

'Oh, my God!'

'It was a big hit in Vienna.'

'What wouldn't be?'

'And Erlanger wants a new story and new lyrics fitted into the score.'

Plum tottered.

'Did you say *Erlanger*?'

'Yes, it's a Klaw and Erlanger production.'

'And I was just going to advise you not to touch it! Why, they might put it on at the New Amsterdam.'

'That's where they're going to put it on.'

'But how did you manage to land a terrific job like that?'

'Apparently all the men up top had a go at it and couldn't satisfy the old boy, so he scraped the bottom of the barrel and found me.

I did a scenario which he liked, thank goodness, and it's all settled. You are to do the lyrics and Jerry some interpolated numbers. You'll have a lot of work, I'm afraid. It's one of those shows where the finale starts half-way through each act.'

'That's all right. I love work. Tell me about Erlanger. He really exists, does he? You've actually seen him? What's he like? To look at, I mean.'

Guy considered.

'He's rather like a toad,' he said. 'Not that I have anything against toads.'

'Nor me. Many of my best friends are toads. I look forward to meeting him.'

'You'll be doing that in half an hour from now. He wants us at his office at eleven. Be careful not to say anything disrespectful about Napoleon.'

'I'll watch myself. But why?'

'Because he has a Napoleon complex. He not only admires Napoleon, he thinks he *is* Napoleon.'

'Reincarnated?'

'I suppose so.'

'What would happen if I kidded him about Moscow?'

'He would probably shoot you. He keeps a loaded revolver in his desk. They say he did shoot a man once.'

'Mistook him for the Duke of Wellington, no doubt. He sounds a bit of a Tartar.'

'That's our expression. The Tartars, meeting a particularly tough specimen, would say that he was a bit of an Erlanger. Still, he's said to be kind to authors and dumb animals, so let's go.'

2

The Erlanger office was large and picturesque. In one corner was a punching-bag, beside it a barber's chair. The barber who came each morning to shave the imperial face had been specially chosen for that high office because he could speak French. When called on to do so, he would take down one of the volumes of Napoleon's letters that filled a wall-bookcase over Erlanger's head and translate. One can picture the stream of small-fry managers and rural 'Opry House' owners who drifted in and out of the office being considerably impressed by this display of culture. A man must be quite something when even his barber can sight-read from French into English.

It being now eleven o'clock, the barber had done his work and departed (no doubt with a respectful '*Vive l'Empereur!*'), and A. L. Erlanger was seated behind the huge desk in one of the drawers of which, probably the open one so as to be handy, lay the celebrated loaded revolver. Lounging in a chair beside him was a small boy in knickerbockers, who gave the two collaborators a cold look as they entered, as if he did not think highly of book writers and lyrists.

'Who's the kid?' asked Plum out of the side of his mouth.

'I don't know,' said Guy.

'*L'Aiglon*, perhaps?'

'I shouldn't wonder.'

It turned out later that the stripling was some sort of a relation, a nephew or the son of a cousin or something, and he was a very valued and esteemed cog in the Erlanger organization. Aged twelve years, he had been selected by Erlanger as possessing exactly the intelligence of the average New York theatre audience. If he liked something, Erlanger reasoned, the public would like it, too. If he didn't, they wouldn't.

It was not immediately that A. L. E. was at liberty to attend to his book writer and lyrist, for he was engaged at the moment of their entry in what – on his side – appeared to be a heated argument with Jack Hazzard. It seemed that Jack had been offered the comedian's part in the Viennese show and was hesitating whether or not to accept it.

This was so perilously near to *lèse-majesté* that Napoleon was not unnaturally incensed.

'I don't know what you're wibble-wobbling about,' he was saying. 'You ought to be down on your knees thanking me for giving you such a chance. Eh, Plymouth?'

'You betcha,' said the knickerbockered child. 'I'm astounded.'

'I'm more than astounded, I'm surprised. It's not only incredible, it's unbelievable. You're nobody. No one ever heard of you. And here I am, offering you—'

Jack stirred uneasily. He was sitting on the edge of a hard chair immediately opposite the desk. Guy and Plum were side by side on a leather settee. The arrangement was faintly suggestive of a courtroom with judge, jury and criminal.

'Well, sir, Mr Erlanger,' said Jack, nervously revolving the hat that dangled between his knees, 'I'm in a hit, you see—'

'A hit? What hit? Where?'

'*Very Good Eddie*, Mr Erlanger. At the Princess.'

Erlanger exploded.

'The Princess? That broken-down little cheesebox under the Sixth Avenue EL?' (The Princess was a Shubert house.) 'Do you realize I'm offering you a chance to appear on the stage of the *New Amsterdam*? And there you sit, humming and hawing—'

'He's crazy,' said Plymouth.

'It sure is a great opportunity,' Jack agreed. 'What's the character like that you want me to play, Guy?'

'He's very loquacious.'

'Yes,' said Erlanger, 'and another thing, he talks a lot.' He looked at his watch. 'Well, think it over,' he said. 'I've got to go down to the theatre to see a run-through of Georgie Cohan's new show. Come along, Plymouth.'

He bustled out, followed by *l'Aiglon*, followed by Bolton, followed by Wodehouse. No actual invitation had been extended to the last-named to join the party, but it seemed to them the prudent thing to do. The first rule a young author learns in the theatre is never to let the manager get out of his sight.

The Cohan show was in full swing when they arrived. They had come just in time for the entrance of the policemen, six chorus-boys in uniform who marched on to a special tune. It was one of those neat tricks in which Cohan specialized, and it should have been very effective. But unfortunately one of the six, a big, awkward young man with red hair, seemed incapable of moving in time to the music. He made the wrong turn, got out of line and generally ruined the thing.

This did not escape Plymouth's observant eye. His voice rang out like that of the daughter of the village Blacksmith.

'Hey!'

'Yes, Plymouth?'

'That one's no good.'

'Which one?'

'The one third from the end.'

Cohan nodded gloomily.

'I've been trying for five weeks to get that boy to march in time, but nothing I say makes any difference.'

Erlanger snorted.

'You're too soft with him. You're too easy. You don't know how to handle these guys. Let *me* talk to him!'

His remarks, filtered for family reading, ran about as follows:

'You filtered fool, what do you think you're doing? Can't you hear the beat of that music? Can't you pick up your feet, you filtered lummox? Don't stand there gaping at me like a filtered half-wit. Go back and make the entrance again.'

Instead of going back, the lummox came forward, right down to the footlights. His manner, if a little reserved, was extremely courteous. At least, it began by being extremely courteous.

'I regret exceedingly,' he said, 'that I have fallen short of the requirements of the part entrusted to me, Mr Erlanger. I am not a professional actor. I gave up a good job in a garage to join this production because I'm married to one of the ladies in the chorus, Miss Pansy LeBoeuf, and I didn't want us to be separated. I informed

Mr Harris that I had a very poor ear for music, and he assured me that it did not greatly matter. If it does, you can of course dismiss me. *But what you can't do, you filtered son of a filter, is to talk to me that way in front of my wife, and if you do it again I'll come down there and knock your filtered block off, and that goes for Cohan too.*'

Erlanger had his coat half off, starting for the stage, but George Cohan was ahead of him. He stuck his hand up to the boy.

'Put it there, kid!' he said. 'And let me tell you you're going to be one of our policemen as long as you want the job. Practise that walk and see if you can't get it, but if you can't, to hell with it.'

The performance continued. Erlanger had slumped back into his seat, baffled. His favourite Marshal had let him down. Guy was thinking how typical that generous gesture had been of George M. Cohan. Plum's mind was occupied with the name he had heard.

'Pansy LeBoeuf, did he say?'

'That's how I got it.'

'Quite a name.'

'Yes, almost as good as Pickles St Clair, who's with Dillingham. But we've got a girl in the *Eddie* chorus who tops them both – Dawn O'Day.'

A few minutes later Erlanger rose.

'It's okay, George,' he said. 'I've seen enough to satisfy me. You open at the Chestnut Street in Philly, and I'll route you west to the Grand in Chicago.'

Without waiting for a reply, he strode off up the aisle. He called over his shoulder to Guy and Plum as he passed them.

'Come upstairs, you two. I'll get Klaw to give you your contracts.'

Next morning Plum called at Guy's apartment.

'Yesterday inspired me,' he said. 'It gave me an idea for a lyric. I've only done a bit of it, but here's how it goes so far.'

> Napoleon was a little guy:
> They used to call him Shorty.
> He only stood about so high.
> His chest was under forty
> But when folks started talking mean,
> His pride it didn't injure:
> 'My queen,' he'd say to Josephine,
> 'The thing that counts is ginger.'

'And the refrain?'

'I haven't done the refrain yet. But here's another verse.'

> He got too fat. We all know that
> From portraits in the galleries.

He never seemed to learn the knack
Of laying off the calories.
But though his waist was large, he faced
And overcame all foemen.
He knew quite well it's brains that tell
And not a guy's abdomen.

'Erlanger's going to love it,' said Plum.

The song was destined for success, but not in an Erlanger production. Jerry Kern wrote a delightful tune and orchestrated it with toy trumpets, and it was sung by Billy B. Van in *Have a Heart*.

3

The new piece was to be called *Miss Springtime*. Guy's title had been *Little Miss Springtime*, but that was changed very promptly by Abraham Lincoln Erlanger.

'We don't have nothing little at the New Amsterdam,' said Abe.

By a great stroke of good fortune Plymouth had picked up a germ and gone down with the mumps, so was not on hand with his sympathy, encouragement and advice, and rehearsals proceeded smoothly. Everything connected with an Erlanger show always moved with the precision of a Napoleonic campaign. The boss kept an eye on things himself and stood no nonsense.

There was once an expensive foreign tenor who was engaged for a leading role in an Erlanger production, and on the night of the dress rehearsal Erlanger, seated in the stage-box, was puzzled and annoyed to note that all that was proceeding from the gifted artist was a faint sound like gas escaping out of a pipe. Stopping the performance and inquiring into this, he was informed by the tenor in a hushed whisper that he, the tenor, was saving his voice for tomorrow night.

Erlanger's eyes bulged slowly from his head. He swallowed once or twice.

'Sing,' he said.

The tenor went into a whispered explanation. When he said he was 'saving his voice', the voice was in fact saving itself.

'She is gone,' he said, alluding to his voice, as serious singers will, as if it were an independent entity. 'Tonight she is gone, but tomorrow she will be back.'

'Sing!' said Erlanger.

'But I'm telling you, Mr Erlanger' – the whisper was even fainter – 'the vo-chay, she is not there. She does this.' He pinched his throat between thumb and forefinger by way of illustration.

'Sing!' said Erlanger.

'Please,' the whisper was now scarcely audible. 'They are delicate, these great voices. They—'

Erlanger rose from his seat, removed his coat and sprang from box to stage. He placed one large hand on the tenor's left shoulder, another large hand on his right shoulder, got a good grip, and shook him backwards and forwards for some moments, then from side to side. He raised him in the air and brought him down with a bump that shook the New Amsterdam stage.

'*Sing!*' he said.

The tenor let out a note that could be heard as far down town as the Battery.

The Emperor had handed over the preparation of *Miss Springtime* to two of his most trusted Generals – Herbert Gresham for the book and Julian Mitchell for the dances. Martial law had been proclaimed on the first day of rehearsals, and Gresham readily adjusted himself to the military atmosphere. Whenever the Little Corporal of 42nd Street strode on to the stage, he would come smartly to attention, and it was clearly with an effort that he refrained from saluting.

Julian Mitchell was much less docile. He was a sort of Marshal Ney, an independent spirit who truckled to no one. He would fight manfully against any suggestion, even from the All Highest, that was in his opinion bad for the show. He knew his job, he did his job, and he was not going to have anyone telling him how to do it. He was fired oftener than a machinegun, but whoever fired him always had to take him back again, for Julian stood alone. He was the real creator of the *Ziegfeld Follies*, for two editions of which Flo Ziegfeld was merely the brilliant pressman.

It was amazing that he should have reached such a position, for he was very nearly stone deaf. His method of hearing a melody was to press his ear closely to the back of the piano. If the piano was in the pit, he would seat himself on top of it like a sort of Buddha. For some reason which aurists may be able to explain he could hear a little better in this position.

Miss Springtime – with Sari Petrass, George Macfarlane, Jack Hazzard, Georgie O'Ramey and Jed Prouty as its principals – opened at the old Forest Theatre in Philadelphia. It moved like clockwork, the beautiful Joseph Urban settings appearing and disappearing without a single hitch. Even the audience did what was asked of them.

As the orchestra struck up the 'play-out', the two authors pressed back through the outgoing crowd to the pass door. Erlanger was already on the stage, the department heads, directors, scene painters, stage carpenters, electricians, head props and costume designer assembled about him. The company stood in lines facing him. Napoleon, with his Marshals about him, preparing to address his troops.

His speech was a eulogy. He scattered medals like birdseed. It was plain that what had occurred tonight had been an Austerlitz. He was particularly enthusiastic about the chorus dancing, the precision and verve of which, he said, had been exceptional.

'The finest line of dancers I've watched in years,' he said and motioned to Julian to say a few graceful words.

Julian, who had not heard a syllable of the speech, stepped forward, a bundle of scribbled notes in his hand.

'I'm ashamed,' he said, brushing away a tear, 'I'm ashamed and mortified at the way you girls let me down tonight. The whole lot of you danced as if you were wearing snowshoes. No precision, no verve, the worst line of dancers I've ever watched.'

He would have spoken further, but at this point a justly incensed Czar of the New York Theatre, speaking carefully into his left ear, fired him. It was not till late on the following day that he was taken back again.

Guy summoned up courage to ask a timid question.

'Do you think it's a hit, Mr Erlanger?'

Plum, on his other side, made a similar query.

'It's a hit, don't you think, Mr Erlanger?'

The Emperor swelled portentously.

'A hit? Of course it's a hit. Do I ever put on anything that isn't a hit?'

'No, no, Mr Erlanger.'

'Certainly not, Mr Erlanger. Of course not, Mr Erlanger.'

'It will run at the New Amsterdam for a year, and as soon as I have the New York opening off my hands I shall organize a Western company.'

The two collaborators beamed at him. People said unkind things about old Abe, did they? He had ruined people, had he? Well, what of it? They probably thoroughly deserved to be ruined, and as for him shooting that man everybody said he had shot, why shouldn't a fellow shoot a chap from time to time if the situation seemed to call for it? What's the sense of having a loaded revolver if you never use it?

Those were the days. None of this modern nonsense about 'hoping they'll like us in New York', and 'We'll have to wait and see what the critics think of us'. 'It will run at the New Amsterdam for a year, and as soon as I have the New York opening off my hands, I shall organize a Western company.' Just like that. And the West was the West then. A full season in Chicago, fifty-two one-week stands, a third season of three-nighters.

And, as a matter of record, Erlanger was right. *Miss Springtime* ran at the New Amsterdam for 230 performances – a very long run for those days – and was an even bigger success in Chicago. It went on touring for several years.

3

1

GUY and Plum were lunching at Armenonville, the charming grill-room of the Knickerbocker Hotel at the corner of 42nd Street and Broadway. This was a step up from their customary Childs', the New York equivalent of London's ABC shops, but they were doing well now and could afford to cut a modest dash. Guy had two hits running on Broadway, and Plum had just sold his novel, *Piccadilly Jim*, as a serial to the *Saturday Evening Post*.

'Tell me about last night,' said Plum, when they had finished the important business of ordering. 'How did you make out with Belasco?'

The question concerned a play called *Polly-With-a-Past*, a comedy which Guy had written with George Middleton.

'I don't quite know,' said Guy. 'It was hard to tell whether he liked it or not. He was hanging pictures.'

'Hanging pictures?'

'While George was reading the play to him. I must say my heart bled for poor old George.'

'Where did this take place? The famous studio?'

'Yes, as sinister a joint as I've ever been in. It looks like the scene of nameless orgies.'

'But this picture-hanging—?'

'Apparently the Master is always tinkering, trying new effects with priest-robes, painted cassones, all that sort of junk. Now he was hanging pictures. Well, he told George to go ahead and read the play. George would read a couple of lines and then there'd be bang, bang, bang. He'd stop, and Belasco would call out, "Go on, I'm listening." '

'Pretty ghastly for George.'

'Yes, he seemed to be suffering. And that wasn't all. Belasco's secretary was there, the one they call Ginty, and the poor thing was suffering from neuralgia. It was in the left eye that it seemed to be troubling her most. She kept applying hot compresses to it and groaning "Oh, my God! This is terrible!" It made her sound like a dramatic critic. George would read a line, and there would be a yell of "Awful! Awful!" It jolted him quite a bit.

'But George is not a man to be lightly stayed in his appointed course. Pausing for but a moment, he ploughed manfully on. Another couple of comedy lines, and there would come a bang, bang, *bang*. ("Don't stop. I can hear you.") And Ginty would shriek "Ow! Ow! This is frightful!" '

Plum drew his breath in sharply, as if he had had a sudden twinge of neuralgia in the left eye.

'So that's reading a play to Belasco! How did this custom of reading plays to managers ever start, I wonder.'

'I believe it's a hangover from the days when most managers couldn't read.'

'Now that a fair proportion of them can, why not let them wrestle with the thing themselves?'

'Yes, if they would do it, that would be fine. The trouble is, the last thing managers want to do is read a play. They think it makes them look important having a great pile of unread scripts on their desks. The higher the pile, the bigger the manager.'

'Then what's the answer?'

'I know the answer, if you could always work it. I managed it once with Harry Frazee. It was one evening after office hours. His staff had gone home, and it seemed that there was nothing to interrupt us. I didn't know then, as I do now, that during the reading of a play a manager has to have something to do that will keep him usefully employed. I believe Arch Selwyn does fretwork, while Crosby Gaige catches up on his burnt-leather bookmarks. Harry Frazee, sticking more closely to business, uses such time for cleaning out the drawers of his desk, getting rid of empty whisky bottles, appeals for charity, cancelled summonses and so on.

'After I had read a couple of pages during which he was entirely invisible, dealing with the contents of his lower right-hand drawer, he suddenly bobbed up and told me to stop reading and leave the play with him. I pointed to the vast pile on his desk.

' "As fairness would demand my play going to the end of the queue, it wouldn't reach you for another two years."

' "All right", he conceded grudgingly. "Read a couple more pages. But those dialects! I can't make head or tail of them." He disappeared again on the left side of his desk.

'I must admit the play was rather rich in dialects, though I was surprised he'd noticed it. It was about a bunch of soldiers, an Italian, a German-American, a coloured boy, etc. I read two more pages as soon as Harry had got back with a pair of galoshes, a bottle of glue and a girl's brassière. He again told me to stop reading. He said he couldn't understand a word I was saying, he hated plays with a lot of foreign accents in them and I was wasting his time.

' "But you've still got several drawers to sort," I said. "You might as well let me read a bit more."

' "I've just told you," he said. "I can't follow you when you do those dialects."

' "Look," I said – I'd had a sudden inspiration – "How about your reading the play to me? If you'd just read to the end of the first act, I bet you won't want to stop. I bet you five bucks!"

'A bet is something Harry can't resist. He grabbed the script and started to read.

' "Gosh," I said. "It's better than I thought it was. You're good, Mr Frazee. You were an actor once, of course?"

' "No, I was never an actor."

' "You should have been – that's all I've got to say." That encouraged him. He started to work harder.

'It went like a breeze. I may not be much of a reader, but I was right there as an audience. A first act by a budding playwright was never better received.

' "I can't wait," I said, "to hear what you're going to do with that second act twist. Gosh, I've got a treat coming to me there."

'From then on he was selling the play to me. He took off his coat and stood up so that he could really act. I went round and sat in his deck chair. I could rock better on the laughs.

'By the time he got to the end of the play he was all in. I had to pour him a stiff drink. I took one myself. We were buddies. He asked me to call him Harry.'

'He bought it?'

'I left the office with a cheque for $1000 in my pocket. The little masterpiece was never produced, because he subsequently came out of the ether, but it got me $1000 at a time when I most needed it. And if you can get $1000 out of Harry Frazee, you're good.'

'Yes, I've always heard he's a pretty hardboiled egg.'

'Most managers are!'

'But not all. There are shining exceptions. One points with pride, for instance, to Savage.'

'Colonel Henry W. Savage? Have you met him?'

'I was in his office yesterday, and he's very different from . . . well, somebody like Abe Erlanger. Mind you, I'm quite fond of Abe. He eats broken bottles and conducts human sacrifices at the time of the full moon, but he's a thoroughly good chap, heart of gold beneath a rugged exterior and all that sort of thing. All the same, you couldn't describe him as a *preux chevalier*. He lacks a certain something.'

'You don't often get a manager who's a Chesterfield.'

'Exactly. That is why I say that, when you do, you should grapple him to your soul with hoops of steel. This Savage, now, of whom I speak, is the answer to an author's prayer, a charming, refined, cultured gentlemen of the old school with delightful, courtly manners, frank blue eyes and a heart as far from fraud as heaven from earth. He radiates benevolence. He is without guile.'

'His heart is as the heart of a little child?'

'You put it in a nutshell. That gentle soul would not harm a fly.'

'How do you know?'

'I've seen him.'

'Seen him what?'

'Not harming flies. He is a sort of modern St Francis of Assisi, dripping with goodwill to all men and running his business in a spirit of pure altruism. By the way, he wants to see us after lunch.'

A man who had been sitting with his back to them turned in his chair.

'Excuse me, gentlemen,' he said. 'I could not help overhearing your conversation. You were speaking, if my ears did not deceive me, of that hornswoggling old pirate and premier louse of the world, Colonel Henry W. Savage.'

'That . . . *what* did you call him?'

' "Hornswoggling old pirate and premier louse of the world" was the expression I used. I could think of nothing stronger on the spur of the moment.'

Guy had recognized the man now. His was a face which since *The Merry Widow* had become a well-known one.

'You're Donald Brian, aren't you?'

'That's right. You're Guy Bolton, I think, and. . . .'

'This is P. G. Wodehouse.'

'How do you do? Mr Wodehouse,' said Donald Brian, 'I will address myself to you, for it was you who were describing Colonel Henry W. Savage as a gentle soul devoid of guile. I assure you, Mr Wodehouse,' said Donald Brian earnestly, 'that that man, that seemingly saintly Hank Savage, is so crooked that he could hide at will behind a spiral staircase. Let me tell you a little story. Some years ago this child of unmarried parents sent for me. He was casting a piece called *The Merry Widow*, of which you may have heard. He wished me to play the hero, a certain Prince Danilo.'

'You were terrific as Prince Danilo,' said Guy.

Donald Brian bowed.

'Thank you. I am a conscientious artist, and I spared no effort to earn my $75 a week.'

'Your *what*?'

'That was my salary throughout the run. I asked a somewhat higher figure. The Colonel refused, and we started arguing about it. "Look, Donny," he said at last – "I'll tell you what let's do. Let's toss for it. If you win, I'll give you what you're asking. If I win, you'll work for $75." Then he pulled a half-dollar from his pocket and said, "Heads or tails?" '

Donald Brian paused a moment. He seemed to be struggling with his feelings.

'Now, psychologists have established,' he resumed, 'that in seventy-seven cases out of a hundred the answer to that question is "heads". I saw no reason to be different, so I said "heads" like all the rest of the boys.'

'And it came tails?'

'It had to come tails, because, as I learned later, it was tails on both sides – one of those freak coins that the Mint has turned out occasionally. You see, the old boy knew all about that quirk of human nature that gives "heads" a big preference. And so through the whole run of the *Widow* I worked for $75 a week. And when the show had been running for a year to capacity business and he had made a fortune out of it, I asked for a rise. "Why, Donny, I'm surprised," the Colonel said. "I thought you were a good sport. That was your end of a bet – $75 a week. You're not going to welsh, are you?" '

Brian sighed, and turned back to his table.

2

It was a tale that provided food for thought, but Plum, as they walked over to the Savage office, was inclined to make light of it.

'These actors!' he said. 'Extraordinary how they love to invent yarns. Anything for a good story.'

'You think it was an invention?' said Guy, who seemed pensive.

'Of course. You aren't going to tell me that a man like Colonel Savage. . . .'

Plum broke off. They had paused in front of the George M. Cohan Theatre to look at the photographs in the entrance. Colonel Savage's star, Mitzi Hajos, was playing there in a piece called *Sari*.

'Someone over on the horizon seems to be trying to pass the time of day with you,' he said. 'He's waving, and I think I caught the word "Guy".'

Guy turned.

'Oh, that's Tom Cushing. He wrote the book and lyrics of *Sari*. Hullo, Tom,' he said, as the other came up. 'Do you know P. G. Wodehouse?'

'We've never met. How are you, P. G.?'

'How do you do? Guy tells me you're the author of this outstanding success.'

'Well, I adapted it from the Hungarian original, and it was a hell of a job, let me tell you. You know what stinkers these Hungarian books are. I had to invent practically a new story. I also fitted new lyrics to all that endless music Kalman writes. It took me months.'

'Still, you must be making a packet out of it.'

A spasm of pain contorted Cushing's face, the same sort of spasm which had twisted the features of Donald Brian when he had been speaking of double-tailed half-dollars.

'Do you know Savage?' he asked.

'Slightly. Guy hasn't met him yet. We're on our way to his office now.'

'God help you,' said Tom Cushing. 'Forgive me if I seem to speak bitterly, but I have passed through the furnace. Do you know what the Colonel paid me for all the work I did on *Sari*? $500.'

'$500 *flat*?'

'That's what.'

'Good Lord!'

'I was to be paid in five monthly instalments, which were to cease if the play should close. That was to keep me up to the mark. Unless I did my damnedest, it might close in three months, and then I would only get $300.'

'It's been running a good twenty weeks, hasn't it?'

'Twenty-four, to capacity. Well, I got my five cheques, and then the generous old fellow sent me another. A darned graceful gesture, I thought, and so I told Madison Corey, the Colonel's manager, when I happened to run into him on the street. I said, "That was nice of Colonel Savage to keep on with those $100 payments because the show is such a success. I appreciated it greatly. What a dear old chap he is!" And next morning there came a letter from the dear old chap saying that his book-keeping department had made a mistake and, unless the $100 was returned immediately, legal proceedings would be instituted.'

Guy had paled a little beneath his tan.

'I can't believe it.'

'It's true.'

'What did you do?'

'I sent him $98.50. I told him I was using the other dollar and a half to buy a frame for his letter. Oh, well,' said Cushing philosophically, 'it'll be something to tell my grandchildren about when they cluster round my knee.'

He passed on, and Guy eyed Plum fixedly.

'You and your answers to an author's prayer! You and your modern St Francises of Assisi! Thank goodness we haven't got to have anything to do with this old devil. What are we seeing him about, anyway? I suppose he has some frightful Hungarian thing he wants us to fix up for $50 paid in monthly instalments.'

Plum coughed.

'Well, not quite that. The fact is. . . .' He paused. He seemed embarrassed. 'You know that thing we roughed out, the one we thought of calling *Have a Heart*?'

'To follow *Eddie* at the Princess?'

'Yes, that was the idea, but I'm afraid I've promised it to Savage.'

'You've done *what*?'

'He's a very persuasive old gentleman. He talked me into it.'

'I wouldn't let him touch it with a ten-foot pole.'

Plum coughed again. His embarrassment had become more marked.

'The trouble is,' he said, 'I'm afraid I rather let myself be carried away and, to cut a long story short, he's got a verbal agreement, and there's no possible way we can get out of it.'

3

Colonel Savage was a man in the middle-fifties, tall and thin and benevolent, his open, candid face surmounted by a handsome mop of grey hair. He walked with a slight limp, having probably in the course of his career been bitten in the leg by some indignant author.

He received the visitors beamingly.

'I want to sign those *Have a Heart* contracts today,' he said, all heartiness and joviality, like something out of Dickens. 'Yes, Miss Stanchfield?'

Miss Stanchfield, his secretary, had entered.

'I've just spoken to the hospital, Colonel,' she said. 'Mr Scarborough seems a little better this morning. I thought you would like to know.'

'Yes, indeed,' said the Colonel. 'I take a fatherly interest in all my authors. Poor Scarborough,' he explained, 'had a breakdown when we were out on the road shaping up his play for New York. He was carried off the train on a stretcher. Well, well. These authors you get today seem very brittle. No stamina. No reserve force. Poor Cushing collapsed while we were trying out *Sari.* And look at poor Browne. There was a sad case.'

'Browne?' queried Plum, as Miss Stanchfield went out. He noted uneasily that all the Savage authors mentioned so far had been qualified by the ominous adjective 'poor'.

'Walter Browne, who wrote *Everywoman*, one of the greatest successes of my career. He died the night the play opened. That's the second one I've had die on me, though the other was only a composer. Ah, well, here today and gone tomorrow. All flesh is grass, I sometimes say. I see,' said the Colonel, following Guy's eye, which had become glassy and was fixed on a picture of a sailing vessel on the wall, 'you are looking at my grandfather's ship. What a beauty! He made a lot of money out of that boat. She was a real clipper. Cargo after cargo she carried.'

'Tea?'

'Slaves. And now,' the Colonel went on, dismissing the subject, 'about those contracts for *Have a Heart*. I like to get these business details off my mind before going ahead. What figure would you suggest? Some authors, I believe, prefer to take a flat sum down—'

'$500?' said Guy with an unpleasant tinkle in his voice.

'Yes, I wouldn't mind going as high as that.'

'We would prefer a royalty.'

'What royalty were you thinking of?'

'The usual 3 per cent.'

'3 per cent is not usual with *me*,' said the Colonel emphatically. 'Still, I'll tell you what I'll do,' he went on, drawing a coin from his pocket. 'I'll toss you for it. 3 per cent if you win, 1 if I win. Heads or tails?' he said, flickering the coin into the air.

'*Tails!*' shouted the authors in unison.

The Colonel picked up the half-dollar and put it in his pocket. He seemed to have aged quite a little in the last few moments. He looked at the authors in silence for a while.

Then he spoke.

'I suppose you boys know quite a few people in our business?' he said reflectively.

4

Have a Heart opened on a cold winter's night – 27th December 1916, to be exact – at the Opera House, Trenton, New Jersey – not quite the best spot for the presentation of a highly sophisticated divorce story in which a honeymooning couple are being pursued by a lawyer bearing the tidings that their marriage is not legal.

The hero was the proprietor of a department store where the heroine worked. When the century was in its teens, there was much talk of model employers and of making conditions luxurious for the workers, and there was a good deal of brilliant satire on the subject in *Have a Heart*.

The clientele of the Trenton Opera House found it all a bit exotic. Their response on the opening night was tepid, and it came as no surprise to the authors to be told by Miss Stanchfield after the final curtain had fallen – to applause of the kind known as sporadic – that Colonel Savage would like to see them in the dining-room of Teller's Hotel for a conference.

The personnel of the meeting, which began shortly after midnight, consisted of the manager, the authors and George Marion, a fine old character actor who, having yet some years to wait for *Anna Christie* to bring him his best role, eked out a poorly paid living as book director for the Colonel's musical productions.

It needed but a glance at the big chief to tell the two partners that the proceedings were likely to take some time. All through the performance he had been dictating whispered notes to Miss Stanchfield, and these, as he dumped them down on the table, looked like the manuscript of a three-volume novel.

'Let's get to work,' he said.

Line by line the script was gone through. Cuts were proposed, changes discussed. The hands of the big, fly-specked clock on the wall pointed to five past two.

'What do you think of that suggestion?' asked Savage, turning to George Marion as Guy proposed a major alteration.

'Let me ponder it,' said George. 'I would like to try to visualize it as it affects the entire dramatic structure.'

He folded his arms on the table in front of him, and rested his forehead on them. Several minutes passed while the authors waited politely for his opinion.

'Go on,' said the Colonel. 'We'll get on to something else while George is thinking.'

They got on to something else, and George continued thinking. He was still thinking when the Colonel rose and announced that he was going to bed.

'We old fellows have to take care of our health,' he said.

'You approve the change I suggested?' asked Guy.

'Certainly,' said the Colonel. It was plain by now that anything in the nature of a change was meat and drink to him. 'And of course there will be those two new lyrics I mentioned. Start on them at once. Miss Stanchfield will meet you at eight-thirty tomorrow morning to collect the material. She will have everything typed and parts extracted by ten. You will then go over the whole thing with George and Teddy Royce, which will give you time to rewrite anything they disapprove of before you get down to rehearsal.'

'May I ask a question?' said Plum.

'By all means.'

'When do we sleep?'

'Sleep?' said the Colonel reprovingly. 'You didn't come here to sleep. You came here to get a show ready for Broadway.'

Plum looked at Guy – Guy looked at Plum. Their thoughts had flashed to George Scarborough, carried off on a stretcher at the end of the pre-Broadway tour, to Walter Browne, dying on the opening night, and – yes, there was another, that unnamed composer who had expired at the close of one of these Savage tuning-up sessions.

'I love the theatre,' said Colonel Savage. 'I love the good old-fashioned show-people to whom the stage came first, whatever crisis might arise. I'd like to tell you boys a little story that will illustrate what I mean. I was a friend of Maurice Barrymore and I knew that in spite of all his peccadilloes he was devoted to Georgie, his wife.

I went to see him the day after she died and found him, his eyes red from weeping, with the newspapers spread about the bed in which he was lying.

' "I've had a cruel loss, Hank," he said. "One I shall never get over. But I must say they've given the old girl some damn good notices." Good night, boys. Don't forget. Eight-thirty sharp.'

He left them. George Marion, still bent over the table, stirred slightly.

'Do you realize,' said Plum, regarding the bowed form sympathetically, 'that this pondering business of George's is the only way the poor devil can get any sleep.'

'Yes,' agreed Guy. 'We only have one tour to cope with. Poor old George goes on, from play to play.'

'Well, we'd better get upstairs and work, I suppose. What do you think we ought to do about George? Should we stir him, do you feel?'

The question was decided for them by George suddenly sitting up.

'Yes,' he said briskly, 'I've gone over the whole thing in my mind and I see no insurmountable obstacles. I therefore vote for the change, Colonel.'

'The Colonel has gone to bed.'

'Really?' said George. 'I was so absorbed in the problem I didn't notice him leaving. Gone to bed, eh? Well, well, I'm afraid the old boy's beginning to feel his age. He's not as wide-awake at these conferences as he was five or ten years ago.'

The two authors went up to their room and settled down to work. By a quarter to six it was done, and Plum stretched himself wearily.

'Have you ever reflected,' he said, 'that 40,000 people were killed in automobile accidents last year, and not one of them was Colonel Henry W. Savage? Looks to me like mismanagement somewhere. Do you believe in heredity?'

'Why?'

'I was only thinking of the Colonel's grandfather, the slaver. Still, I believe the show's a hit, don't you?'

'A hit? Of course it's a hit. Do we ever put on anything that isn't a hit?' said Guy, making use of A. L. Erlanger's non-copyright material.

'But I was disappointed in the way "Napoleon" went.'

'They've probably never heard of Napoleon in Trenton.'

'No, it wasn't the audience. It was the fellow who sang it.'

'Napoleon' had been sung by the principal comedian, who played a brash elevator-boy named Henry. It was Henry's boast that he had told more women where they could get off than any man in New York.

'He's too old. Too old and too large.'

'There aren't many comics who can look like boys of sixteen.'

'I know one who can. I've seen him in vaudeville. Billy B. Van. But would the Colonel engage him? He's expensive.'

'Well, what's money? You can't take it with you.'

'I know you can't, but nobody ever told that to Hank Savage.'

'Listen,' said Guy. 'Let's snatch forty minutes' refreshing sleep, which seems to be the most we shall ever get a night during this tour, then we'll be all rested and alert for taking it up with him before rehearsal.'

Colonel Savage, approached an hour or two later, agreed that Billy B. Van would be ideal for the part of Henry.

'But his salary!' he said, a look of pain coming into his fine eyes. 'I doubt if you could get him under $300.'

'$300 isn't much.'

'It is to me,' said the Colonel, who, having only $27 million tucked away in sound securities, had to be careful. 'But I'll tell you what I'll do. . . .'

'*Tails!*' cried the two authors, speaking as one author.

The Colonel smiled faintly and very wryly. The old wound still troubled him.

'If you boys will pay half his salary for the first three months, it's a deal.'

Guy and Plum looked at one another. The same thought was in both their minds – viz. that for an author to pay out money to a manager instead of taking it off him was like rubbing velvet the wrong way. Then they thought of Billy B. Van singing 'Napoleon', and the sensation of nausea passed.

'I'm game,' said Guy.

'So am I,' said Plum.

So the matter was arranged. Billy B. Van was engaged and was an instantaneous success in New York, rolling the customers in the aisles with his comedy and singing 'Napoleon' like a linnet. And all through the first three months Guy and Plum duly paid up $75 per week per person, their contribution to his salary.

At the end of the third month the Colonel fired him.

4

1

HAVE A HEART was one of those semi-successes in New York. It played to capacity for three months, but after Billy Van left business dropped. Old Hank didn't seem to mind. The fact that he had engaged a new comedian cheaper than Billy by $150 apparently compensated him for the loss of thousands at the box-office. He was not, as a matter of fact, very interested in a New York run. What he liked was the road. *Have a Heart*, which had done only five months and two weeks on Broadway, played for six years outside New York.

Shortly after it had opened at the Liberty Theatre on 42nd Street (now a second-run movie-house) its authors had a call from Ray Comstock, Bessie Marbury's partner, asking them to come to the Princess and confer with him about a show to follow *Very Good Eddie*, which had just passed its 200th performance.

Plum, as they started off for 39th Street, was at the top of his form. This business of being asked by managers to look in and confer about shows was still an exhilarating novelty to him. It pained him, accordingly, to see that his colleague was moody and preoccupied.

'Girl trouble,' said Guy briefly, in answer to a sympathetic query. 'I had a little girl trouble last night.'

'Who was the little girl?'

Guy stiffened. There came into his eyes that cold, stern look which had caused him to be known in the old regiment as Chilled-Steel Bolton.

'Does one bandy a woman's name in mess, old boy? If one does, Emily Post has been fooling me for years.'

Plum flushed. The rebuke had been a just one.

'Forgive me, old chap. I should not have said it. Call her X and tell me what happened.'

Guy was silent for a moment. His finely chiselled features twisted a little, as if the memory pained him. With men of the Guy Bolton type memories are like mulligatawny soup in a cheap restaurant. It is wiser not to stir them.

'I can't imagine what induced her to come to that elevator,' he said at length.

'She wished to go up . . . or possibly to go down?' hazarded Plum.

'True, we had parted in anger, but that was no reason why she should have come to the elevator. What happened was that we disagreed on the subject of her new hat and, one thing leading to another, she threw a vase – containing, if I remember correctly, roses – at my head, and I, thinking I might as well be going, walked out and rang for the elevator. It arrived, full of people, and I was just about to get aboard, when X came dashing down the hall, screaming loudly, and attached herself to my coat-tail.'

'Embarrassing.'

'Most. I disengaged myself and stepped in, she still screaming, and as we started to descend I was aware of a figure standing at my elbow, a grey-haired figure in a clerical collar.'

'Not—?'

'Yes. Belasco. He was looking at me austerely, like a clergyman who had discovered schism in his flock.'

'Did he say anything?'

'He said – very coldly – "Good evening, Mr Middleton." '

'And what did you say?'

'I said, "Oh, good evening, Mr Belasco. I didn't think you would remember me." '

They arrived at the Princess, which for years now has ceased to be a theatre. Today it is not even a second-run movie-house, it is a television den, God help it! The lion and the lizard keep the courts where Comstock gloried and drank deep. They found Ray seated at his desk with a bottle of whisky beside him for purposes of reference.

'That must be powerful stuff you're drinking,' said Guy. 'You can smell the fumes as you come up the stairs.'

'It isn't this bottle,' said Comstock. 'It's the ceiling,' and they saw that it was covered by a dark stain on which beads of moisture had formed. 'Whisky,' said Comstock mournfully. 'The finest money can buy. I stacked it up in the loft, twenty-four cases. I forgot the steam-pipes run through there. The stuff got so hot it exploded.'

Ray Comstock was a thin, rangy individual who looked like a boy and had almost as much charm as Charlie Dillingham. He seemed to be perpetually telephoning and had a telephone receiver that he could balance on his shoulder, thus leaving his hands free for opening letters, pouring drinks and so forth.

His mind seemed equally detachable. He could listen on the telephone and talk to visitors simultaneously. There was never any clue as to who was on the other end of the wire. His part in the conversation was mostly monosyllabic, the other person evidently doing the major part of the talking. He addressed all these callers as 'Honey'.

He had sent for Guy and Plum, as he had hinted over the telephone, to tell them that the time had come to be thinking of something to follow *Very Good Eddie. Eddie* he proposed to move to the Casino, where there were 1500 seats. It would thus become available to a public that could not afford to pay the high scale of $1–$3 charged at the Princess.

This was the policy adopted from now on with the Princess shows, and a very good one, too.

He then told them something else. Bessie Marbury was out. She had withdrawn from the partnership.

'She didn't like the play.'

'What play?'

'The play you boys are going to turn into a musical. Charlie Hoyt's *A Milk White Flag.*'

Plum remained calm – he had never heard of *A Milk White Flag* – but Guy nearly hit the dark patch on the ceiling.

'You're crazy, Ray. You can't be thinking of making that into a Princess musical.'

'Why not?' said Comstock. He spoke into the telephone. 'I said, "Why not?" to somebody else, honey. "Decidedly not," is what I say to you.'

Guy was still staring incredulously.

'I've read *A Milk White Flag,*' he said. 'It's about a man who pretends to be dead so as to evade his creditors and collect on his insurance. He's laid out on ice and catches cold.'

'That's right,' said Ray, laughing heartily. 'I had forgotten about him catching cold. I remember now it was terrific. Every now and then there would be a sneeze from the room where the body was laid out. The family were scared popeyed.' He laughed again at the recollection of this rich comedy, and spoke into the telephone. 'No, honey, you needn't get sore. I'm not laughing at you.'

'But listen, Ray. The thing that has made the Princess shows is charm. We must have charm.'

'Be as charming as you like. No one's stopping you.'

'Well, you can't say *A Milk White Flag* has charm, with a corpse that keeps coming on the stage without any trousers on.'

'Why would a corpse have trousers on? Only the upper half of the body would be on view. No, honey, I'm not talking about the party last night. This is in a play, the new Princess show.'

'And he makes a buffet dinner off the sandwiches set out for the mourners.'

'We'll change it to a sit-down dinner.'

'A *what*?'

'I was speaking on the telephone.'

'Perhaps we had better wait until Ray's finished phoning,' suggested Plum.

'He's never finished phoning,' said Guy. 'As soon as he hangs up on that call, there'll be another.'

'Look, Ray,' said Plum. 'Guy doesn't seem to like this *Milk White Flag* of yours. Why not do the piece we've been working on?'

He was referring to a fantasy which Guy had written called *The Little Thing*, a whimsical trifle about an orphan girl in a Greenwich Village boarding-house. Every young playwright has something of this sort tucked away in a drawer, and it is always something which managers refuse to consider. Shakespeare, as he sat listening to the audience at the Globe whistling and stamping its feet at the end of the 'To be or not to be' soliloquy, was probably not congratulating himself that *Hamlet* was a sell-out and that if business kept up like this they would do fifteen ducats, eleven rose-nobles and four pieces of eight on the week. It is far more likely that he was thinking wistfully of his masterpiece, that *Tragedy of Alexander the Great* which he could never get Burbage to look at.

'What piece is that?' asked Comstock.

'It's called *The Little Thing*. It's a fantasy.'

'It's wonderful,' said Guy.

'Terrific,' said Plum. 'Strikes a new note.'

'Yes, honey,' said Comstock. 'No, honey,' said Comstock. 'Just as you say, honey. Good-bye, honey.' He hung up the receiver. 'I'm glad you like the idea, boys,' he said. 'A big hit in its day, the *Milk White Flag*.'

Guy clutched his forehead.

'But what about the numbers?'

'Oh, hello, honey,' said Comstock as the telephone tinkled. He tucked the receiver between ear and shoulder and poured himself a drink. There was nothing to indicate whether this was the previous honey, playing a return date, or another honey. 'What's your trouble?' he said. 'Not yours, honey. I have some authors with me.'

'Who does the numbers?'

'The corpse has two daughters, and they have beaux. What more do you want?'

'But the daughters think their father is lying dead on ice in the next room. They'll scarcely be in the mood to sing.'

'That's up to you. I'm not writing the show. Would you mind repeating that, honey, somebody was talking. No, I *can't* throw them out on their fannies, honey, this is business. I have to work, don't I, honey? If I didn't, where would you be? Oh, you would, would you? Oh, they do, do they? Begging you on their bended knees, are they? Well, why don't you? Darned good idea.' He seemed not in the least perturbed. His tone was mild, even affectionate. 'Go to hell, honey!' he concluded almost lovingly and, hanging up the receiver, turned to Bolton. 'What were you saying about a fantasy?'

'I was speaking about the show we've written, *The Little Thing*.'

'I don't like fantasies.'

'You'll like this fantasy.'

'Who says so?'

It seemed to Plum that it was a case for compromise.

'Well, if *The Little Thing* doesn't appeal to you, Ray, how about *Oh, Boy!*?'

'What's *Oh, Boy!*?'

'Another show we've been working on. It's got a good story, and Jerry and I have finished half the numbers. There's one called "Till the Clouds Roll By"—'

'Perfect for the *Milk White Flag*. One of the beaux is trying to cheer up one of the daughters. "Too bad your old man shuffled off," he says. "Yes, damned shame if you ask me," says the daughter. "Still, nothing to be done about it, of course," says the fellow. "No," says the girl. "Let's wait till the clouds roll by." And into number. Fits like the paper on the wall.'

Guy rose.

'The charm dissolves space,' he said. 'I quote Shakespeare.'

'That's the trouble with you,' said Comstock. 'You've been reading Shakespeare. You've gone highbrow on me. This *Oh, Boy!* What's it a musical version of?'

'It isn't a musical version of anything. It's original. Our own unaided work.'

Comstock shook his head.

'I don't want an original. I want something I've heard them laugh at. Then I know what I'm getting. Now, *A Milk White Flag*—'

'No,' said Guy firmly. 'Shoot, if you must, this old grey head, but don't ask me to make a Princess musical with half the numbers done by a corpse with no trousers on. I'm sorry.'

'I'm sorry, too,' said Comstock. The telephone tinkled. 'Oh, hello, honey,' he said. 'Haven't heard from you in some time.'

2

For some months after that a number of writers wrestled with *A Milk White Flag*. Otto Harbach made a start, but gave it up. Henry Blossom, Victor Herbert's writing-partner, had a go, and turned in his portfolio. It was finally taken on by a triumvirate consisting of John L. Golden, Anne Caldwell and Jack Hazzard. The music was by Baldwin Sloane, and the piece had been called *Go To It*, one of those unfortunate titles which spell disaster from the outset. Offer a dramatic critic something called *Go To It*, and he is immediately struck by the happy thought of saying that it should have been called *Don't Go To It*, for these dramatic critics are as quick as lightning.

Bolton held his breath. Wodehouse held his breath. Kern, in his Bronxville home, was also holding his breath. They realized that this was a crisis. If *Go To It* was a hit, their hold on the Princess was gone, and the chance to put on an original anywhere would vanish for ever. The adapted farce would seem to every manager, as it seemed to Ray Comstock, a safer bet, and their *Oh, Boy!* (retitled *Oh Joy!* for its British production in 1919) would not have a hope of production.

They journeyed down to Atlantic City for the out-of-town opening, and were able to breathe again. The thing was awful, just as they had predicted it would be. Not even the corpse on its bed of ice was colder than the audience. It was with uplifted hearts that they returned to the Traymore. In the lobby they encountered Freddie Zimmerman, the son of the owner of a large chain of theatres in the provinces, who invited them to his suite for a nightcap. He had come over from Philadelphia as an emissary of his father to view the new Princess show and decide whether to accept it as tenant of one of the Zimmerman houses. After the first intermission he had phoned his old man and told him to let *Go To It* go elsewhere.

In Freddy's suite they found Joe Urban. Joe, who was making history with his stage settings and even more with his revolutionary stage lighting, had done a beautiful job with *Miss Springtime*. He eyed the trio with momentary anxiety.

'This *Go To It* – you boys did not write it?' he asked.

With considerable emphasis the boys assured him they did not.

'I am so glad,' he said. 'For me it is a very bad smell. It should be taken away by the grubbage collector to the city dumpings.'

Joe, a charming Austrian, spoke a language of his own. He couldn't drink milk because it curdled in his stomach; he promised that he would have his sketches ready at the drop of a bucket, and, when he grew emphatic, his favourite expression was 'just mock my words'. In those days people collected Urbanisms as they later collected the quaint sayings of Samuel Goldwyn.

Joe remarked that he loved Atlantic City. The air was so embracing.

'I can remember a time when it wasn't as embracing as you would have liked it to be,' laughed Freddy.

'No,' agreed Joe, 'I get a sock in the pants that time I shall never forget.'

It had happened during the war when Atlantic City was full of volunteer spy-chasers, dollar-a-year men, proud of the federal badge they carried under their lapels and all anxious to make a name for themselves by uncovering a trail of espionage. One of these had his eye on Joe. The *Follies* scenery had been damaged in transit and Joe had sent for his Austrian business manager, who had arrived with three Austrian scene-painters, and, while they worked, the manager would whisper to Joe asking how chances were for getting some money out of Ziegfeld, and Joe would whisper back that they were not good, explaining that, while fantastically generous about anything he didn't owe, Ziegfeld had a constitutional objection for paying what he did.

It was these Teutonic whisperings that had aroused the suspicions of the spy-chaser, who was lurking in the background, but what really set him hot on the trail was the signalling.

'In the mornings,' said Joe, 'I do always my sitting-up exercises. We are staying at the Shelbourne that time and I open the window and breathe the invizerating sea's air while I go oop, down, out, back with the arms.'

'The sleuth-hound was down below,' supplemented Freddy, 'making notes.'

'What did he think you were doing – signalling to Germany?'

'To Germany, no. To someone in the Bellevue – Stratford. It is you know only a stone's jump from the Shelbourne. This dumkopf think when I go oop, down, out, back it is a code – a wag-wag.'

It seems that the thrill of sharing a hotel with the *Follies* beauties had been too much for Joe. He had fallen in love. What is more he had fallen in love with the gorgeous prize peach of the 1917 crop. And Joe's Austrian charm, his soft, vibrant voice breathing words of adoration, had found ready response from a heart which, like the US Navy, was 'open to all men from eighteen to forty'.

Joe, somewhat falteringly, had suggested that if she would come up to his suite he would show her a collection of his drawings and, at the same time, they could deal with another bottle of Bollinger non-vintage. She accepted on both counts, and they made their way to the Shelbourne. When they got in the elevator a man stepped in with them. When they got out he followed. As Joe was putting the key in the lock he felt a hand on his shoulder and a voice said, 'You are under arrest.'

'I think it is someone pushing my leg,' said Joe. 'I say to him in my most chalant manner, "This is no time for clown-making." He say it is no clown-making but honest-to-level and that I must come with him. I make pleadings. I say I do not know what I have done but can he not, for a little while, let bygones be hasbeens? All he does is say like a parrot, "You are under arrest." '

Ziegfeld was sent for and he explained who Joe was, adding that, while the United States was important, the *Ziegfeld Follies* wasn't to be kicked around either. He needed Joe to get his scenery right. Finally a compromise was effected. The Sleuth would give Joe a week before hauling him into court but, during that time, the artist must remain in his custody. Not for a single moment was he to be out of his sight.

'Everywhere I go,' said Joe, 'there he is dodging my feetsteps. Whenever my girl and me went chair-riding it must be one of those big for-three chairs. She has heard of a wonderful fish ghetto where they make special fine lobster-humidor. This lowlife goes with us to the ghetto. He also eats lobster-humidor.'

When the week was up Joe was carted over to Philadelphia, taken before a judge – and cleared. He returned to New York just in time for the *Follies* opening.

'So it all ended happily?'

'Not so much happily,' answered Joe. 'I ask my girl to have supper with me opening night, but she say she cannot. And then when I walk into Rector's after the show, what do I see? She is sitting handholding with the verdampte spy-chaser!'

3

Go To It duly opened at the Princess. All the critics – except one, who headed his review with the word 'Why?' – said that it should not have been called *Go To It* but *Don't Go To It*. Jerry Kern had a call from Comstock soon after breakfast, asking him to come at once to the office and bring Guy and Plum.

In the Comstock office there was a hushed, funeral atmosphere. The customary row of actors sat in the waiting-room, looking rather more animated than usual. One gathered that the newspaper each one held contained a message of hope for the artist who was resting. They would soon be casting again at the Princess.

Ray Comstock was at his desk, the receiver wedged against his ear.

'Come in, boys,' he said. 'Yes, honey, it's a flop. . . . So am I, honey. . . . Thanks, honey. . . . Good-bye, honey.' He hung up. 'Now, boys,' he said with, for him, a surprising briskness, 'we've taken a kick in the pants, as I'm sure you all know. I blame you fellows, partly. Oh, hello, honey. If you'd tackled the job as I asked you to, things might have been different. You've got something – maybe it's this "charm" you talk about. No, honey, I'm not talking to you, I'm talking to the boys. I saw *Miss Springtime* the other night. It's a swell show, a clever show, plenty of laughs, too.'

'It isn't in it with *Oh, Boy!*' said Guy.

'That's what I wanted to see you about. Get off this damned line, will you, honey. I'll give you a contract for *Oh, Boy!* right now.'

'But you haven't read it.'

'I don't need to. You fellows know what you are doing. I'll see it opening night. The only question is how soon can we get into rehearsal?'

Guy reflected.

'A month for writing, a couple of weeks for casting – we should be ready by December.'

'Okay, boys, go to it.' Comstock coughed apologetically. 'Sorry, it slipped out. I shall try never to use those words again.'

'You really mean that you'll buy the show without reading it or hearing a note of music?'

'That's right. Tell your agent to draw the contracts, 7 per cent, no more. You choose the directors and the cast. If they'll fit in the budget, you can have anyone you name.'

'I'd like Robert Milton to stage the book,' said Guy.

'Isn't that the red-headed Russian who talks about "pear-shaped tones"?'

'Yes, but he's clever just the same, and he's begging for a chance to do a musical.'

'That's what I like,' said Ray, 'people begging. It's when you got to beg *them* that things get expensive. Now run along. Don't waste time talking. Go to—' He checked himself.

'Get busy,' he amended.

The three rose. Plum pulled a cigar from his pocket and held it out.

'Have a cigar, Ray,' he said. It was the first and perhaps the last time an author ever gave a cigar to a theatrical manager. Ray took it with a slightly dazed air.

'Thank you, honey,' he said mechanically.

5

1

THERE were two small female roles in *Oh, Boy!* which still remained to be filled after the rest of the cast – Anna Wheaton, Marie Carroll, Edna May Oliver and the others – had been signed up: and one morning Comstock asked Guy and Plum to look in at his office. They found him telephoning as usual.

'Can you fellows . . . I haven't time to talk to you now, honey, we're casting. And don't ask if there's anything for you, because there isn't . . . keep a secret?' he said.

They thought they could.

'Well, I don't promise, but I think I'm going to steal the two top *Follies* beauties away from Flo Ziegfeld.'

'You don't mean—?'

'That's right. Marion Davies and Justine Johnstone.'

'You're kidding, Ray. Why would they leave Flo? Look at the publicity he gives them.'

'They want to be actresses.'

'Ah!'

'And I caught them at just the right moment. They're sore about the dressing-room sketch.'

'What's the dressing-room sketch?' asked Plum.

'I know all about that,' said Guy. 'It's a thing Gene Buck wrote for the *Follies*, but it has never been used. It never will be, either. It's much too valuable to Flo for him to waste it on the public. You see, every year Flo has this same trouble with some of the girls getting ambitious. They tell him they won't sign on unless they're given lines to speak. So up pops the dressing-room sketch. The girls get their parts, and everybody's happy.'

'And then he says it's so bad it must come out?'

Guy was amazed.

'*Flo?* You think Flo would do anything as crude as that? Of course not. He tells them the sketch is great stuff and they're going to knock the customers endways. He says he never realized before how wonderful they were and thanks them for making him give them the opportunity of showing what they could do. But, come opening night at Atlantic City, he's all broken up to find that the costumes, owing to somebody's inexcusable carelessness, have been left behind. He yells and storms at the wardrobe mistress, but there's nothing to be done about it, of course, till tomorrow night. And before tomorrow night they've found out that the show is an hour too long and he's all broken up but the dressing-room sketch will have to go. Meanwhile, the girls have signed up for another year.'

The following afternoon when Guy and Plum arrived at the Princess, there were two 'town cars' parked at the kerb, a pair of uniformed chauffeurs standing beside them. The Delage bore no identifying insignia, but on the door of the Pierce-Arrow were two Js intertwined back to back like the double Ls emblazoned on the royal coach of the *Roi Soleil.*

Everything seemed to indicate that here were the Girls.

As the two authors entered Ray's office, it was evident to them that they had guessed right. The air was vibrant with silvery laughter, and the characteristic smell of a theatrical manager's office, which is a blend of dust, whisky, and old, dead scripts, had given place to something more pleasing, possibly Coty's 'l'Origan' or 'Quelques Fleurs'. The place was practically a boudoir.

The girls were quite breathtakingly lovely. Marion was eighteen, Justine a year and a half older. Both wore mink coats that even a masculine eye could see were the best that the mink family had to offer. Both wore a spray of orchids as if orchids were an everyday affair – which for them they were. Diamonds sparkled at their wrists and glistened more discreetly through the sheer black silk stocking that covered Marion's slender ankle.

Bob Milton, a mature and serious man, sat on the sofa beside Marion, gazing at her as Bernard Berenson would gaze on a Botticelli Venus.

'Don't waste your time with them,' he said, as Guy and Plum were 'presented'. 'They're only writers. I'm the man that's going to make you into an actress.'

'Yes, b-but they'll have to write the w-words I'm to say.' Marion had an ever-so-faint and ever-so-attractive stammer.

Justine Johnstone was, if anything, even more likely than her friend to provoke the long, low whistle. Daughter of a Norwegian sea captain, she had that touch of aloofness and that faintly haughty carriage that seem to characterize the beauties claiming Viking ancestry.

'The girls are ready to sign up with us,' said Ray, 'provided they get parts.'

Guy assured them that they would have parts.

'And names,' said Justine. 'Not just "first girl" and "second girl".'

'Of course you have names. Yours is Polly Andrews.'

'Is that a play on polyandrous?'

'Good heavens, no.'

'It sounds like it.'

'What does polyandrous mean?' Bob Milton inquired. He was a Russian whose real name was Davidoff and a surprisingly short time before he had known no English words at all.

'It means the same thing about a woman that polygamous does about a man.'

'You're too well-educated,' said Marion. 'I just say snuggle-hound – that's what I hear Ray is. I hear he's the worst old snuggle-hound on Broadway.'

'I'm not a patch on Guy. A flick of the finger, a broken heart – that's Guy Bolton.'

'Really?'

'He once kissed a girl on Broadway, and she shot clear up to the top of the Woolworth Building.'

'You don't say?'

'I'm telling you. Just closed her eyes with a little moan and floated up and up and up.'

'And he looks so good. Are you married, Guy?'

'Not yet.'

'But you are?' said Marion to Plum.

'Oh, yes,' Guy told her. 'Plum is very happily married and he's constantly telling me I should be too.'

'You get married,' said Marion, 'and first thing you know you have a baby. Then in a few months – there's another baby. Mind you, I like babies, I like them a lot, but I'm glad I haven't one now.'

Then, as if it were an afterthought, she leaned over and rapped the top of Ray's desk. The laugh that rewarded her carried her to the door.

'Write me some funny stuff, boys,' she said. 'I want to be a comic.'

She went out.

'Marion will say anything to get a laugh,' Justine commented in her low, Ethel Barrymore voice, 'but really she's a perfectly good girl and lives at home with her mother.'

She gave a little gurgling laugh as if she too had said something funny, then raised her hand in the straight forearm salute associated with royalty. Her hand fluttered a farewell. 'Good-bye, boys.'

She followed Marion out. Through the open door they could see the actors craning their necks after her. There was a buzz of comment. Plum, who had been the little gentleman to spring up and open the door, closed it behind her.

'I feel as if I had stepped back into Good King Charles's golden reign,' he remarked. 'Saucy Nell must have been very like Saucy Marion.'

'Yes, Charles would have made them both duchesses,' agreed Guy.

'They'll get us a lot of publicity,' said Ray. 'But, great Godfrey, how the rest of the women in the show are going to hate them!'

2

The rehearsal period passed swiftly and uneventfully. It seemed no time before a day arrived when the company were gathering on a platform in the Grand Central, with the usual collection of dogs, fiancés, and anxious mothers that appear whenever a theatrical troupe is setting off 'on the road'.

The manager in charge was a young man named Jefferson Perry. He was new at the game, but anxious to learn all he could about it before embarking on some private ventures of a highbrow nature beside which *Oh, Boy!* seemed trivial indeed.

His wife, of no special moment – or so the boys supposed – was a rather severe-looking young woman with glasses, who wore a small brooch on which the letters 'D.A.R.' appeared in red-white-and-blue enamel.

Schenectady was the first stop, and there the authors were plunged into the depths of despair by a dress rehearsal at which all the things that can go wrong at dress rehearsals did.

The shoes, for instance. The gentleman from I. Miller sitting stolidly out front was a constant object of attack.

'These are my own shoes, Mr Comstock. The shoes from Miller don't fit.'

'You need them larger?'

'Larger on the inside – yes.'

The prop department had its share of blame.

'I'm supposed to have a letter to read but no one's given it to me.'

Then, most nerve-racking of all – the stage wait. 'What's the matter? What's supposed to be happening?' 'Miss Wheaton says she can't make the change. There'll have to be more dialogue.'

The two Ziegfeld lovelies appeared on the stage for a brief scene that lit the depressing gloom with a moment or two of comic relief. Marion, it seems, had suffered an attack of stage fright and, in an effort to dispel it, had downed a glass or two of champagne. This had the unfortunate effect of increasing her charming little stammer to a point at which she was unable to deliver her lines.

To cope with this situation the girls had arranged between them that Justine should speak not only her own lines but Marion's as well. The remarkable monologue ran as follows:

'Oh, so you're here? Yes, I'm here – what about it? You won't leave George Budd alone. That's my business. You don't stand a chance with him. Why not? He's in love with that little Carter girl. He isn't.

Yes, darling, he is. I don't care. I'll tell you something else, darling. They're married. They're *not*. Yes, they are – secretly married.'

Some effort at verisimilitude was made by Justine changing her voice on each alternate line, speaking first in a piping treble then in her own rich contralto. On the treble lines Marion kept moving her lips as if she were actually speaking. But mouthing and sound were a very poor fit.

The scattering of dressmakers, scene-painters, music-arrangers, house-managers, not to mention the gentleman from I. Miller, burst into shouts of laughter.

'Keep it in, Guy,' said Comstock grimly. 'At least you'll be sure of one laugh.'

The climax came with the sudden appearance of a reporter and a press photographer shepherded by the show's press agent. There was a whispered exchange with Ray Comstock who shook hands with the newcomers and then called Milton over.

'Stop the rehearsal,' he said. 'We're going to get a spread in the papers.'

The actors gathered together in little groups as the newsmen made their way on to the stage.

'Who do you want first?' asked the stage manager.

'We only want Miss Davies and Miss Johnstone.'

'You mean you're not going to take any pictures of the rest of the company?'

'No, that's our orders – just Miss Davies and Miss Johnstone.'

The company had come out front and sat watching the girls as they moved from pose to pose. The expressions on the faces of the female members of the cast were much the same as those of the bonnet rouge leading the mob in Delacroix's famous painting of the storming of the Tuileries. One heard the mutterings of the crowd coming from the seats where the chorus had grouped themselves.

'They're just a bunch of amateurs.' Guy and Plum, sitting together, numb and despairing, heard it without knowing who said it.

Then someone added, 'Like a college show.'

Finally the picture-taking was finished.

'Let's get on with the rehearsal,' Comstock called from the back of the theatre.

'Sorry, Mr Comstock, Miss Wheaton and Miss Carroll have gone. They said they'd have no voices tomorrow if they sat around in this cold theatre any longer.'

Comstock rose. 'Send 'em all home,' he said. 'No use going on. You'll just have to trust to luck tomorrow – and God knows you'll need plenty.'

He turned to Jerry Kern, ignoring the pair seated behind him, and delivered the *coup de grâce*.

'This is the lousiest, awfullest show I ever saw,' he said. 'I thought *Go To It* was bad, but it was a sweetheart compared to this turkey. It hasn't a hope.'

3

The two who had planned and written the atrocity made no reply. They slipped out of a side exit to avoid meeting anyone either on the stage or in the lobby. No conference was called. The thing was beyond conferences. The scribbled notes of errors detected earlier in the evening seemed too trivial to mention. To have wasted time on them would have been like cleaning spots off the deck of a vessel about to founder.

There was a bitter wind blowing, and when a bitter wind blows in Schenectady it is a matter of civic pride with the citizens that no other upstate city can claim a bitterer. Guy and Plum turned up the collars of substantial overcoats that felt as if they were fashioned of gossamer.

The empty streets were dark as were their thoughts. It was very late. The Schenectadians were abed, dreaming no doubt of the treat that awaited them tomorrow evening at the Gaiety Theatre.

They rounded a corner and were met by a blast that seemed to say, 'You thought it was cold on Main Street, did you? Now we'll show you what Canal Street can do.' They bowed their heads and pushed forward like Robert Peary and his Eskimo companion on 8th April '99.

A figure suddenly appeared beside them. It was the red-headed boy who played the waiter at the country club in Act Two, a part of less than a dozen lines.

'How was I?' he asked, barring their path.

'You were fine, Eddie.' It was hard to speak without losing your breath. 'You were wonderful.'

'I'd like to have a little chat about my part,' said Eddie. 'I guess some of the things you wrote have more meaning than I'm putting into them.'

'Not a bit, old man.'

'If I could go over them.'

'But for God's sake, Eddie – not here.'

'That last exit of mine. I'd like a laugh, if you could give me one.'

'We haven't a laugh in us, Eddie.'

'I thought of something myself. I'd like to tell it to you, if you won't get sore.'

'We won't get sore, but we may get pneumonia. I feel like the corpse on ice in *Go To It*.'

'Yes, it's a bit chilly tonight, isn't it?' said Eddie, apparently having just noticed it. 'But this won't take a minute. Of course, it's a pretty fresh of me to be trying to put a line in a wonderful show like *Oh, Boy!*'

'You think *Oh, Boy!* is wonderful?'

'I sure do.'

'Then,' said Guy, 'we're at your service until Hell freezes over. And that, I should think, is liable to happen almost any minute.'

'Well, you know the situation,' said Eddie, getting down to it. 'Miss Wheaton has just got a flash of Sheriff Simms through the window. He's been looking for her ever since she escaped from that raid in the speakeasy—'

'Yes, yes, we know the plot.'

'Well, she runs into the Ladies' Room just as I'm going off on the other side, and I thought maybe I could call to her, "When you come out, would you mind bringing me my umbrella?" Would that be okay?'

'Absolutely okay,' said Guy. 'And if you'd like to rewrite the rest of the show you're more than welcome.'

4

The next night was a riot. Everything went like clockwork. The hand-props were all there, I. Miller's shoes were all there. When it came to the quick change, Anna Wheaton was there. Most important of all, the laughs were there, and none topped that put in by Eddie, the red-headed waiter.

Ray Comstock beamed.

'I knew it was all right last night,' he said. 'You could feel success in the air.'

They moved on to Syracuse, Rochester, Buffalo and Albany, the weather getting colder and colder and the audiences warmer and warmer, and the company, after the manner of theatrical touring companies, becoming what someone has cleverly described as 'one big happy family'. No team, no clique, no sworn band of blood-brothers has such a tendency to gang up as a company of travelling actors. They move like Xenophon's Ten Thousand through an alien country, speaking a different language. They think of nothing but the show. Newspapers lose their interest. Burning questions may be exercising the rest of the populace, but to actors on the road the only burning question is, 'How's the show going to go tonight?'

But even a big happy family can have its rifts within the lute. The trouble with the *Oh, Boy!* one was, as might have been, predicted, the Girls. Not that they weren't nice to everybody, not that they were not good troupers. But they were too pretty.

And then there were the hotel suites, which rankled a little with important members of the company who had to rough it in humble bedrooms. These had started quite modestly, but as the tour progressed they became larger, and the flowers with which they were bedecked appeared in more lavish profusion. Somebody – possibly her mother – was intent on seeing to it that while on the road Marion got all the comforts of home, and this mother – or it may have been an aunt – was plainly a woman of spacious ideas. In the Hollenden Hotel in Cleveland what Marion drew was a reception room, a large sitting-room, a small sitting-room, a dining-room, two bedrooms, two baths, a clothes-pressing room, maid's room and maid's bath.

Invited to share it, Justine looked dubious. 'Where do I put my maid?' she queried.

'That's all right,' said Marion cheerily. 'We'll tell them to tack on another room and bath.'

5

It was in this cosy little chummery that the famous party was given, but before the party came the arrival of Ethel Wodehouse and before the arrival of Ethel Wodehouse came the contretemps.

Mrs Jefferson Perry, the wife of the company manager, was, here in Cleveland, treading her native heath. Her mother, still extant, was of the *crème de la crème* of Cleveland society. And in those days there was no nonsense about 'café society'. As Ward McAlister could tell you, you were either born to it or you weren't.

Mrs Jefferson Perry, Mrs Jefferson Perry's mother, Mrs Pell and the Kerns were having supper following the Cleveland opening of *Oh, Boy!* the reception of which had been all that could be desired. At another table in the Hollenden dining-room the Girls were the guests of Plum and Guy. Their meal was the first to finish and the quartette filed out, passing the Kern-Perry-Pell table. A pause was indicated.

'Went well, didn't it?' said Guy, and turned to Mrs Perry who with downcast eye was busying herself with a Nesselrode pudding.

'You don't know Miss Davies and Miss Johnstone, do you, Mrs Perry?'

'No, and I don't care to,' said Mrs Perry.

This devastating rejoinder broke up the little gathering.

The one big happy family was no longer one and no longer happy. The story quickly went the rounds and produced varying reactions. Most of the company sided with the Girls but there were exceptions. At least two of the members of the company laughed when they heard the story and said 'Good'. This was duly reported to the Girls by one of those little birds that goes around poking his bill into other people's business. Also Eva Kern continued to be seen about with Mrs Jefferson Perry. It made her a marked woman.

It had reached the point where certain members of the company were not speaking to each other, and at which unpleasant words were muttered half audibly as some member of the opposing camp passed by, when the party was augmented by the arrival of Ethel. She loved the show, but was appalled by the 'atmosphere'.

'It's the best way to get a failure,' she said. 'You can't have a company bickering and quarrelling. People can't work together unless there is harmony.'

'Nonsense,' said Plum. 'Look at Gilbert and Sullivan, they were like a dose of Paris green to each other but they worked together all right.'

'There may be exceptions, but that doesn't alter the fact that in most cases dissension destroys the team spirit.'

'What can we do about it?'

'You must give a party, you and Guy – Jerry too if you like. A real bang-up "get-together". And when they're all there and have had plenty to drink you must make a little speech about the importance of harmony.'

'My instinct is against it, but I know from experience that once you make up your mind to give a party, no man or elemental power may stay your course.'

'I'm only doing it for you and Guy. You neither of you seem to think it important to have everyone pulling together, but I feel sure that it is.'

'What do you think, Guy?'

'I think if Ethel wants us to give a party we'll give a party.'

'It needn't be anything elaborate. Lots of beer and a few bottles of whisky.'

'And sandwiches?'

'Yes, and a few other odds and ends. "Picnic style" I'd call it. Songs round the piano. By the time it's over they'll all be one big happy family.'

6

Two evenings later the party took place. Ethel assured Plum and Guy that they need not involve themselves in the preparations. She would take care of everything. Ray Comstock, she said, had promised to find a room of suitable size. Everyone was coming, chorus as well as principals.

The two hosts were the first to arrive. Ethel had said that they would find her there, but she wasn't visible.

'Anybody here?' called Plum.

'Only us tables and chairs.'

'And a hell of a lot of expensive-looking flowers.'

They peered into adjoining rooms. In the dining-room was a U-shaped table with American Beauty roses strewn about artistically between the places. Standing at one end of the room was a marvellous buffet of cold dishes that included a big salmon encased in ice. There was a platter of Chicken Jeannette and another of some small birds that looked like quail in aspic.

Guy pointed to it. 'Picnic style,' he said. 'For the love of Pete, what has Ethel been up to? The show will have to run six months for us to break even.'

'Gosh, yes, look at this – there are music stands. She's engaged an orchestra.'

'And what about these champagne buckets? There are bottles and bottles.'

'What kind of champagne is it?'

'I'm afraid to look.'

'Suffering Pete – Bollinger 1911.'

Max Hirschfeld, the company's conductor, arrived with three or four of his musicians. He said that Ray Comstock had told him there would be dancing. The musicians started in to play the music from the show. Some of the girls and boys came trooping in and took the floor. Then came the magnetic Anna Wheaton and her opposite number, Hal Forde. Marie Carroll and Tom Powers followed, then the Kerns accompanied by the Perrys and the inevitable Mrs Pell.

'Say, what *is* all this?' exclaimed Jerry. 'Putting on the dog a bit, aren't you?'

'What about yourself? What about those pearls Eva is wearing?' countered Plum.

'Aren't they lovely?' said Eva. 'Jerry said he'd get them for me when he was sure the show would be a big hit.'

'Expensive, of course,' said Jerry. '$7500, no less.'

As he spoke they became aware of a sudden hush in the room. All eyes had turned to the door. It was the Girls. They paused just inside the door waiting for the lovely ermine wraps to knock 'em dead. They looked ravishing in sheath-like dinner dresses that showed off the flowing lines of their young figures. They both wore sprays of orchids and pearl necklaces. The other women, looking them over with microscopic carelessness, knew that they might as well pack up and go home. They'd had it.

The two hosts went forward and greeted them. 'Let's dance,' said the Girls simultaneously.

As Guy danced with Justine, she asked him what it was Jerry was saying when they arrived. 'Something about a pearl necklace.'

The music stopped and Plum suggested they come in to supper. Four waiters had appeared. The champagne had begun to flow.

'Don't look now,' said Plum to his fellow-sufferer, 'but I think the stuff in those crocks the waiters are passing is caviar.'

It was caviar – the big grey kind that nowadays never gets farther than the tables of particular friends of the boys in the back-room at the Kremlin.

Then at last, pale and scared, Ethel appeared. She drew the hosts aside.

'I've been looking everywhere for Ray Comstock. I gave him my lists, but left the ordering to him. He's changed everything.'

'You didn't order caviar?'

'Good Heavens, no.'

'How about Bollinger '11?'

'I asked for whisky and beer as I said I would – everything Bohemian and informal.'

'And the performers on sackbut and psaltery?'

'No, I told Ray to make sure there was a piano for Jerry and whoever else might play.'

'Ray thinks it's a joke, I suppose. He's always making cracks about all the money we have rolling in.'

Save for the bad moment when the Girls appeared, Mrs Jefferson Perry was having a good time.

'I adore caviar,' she said. 'I've never had enough, but I'm really making the most of my opportunity tonight. And this champagne is the last word.'

'I love the peeled hot-house peaches in the glasses,' chimed in her mother.

Ethel closed her eyes and drew a long breath. 'Hot-house peaches!' she murmured.

The Girls seated across the table from Jerry, Eva and the Perry contingent, were engaged in a conversation about jewellery.

'Lillian Lorraine has a new pearl necklace,' said Miss Johnstone casually.

'What, another one?'

'Oh, this isn't like her real one. It's just something to wear when she's slumming. It only cost $7500.'

'I wouldn't be seen dead in a thing like that,' said Miss Davies disdainfully. 'My motto is don't have it if you can't have it good.'

'You're so right, darling,' agreed Miss Johnstone. 'Of course, for $7500 all you get is one of those cultured Japanese jobs. The Japs tease the oyster into making the pearl by pushing a bit of grit into his shell. He makes a pearl, but his heart isn't in the work.'

'Serves the Japs right,' said Miss Davies. 'Why should an oyster be annoyed like that just to make second-class pearls for cheap necklaces? Left alone he might some day make a really good pearl – something an oyster could be proud of.'

It was at this point that Eva said that she had a headache and thought she'd go to bed. Mrs Jefferson Perry downed a final glass of Bollinger and said if Eva was going she would go too.

'Oh, don't go yet,' protested Marion. 'I ordered Nesselrode pudding especially for you – I know how fond you are of it.'

'*You* ordered it?' cried Mrs Perry. 'I was told this party was being given by Mr Wodehouse and Mr Bolton.'

'Not *this* party, dear,' said Marion. '*This* party is mine. I believe their party is in one of the banqueting rooms on the second floor.'

'But we were told to come here.'

'Yes, Ray thought you might all enjoy coming to my party first.' She turned her charming smile full on Mrs Perry. 'Perhaps he knew how fond you are of caviar.'

'Are *we* invited to your party?' asked Marion, turning to the authors.

'Of course,' said Plum, fastening his gaze on Ethel. 'Ours is for everybody – a get-together. The entire big happy family.'

'That's lovely,' said Marion, 'but anyone who wants to stay here can. How are you doing, girls?' she asked, addressing the female principals at their table. 'Are they giving you plenty of champagne?'

It was the day of the gold-mesh bag. Each of the girls was carrying one. Marion opened hers.

'Oh, dear,' she said, turning to Justine. 'Have you a loose $100 on you, darling? I want to leave something for the waiter.'

6

THE definition of a smash-hit in the theatre is one that has varied a good deal from age to age. In Shakespeare's time anything that ran two nights was good, and if you did three you went out and bought a new fur coat. In the nineties authors became offensively conceited if they broke the hundred mark. Today a musical comedy which runs less than five years is presumed to have had some structural weakness in it. It ought to have been fixed up out of town, people say, even if it meant calling in a couple of play-doctors.

It is difficult, therefore, to estimate the degree of success which *Oh, Boy!* achieved. One can only say that it was sufficient to make one chuck one's chest out quite considerably when it happened. It did not run five years, but it did do 475 performances in New York, and during its Broadway run there were four companies out on the road, one playing Chicago, another Boston, a third the one-week cities and a fourth the one-night stands. It cost $29,262.56 to produce, this including a seven-week tour during which two authors, a composer, a book director, a dance director and a manager had to be supported in luxury, and it made a profit of $181,641.54.

For those days it was a socko, and it left Bolton and Wodehouse – the latter now better known as the Sweet-Singing Thrush of 39th Street – sitting on top of the world and loving it. It seemed as though Fate had decided that there was nothing she could deny to these favourite sons of hers. They were in. As they sauntered past Cain's Storehouse of a morning, taking snuff from their jewelled snuff-boxes and sneering at the lower orders whom they jostled off the pavement, there was never a thought in their minds that the time was coming when that gaunt building would play an impressive part in their lives and that before many more suns had set its proprietor, when asked by friends how business was, would be saying, 'Quiet at the moment, boys, a little quiet at the moment, but it'll pick up. Bolton and Wodehouse have a couple of shows coming on.' Like most young authors who get a run of luck, the unhappy saps had taken on much more work than they could do even fairly well. They had so many irons in the fire that they put the fire out.

Writing musical comedies is like eating salted almonds – you can always manage one more. Every time the two partners met, they vowed that they would go on the musical comedy wagon, but nothing ever came of their good resolutions. Somehow they found themselves in Charlie Dillingham's office, and there was the box of cigars on the desk and Mr Ziegfeld in a chair by the window and Mr Dillingham saying, 'Wouldn't it be fun to get up some theatricals?' and Mr Ziegfeld saying, 'Yes, wouldn't it?', and then a voice through the smoke cooed, 'Sign here, boys,' and the boys woke up and found that they were booked to do a colossal revue for the Century Theatre.

And after that . . . Cain's hospital storehouse.

Cain's Storehouse, like so many monuments of the past, no longer exists. One is not quite sure what happens now to the scenery of shows that have failed to attract. You probably have to cart it out into the wilds somewhere and set fire to it with matches. But in the days of which we are writing Cain's was a great institution, a sort of Sargasso Sea into which the wrecks of dramatic Hesperuses drifted automatically. Or you might call it a morgue. To this morgue it was inevitable that sooner or later Bolton and Wodehouse would be contributing a corpse or two. In actual fact, they contributed three, one after the other.

There was once a manager who, examining his books, made the discovery that his box-office man had been cheating him for years. He sent for the culprit.

'How much do I pay you a week?' he asked.

'$60, sir.'

'It's raised to $75.'

'Oh, thank you, sir!'

'Or, rather, $100.'

'Oh, thank you, sir!'

'No, wait. That's not enough. $150. And when I say $150, I mean, of course, $200.'

'Oh, *thank* you, sir!'

'Just one thing more,' said the manager, beaming at him like a Cheeryble Brother, 'You're fired. You see,' he explained to a friend when telling him of the incident later, 'I wanted to fire the son of a what-not from a really *good* job.'

It is in a precisely similar way that Fate likes to work, waiting with the brass knucks and the sock full of sand until its victims are at the peak of one of those boom periods when life appears to be roses, roses all the way. As Shakespeare, who often hits off a thing rather neatly, once said:

> This is the state of man. Today he puts forth
> The tender leaves of hopes, tomorrow blossoms,
> And bears his blushing honours thick upon him.
> The third day comes a frost, a killing frost;

And when he thinks, good easy men, full surely
His greatness is a-ripening, nips his root.

It was just like that with Guy and Plum. They couldn't have put it better themselves.

The first V-shaped depressions to darken their lives after the unbroken fine weather in which they had been basking came along, ironically, in the season when they had set a mark for all other authors to shoot at by having five shows running simultaneously on Broadway . . . or, in Guy's case, six, for Belasco had taken sufficient time off from his picture-hanging to produce the Bolton-Middleton comedy, *Polly With a Past*, starring Ina Claire, and it had settled down to a long and prosperous run.

These were the five: *Oh, Boy!*, *Leave it to Jane*, *The Rose of China*, *The Riviera Girl*, *The Second Century Show*.

Oh, Boy!, as we say, was a smash-hit, and so to a lesser extent was *Leave it to Jane*, a rather free adaptation of George Ade's *College Widow*.

But the others . . . .

1 *The Rose of China*

The writing of this blot on the New York theatrical scene was due entirely to too much rich food, too much potent liquor and the heady effect of Oriental music on top of these. The consumers of the food and the liquor were the pair so shortly to become the toast of Cain's Storehouse, and the music was that of Armand Vecsey, rendered by himself in the Oval Room of the Ritz-Carlton Hotel, where he was the *chef d'orchestre*.

In the song 'Yip-i-addy' we are told that,

Young Herman von Bellow
A musical fellow,
Performed on the 'cello each night
At a restaurant where
All the brave and the fair
Would look in for a chat and a bite.
He played tunes that you know
From Wagner and Gounod
To give the gay building a tone,
But the place started swaying
When he began playing
A sweet little thing of his own.

It was precisely the same with Armand Vecsey, except that his instrument was the violin. He played superbly, and when he dished out the Chinese suite he had composed, the brave and the fair curled up like carbon paper and the Messrs Bolton and Wodehouse, puffing their cigars and taking another beaker of old brandy, told each other emotionally that this was the stuff. Not realizing that practically anything sounds good after a well-lubricated dinner, they agreed that a musical play written around these marvellous melodies could not fail to bring home the gravy. A week later they were writing *The Rose of China*.

It just shows how overwork can dull the senses that neither of the gifted youths realized what was bound to happen if they started getting mixed up with things of that sort. The advice that should be given to all aspiring young authors is: Have nothing to do with anything with a title like *The Rose of China* or *The Willow Pattern Plate* or *The Siren of Shanghai* or *Me Velly Solly* . . . in fact, avoid Chinese plays altogether. Much misery may thus be averted.

What happens when you write a Chinese play is that before you know where you are your heroine has gone cute on you, adding just that touch of glucose to the part which renders it unsuitable for human consumption. She twitters through the evening saying, 'Me Plum Blossom. Me good girl. Me love Chlistian god velly much,' and things of that sort, like the heroine of Sammy Shipman's *East is West*, by which, one supposes now that the agony has abated and it is possible to think clearly, the Bolton-Wodehouse opus must have been – if that is the right word – inspired.

It is the view of competent critics that – with the possible exception of *Abie's Irish Rose* and *Grandma's Diary* – *East is West* is the ghastliest mess ever put on the American stage, but this is an opinion held only by those who did not see *The Rose of China*. It was of *The Rose of China* that Ring Lardner, one of the scattered few who caught it during its New York run, said, 'Cain's horses are *snorting* for this one,' and how right he was. It was the sort of piece where the eyes of the audience keep wandering to that cheering notice at the top of the programme: 'This theatre can be emptied in three minutes. Look around, choose the nearest exit to your seat and walk (do not run) to that exit.'

Without referring to the script, a thing they are naturally reluctant to do, the authors cannot say after this length of time whether or not the heroine of *The Rose of China* turned out in the end to be the daughter of an American missionary, kidnapped by Chinese bandits in her infancy, but it would seem virtually certain that she did. All heroines of Chinese plays turn out in the end to be the daughters of American missionaries, kidnapped by bandits in their infancy. This is known as Shipman's Law. There is no reason to suppose that in this instance there would have been any deviation from the straight party line.

2 *The Riviera Girl*

By all the ruling of the form book this one should have been all right, for it was a Klaw and Erlanger production, put in with Joseph Urban scenery at the New Amsterdam, and the score was by Kalman, the composer of *Sari* and *Miss Springtime*, with additional numbers by Jerome Kern.

The Kalman score was not only the best that gifted Hungarian ever wrote but about the best anybody ever wrote. After thirty-odd years it is still played constantly on the radio, and in the early fifties it was revived, with another libretto, in Paris, and pulled in the cash customers in their thousands. Which seems to place the responsibility for its deplorable failure on Broadway squarely on the shoulders of the boys who wrote the book. They feel that where they went wrong was in being too ingenious in devising a plot to replace the original Viennese libretto, which, like all Viennese librettos, was simply terrible.

It was one of those plots where somebody poses as somebody else and it turns out that he really was somebody else, they just think he is pretending to be somebody else. (It would be nice to make it a little clearer, but that is the best we can do.) And the odd thing is that – till the critics got at it with their hatchets – both authors thought highly of it. 'Boy,' Guy would say to Plum, his eyes sparkling, 'you could take that plot down to the bank and borrow money on it,' and Plum, his eyes sparkling, too, would agree that you certainly could.

And then the rude awakening.

3 The Second Century Show

This was the one mentioned earlier, into which the authors were lured by the combined persuasiveness of C. B. Dillingham and Florenz Ziegfeld, the former of whom alone was capable – for there never was a more genial man than Charlie Dillingham – of luring an author into anything. The two had gone into partnership in the previous year to produce a mammoth revue at the Century Theatre called *The Century Show*, and they now wanted another, equally mammoth, to follow it. The Century, long since pulled down, stood at the bottom of Central Park West and was the last word in theatres, its girders made of gold and $1000 bills used instead of carpets. It was built by a syndicate of millionaires. At least, they were millionaires when they began building it.

The thing that turned the scale and decided the Bolton-Wodehouse duo to sign on the dotted line was the fact that the latter a few years earlier had collaborated on a revue for the Empire Theatre in London and had found it the most delightful experience. As he told Bolton, all the author of a revue had to do was put his name on the thing. The dialogue was written by the artists, worthy fellows who asked nothing better than to write their own stuff, while publishers vied with one another to contribute songs. Doing *The Second Century Show*, he said, would be a nice rest.

The awakening – another rude one – came with the discovery that the New York method of assembling a revue differed from that in vogue in London. The authors found that they were expected to do the work themselves. It was an unpleasant shock, but they rallied from it and sat down to think what sort of a masterpiece they should give the customers.

On one thing they were resolved – there should be a plot, a real, coherent, consecutive story. Not like that show last year. They were frightfully contemptuous and superior about that last year's show. They called it a mere vaudeville entertainment and other harsh things. They could do a little better than that, they rather felt.

The first jarring note was struck when they learned that the cast of principals as selected – and given contracts – to date consisted of three classical dancers, three acrobatic dancers, a Spanish dancer, forty-eight buck-and-wing dancers, two trained cows and Harry Kelly and his dog Lizzie. (Does anybody remember Harry Kelly and Lizzie? 'She's a hunting dog. Sometimes she hunts here, sometimes she hunts there.' Harry would say, 'Roll over,' and Lizzie would take not the slightest notice, and Harry would say, 'Good dog,' and the act would proceed.)

This did not seem what you might call a balanced cast for a plotty show, but the management urged them to go ahead and fear nothing. They said they would see to it that performers were provided, and they certainly were. Scarcely a day went by without the addition to the cast of some new juggler or trapeze artist, and the gallant little plot swallowed them all like a frog swallowing flies, till at last, in a heroic attempt to absorb a performing seal, it burst and died, regretted by all.

You could find fragments of it splashed about all over the final version of *The Second Century Show*, gruesome fragments like the remains of the man who died of spontaneous combustion in *Bleak House*. Guy was at the sick-bed to the last, hoping for the best, for he loved that plot. He would pick it up and nurse it back to consciousness after some frightful blow had stunned it, but just as it was beginning to recover, along would come somebody and cram a couple of cross-talk comedians down its throat, and all the weary work was to do again.

Plum was more occupied with the lyrics. Occasionally a sharp scream from the tortured plot would make him wince, but it was the lyrics that etched those lines on his face and were responsible for the dark circles under his eyes.

A revue lyric of that period was a monstrous freak with one verse and twelve refrains, each introducing a separate girl in some distinctive costume. The lyric was written round the dresses. On arriving at the theatre in the morning, the sensitive poet was handed a pile of costume designs. One would represent a butterfly, another the Woolworth Building, a third a fish, a fourth a bird, a fifth a fruit salad and the others the Spirit of American Womanhood, Education Enlightening The Backward South, Venus Rising From The Sea, and so on, and

Mr Ziegfeld says will you please have it ready for tomorrow's rehearsal, as the girls are threatening to walk out because they have nothing to do. ('Walking out' was the technical term when a show-girl stepped into her Rolls-Royce, said, 'Home James,' to the chauffeur and drove off, never to be seen again.)

When the bard had finished twelve refrains, cunningly introducing the butterfly, the Woolworth Building, the Growing Unrest In The Balkans and Venus Rising From The Sea, the management decided that they didn't want to use those costumes after all, and handed him another batch. Critics have often commented on the sombre gloom which permeates all Wodehouse novels like the smell of muddy shoes in a locker-room and have wished that, fine as they are, there was not quite so much of the Russian spirit of pessimism and hopelessness in them, but now that it has been revealed that he wrote the lyrics for *The Second Century Show*, they will understand and sympathize.

It was an axiom in the theatre of those days that if you had a clientele you could not fail to bring home the bacon. The Empire had its clientele. So had the Princess and one or two other houses. But the real clientele boys, head and shoulders above all the rest, were C. B. Dillingham and Florenz Ziegfeld. With the two of them joining forces, it seemed obvious that *The Second Century Show* must be a success. But it was not. In the immortal words of whoever it was, the clientele didn't come to that one.

Have you ever been distressed and mortified at the unexpected refusal of your dog to accept the proffered morsel? You are enjoying a quiet meal, when the hound intimates by every means at his disposal that he wishes to come in on the ground floor. You offer him a bit of the delicacy you are consuming, and he sniffs at it and then turns away with an expression on his face that suggests that you have wounded him in his finest feelings, leaving you piqued, chagrined and frustrated. Just so does an author feel when the public, who have been pawing and whining at him for some particular brand of entertainment, turn away on being offered it and leave it untouched.

If there was one thing it was certain that the New York public wanted at this time, it was large, lavish revue crammed with lovely girls, and this was what they had been given. Nothing could have been larger and more lavish than *The Second Century Show*, and there were lovely girls in every nook and cranny of it. And yet it was withdrawn after thirty performances. Which was perhaps just as well, come to think of it, for it was discovered later that it was so large and lavish that if it had played to absolute capacity with two rows of standees every night, the weekly loss would have been between $3000 and $4000.

There was only one thing about *The Second Century Show* that is of historic interest. The pianist who played the piano at rehearsals was a young fellow named George Gershwin.

7

1

FOR two ardent young men who have made it their mission in life to raise the lighter musical drama to new heights there are few things more unpleasant than a resounding flop. Let them have three such flops in rapid succession, and they begin to feel like a couple of lepers who have been expelled from their club for cheating at cards. After *The Rose of China, The Riviera Girl* and *The Second Century Show* the guilty pair were afraid to walk past the Lambs Club lest they run into some reproachful ham who had appeared briefly in one or other of these outstanding turkeys. A jocular boulevardier induced in them a strong distaste for all jocular boulevardiers by saying to the jocular boulevardiers with whom he was drinking synthetic Scotch that he felt nervous about leaving town for the weekend these days because he might be missing a Bolton-Wodehouse show.

It was the tragedy of *The Rose of China* that they found hardest to bear. The other two had been commissions, and nobody could have been expected to turn down a commission for a big musical from Klaw and Erlanger and what had seemed like an even bigger musical from pre-eminent managers like Dillingham and Ziegfeld. But they had gone into *The Rose of China* entirely on their own initiative, just because a fiddler had hypnotized them with his violin at a moment when their better judgment had been clouded by a good dinner at the Ritz-Carlton.

They were not eating at the Ritz-Carlton now but at the Columbus Circle Childs'. There were three reasons for this – the first the prices on the right-hand side at the former of the two hostelries, the second the understandable shrinking from being pointed out as the pariahs of Broadway, and the third, most potent of all, a desire never again to lay eyes on or lend ears to the Ritz-Carlton's *chef d'orchestre*.

At this very moment, they felt, as the waitress slammed down their buckwheat cakes and coffee, Armand Vecsey was probably tying himself in knots as he rendered some excerpt from *The Rose of China* designed to show the luncheon patrons that its failure had not been the fault of the composer.

They were just squaring their elbows and getting at the wholesome foodstuffs when Plum gave a start and sat rigid, the buckwheat cake frozen on his fork. The expression on his face was that of someone passing a sewer excavation.

'What's that noise I hear?' he asked in a low, toneless voice. 'I don't mean the waitress throwing used dishes down the chute, I mean that music. It's Chinese music!'

'Nonsense. You're hearing things.'

'Don't tell me. That's Chinese music. Listen.'

'Do you know, I believe you're right.'

They hailed a waitress, who explained that the music was indeed Chinese music and was filtering through the ceiling from the Far East restaurant immediately above.

'We shall not be coming to this Childs' again,' said Plum coldly.

'Decidedly not. I'm darned if it isn't *The Rose of China* they're playing. They must have got hold of one of the records. Even here we can't escape it. And do you realize,' said Guy, 'that if a certain man had not happened to walk down a certain street in a certain Hungarian town on a certain evening *The Rose of China* would never have happened?'

'What do you mean?'

'It was owing to this son of a Hungarian that Armand Vecsey got his musical education. I had it from Armand himself. It seems that he began life as a poor boy in a farming district near Budapest called the Puszta. He wanted to be a violinist, but his family wouldn't hear of it, so one day he ran off with his fiddle, and what little money he had managed to save, to a place with the impossible name of Papa. It's the Heidelberg of Hungary, I gather, and there is a famous Conservatory of Music there.'

'How do you spell Papa?'

'P-a-p-a.'

'The students, no doubt, refer to it as their Alma Pater.'

'Please! Not now. Well, in next to no time, of course, Armand ran out of money, and his landlady said that if he didn't pay his back rent, she would kick him out and keep his violin.'

'So he packed it in his trunk and tried to sneak away?'

'Exactly. And he got it as far as the front door when this man came along. Seeing that Armand was in difficulties, he stopped and asked if he could give him a hand. Armand explained the situation, and they started down the front steps, carrying the trunk. At this moment the landlady appeared.'

'Embarrassing. I suppose Armand was nonplussed.'

'He was. But the man wasn't. He told the landlady that he was a friend of Armand's, and Armand had inflamed him with his stories of what a delightful dump this of the landlady's was, so here he was with his trunk and he would like, if possible, a room with a southern exposure.'

'Ingenious.'

'Yes, he was one of those quick-thinking Hungarians. Well, the landlady not unnaturally blew her top. "I don't want any friends of this little so-and-so in my house," she said, speaking of course in Hungarian. "You take that trunk and get out of here!" Which they did. Are you laughing heartily?'

'Very.'

'Well, save it up, because there's a lot more coming. When they were out of sight of the house, they put down the trunk and sat on it. Armand thanked the man, and told him all about his ambition to become a violinist, but how on earth he was ever going to become a violinist he didn't know, he added, because he hadn't the cash to study at the Conservatory, and if you're a musician and don't study at conservatories, you haven't a hope.'

'Like that line in *Leave it to Jane*. "If you don't get an eddication, you can't be a lawyer." '

'Exactly. Well, when he heard this, the man pricked up his ears. "Now, that's a funny thing," he said. "I've been sent to the Conservatory to study, and I want no piece of it. What I like is pottering around and having a good time. I've not been near the place yet. How would you react to the idea of going there and studying in my place?"

'Armand felt that this must be some beautiful dream.

' "You're offering me a musical education? Your education? "

' "Why not? I don't want it. I hate music. But my grandmother told me to come here, and her word is law. She has supplied me with ample funds to see me through the Conservatory, so it seems to me our path lies clear before us. We split the money, you taking one quarter, me three quarters, and you go and study till you're blue in the face, leaving me to continue pottering around and, as I say, having a good time." '

'Gosh! This thing's beginning to shape. Armand, who of course takes the other fellow's name, is a great success at the Conservatory and writes a diploma-number that enchants one and all, and the grandmother comes hot-footing to applaud the young genius—'

'And the chap who knows nothing about music has to play for the old lady, so he sits at the player-piano and—'

'—half-way through he gets absent-minded and gets up—'

'—and the piano goes on playing. . . . There's a show there.'

'If we were going to write any more shows.'

'But we aren't.'

'No. Still, it's a good story.'

'Very good.'

'The only thing wrong with it,' said Guy broodingly, 'is that, to make it dramatic, after a start like that Armand should have finished up as a world famous composer instead of sawing a fiddle in a New York hash-house. In which event he wouldn't have intrigued us with a lot of pseudo-Chinese music and we wouldn't have written a prize bust called *The Rose of China*.'

2

Despondency continued to grip the two. After three failures in a row it seemed impossible that they would ever again find a manager with confidence enough in their moth-eaten talent to entrust them with a commission. And it was just when Guy was saying that, come right down to it, there was no life like the architect's, and Plum had begun to mutter that if he had to do it all over again he would certainly think twice before he gave up a steady job at $3 a week, that Ray Comstock brought the sunshine back into their lives by asking them to look in and discuss a new piece for the Princess. They were in his presence twenty minutes after the receipt of the telephone message, not even stopping to wonder how Ray could have staved off the honeys long enough to be able to give them a call.

In the familiar surroundings of the Princess their flagging spirits revived. True, the actors on either side of the waiting-room eyed them distrustfully as they appeared at the wicket and one of their number rose, pocketed his *Variety* and left, glancing at them in a meaning way as he passed through the door.

'There's a fellow doesn't want to be in anything of ours,' said Guy, as they went into the inner office and found Ray with the receiver propped on his shoulder as usual. The conversation he was conducting had apparently reached its end, for he said, 'Good-bye, sugar,' and hung up.

'*Sugar*?' said Plum, startled. It seemed very unorthodox.

'He's giving the South a play,' said Guy.

Ray smiled his Sphinx-like smile.

'Where have you boys been keeping yourselves?' he asked genially. 'Time you stopped loafing and got down to work.'

They exchanged glances. Was this tact, or had he not noticed certain things that had been happening around the corner on Broadway?

Presumably he had not, for his faith in them appeared to be unimpaired.

'Another *Oh, Boy!* is what we want,' he said. 'Oh, hello, honey.'

'How do you like *Oh, Lady, Lady* for a title?' asked Guy. It was a phrase which Bert Williams, the negro comedian, was using at the moment.

'H'm. . . . Go jump in the lake, honey. . . . Yes, good. Well, if you boys want contracts, you can have them now, and an advance of $1000 apiece. I'm adding a half per cent to your royalty. Every time you give me a hit, the next time. . . . I said Go jump in the lake, honey . . . will be a half per cent more.'

The two partners were so moved by the thought that somebody still considered them capable of writing hits that they nearly broke down. As they left the office, they agreed that there was no manager like Ray Comstock and no theatre like the Princess.

'I shall be practically next door to it, which will be convenient,' said Plum. 'Ethel's taken an apartment for the winter in the Beaux Arts.'

This new abode was a handsome studio-apartment recently vacated by the well-known artist, Leon Gordon. It was here that Guy and Plum met one morning to work on *Oh, Lady, Lady*. Ethel had gone out, leaving them to get on with it.

But they had struck a snag. A story was shaping itself, but they could not decide where the action was to be laid. Also, what to do with the second love-interest was bothering them. 'Bill', the hero, and 'Molly', the heroine, would take care of the main plot, but running parallel with it there had to be a second love-interest, and it had to be funny. And to make the process of composition tougher, they had run out of tobacco, without which it was impossible to think properly. Guy said he would go out and buy some.

'I wish you would,' said Plum. 'I ought not to leave here. There's a lady decorator coming to collect that settee there.'

'A bastard piece,' said Guy, surveying it. 'Early American top with Victorian legs.'

He went out, and in the lobby encountered Audrey Munson, New York's leading artists' model, whose acquaintance he had made in a friend's studio. It is Audrey Munson whom the passer-by sees when he walks down Fifth Avenue and arrives at 59th Street, for she is the lady on top of the fountain in the Plaza, who seems to be awaiting, from the other side of 59th Street, the imminent arrival of General Sherman, rather inconveniently chaperoned by an angel. She may also be seen in the Modern Room of the Metropolitan as Phryne dropping her cloak at the trial, as Hagar driven into the wilderness, and as an unnamed female strolling in the nude along a presumably unfrequented beach.

'What are you doing?' asked Guy after the customary greetings and civilities had been exchanged.

'Oh, I'm making the rounds of the artists' studios, seeing if I can't drum up a little trade,' said Audrey. 'In my line you've got to make the most of what you've got while you've still got it.'

Guy went on his way, and Audrey looked in on a few likely prospects. None of them wanted a model at the moment, but one of them suggested she try Leon Gordon. To the Leon Gordon studio she went, and in response to her ring Plum opened the door.

'Oh, come in,' he said cordially. He waved a hand toward the settee. 'There's the old sofa.'

Miss Munson interpreted this as an invitation to be seated.

'I'm Audrey Munson,' she said. 'Have you any work for me?'

Plum had not paid much attention to the name of the lady decorator when Ethel had mentioned it, but it seemed to him that it had been something like Munson. (Actually, it was McFarland.)

'Oh, rather, quite a bit of work,' he chirruped brightly, and, remembering his instructions, added, 'and more to come later, if your figure is all right.'

Miss Munson bridled slightly.

'My figure is generally supposed to be all right.'

Plum knitted his brow, trying to remember just what Ethel had told him about that settee. The back and the arms were okay, if he recalled, but. . . . Ah, yes.

'It's the legs that are the problem.'

'You need have no anxiety about those.'

'That's good. And how much will it be altogether?'

'You want the altogether.'

'Oh, while I remember, the seat. It should be covered with a piece of chintz. To hide the legs, if they show too much sign of wear and tear.'

Miss Munson smiled indulgently.

'I guess I'm being kidded,' she said. 'You fooled me at first with that deadpan stuff.' She rose and glanced about the room. 'Do you have a screen?'

'I don't believe so. Should we, do you think?'

'It doesn't matter. I can manage. You want to work now, right away?'

'Yes, I've got to get to work.'

'Fine,' said Audrey. She walked over to the bedroom door. 'Anyone in there?'

'No, I'm all alone.'

'Good. I'll only be a minute.'

Plum told Guy later that it did occur to him as a trifle odd that a lady decorator should have accompanied the foregoing remarks by starting to unfasten the buttons of her dress. However, he knew that lady decorators had their own way of doing things. Assuming that she had gone into the bedroom to inspect something Ethel had asked her to inspect in there, he dismissed her from his thoughts and turned back to the lyric he had been working on for *Oh, Lady*, a trio for Bill, the hero, Hale, his friend, and Cyril Twombley, the aristocratic private detective subsequently played so perfectly by Reginald Mason. It was entitled – appropriately in view of what was so soon to happen – 'It's a Hard World for a Man'.

He had just written the last line when the door of the bedroom opened and Audrey Munson emerged in an advanced state of nudity. And as he stood gaping, with the feeling that this was pretty eccentric even for a lady decorator, there was a ring at the bell and there entered another strange young woman.

'I've come for—' she began, then stopped, having caught a glimpse of what should have been covered with a piece of chintz disappearing upstage left. 'Perhaps it would be more convenient if I were to look in some other time,' she added frigidly, and Plum observed that behind her there was standing a man in overalls, obviously one of those sons of toil whose function it is to heave furniture about. Quick on the uptake, like all the Wodehouses, he saw that this new arrival must be the authentic female decorator. Who the other had been, he could not say. Probably just one of the neighbours making a social call.

'Oh, good morning,' he said, and was about to add that that was the settee over there and, as he had been saying only a moment ago to the lady who has just left us, the legs didn't match with the upper part, when his visitor withdrew, taking the man in overalls with her. The latter, he noticed, seemed reluctant to leave, as if he were feeling that by doing so he might be missing something of more than passing interest. His eyes, as they rested on the bedroom door, were protruding some inches from the parent sockets.

It was a few minutes later that Guy returned with the tobacco. Plum welcomed him warmly. He was glad to have at his disposal the advice of this seasoned man of the world.

'Listen, old boy,' he said. 'I have a problem, and one that seems to me to call for sophisticated handling. There's a girl in there.'

'A girl?'

'Yes, it's a girl, all right.' It was a point on which no room had been left for doubt. 'She came in while you were out and after a few civil remarks had been exchanged took all her clothes off.'

'Took her *clothes* off?'

'Yes. It struck me at the time as peculiar. And the problem, as I envisage it, is: Taking into consideration the fact that Ethel will be back at any moment, what do we do for the best?'

Even as he spoke, the inspiration of Puvis de Chavannes and Homer St Gaudens came out, fully clad, and Guy was able to effect the introductions. Plum apologized gracefully to Miss Munson for having proved so distrait a host, and Audrey, as good a sport as ever sat on a model throne, apologized for having made it necessary for him to apologize to her. They sketched out for Guy's benefit the story of the recent misunderstandings, and it was just after Miss Munson had left that Guy leaped from his chair as Archimedes leaped from his bath when he made that historic observation of his – 'Eureka!'

'That's it,' he said. 'There's our scene.'

'What scene?'

'The comedy scene we want for the first meeting of Bill's friend Hale and our soubrette – "May Barber", or whatever we were going to call her. Bill must be an artist, and he leaves Hale with instructions about the settee, and in comes May, who's a model. The thing will write itself, and it gives us our setting – Greenwich Village. I can't remember a Greenwich Village set in a musical comedy, so it'll be brand new. There ought to be a Greenwich Village lyric.'

'There will be,' said Plum, and next day he was able to hand it over to Jerry, complete.

Way down in Greenwich Village
There's something, 'twould appear,
Demoralizing in the atmosphere.
Quite ordinary people,
Who come to live down here,
Get changed to perfect nuts within a year.
They learn to eat spaghetti
(That's hard enough, as *you* know)
They leave off frocks
And wear Greek smocks
And study Guido Bruno.
For there's something in the air
Down here in Greenwich Village
That makes a fellow feel he doesn't care:
And as soon as he is in it, he
Gets hold of an affinity
Who's long on modern Art but short on hair.
Though he may have been a model,
Ever since he learned to toddle,
To his relatives and neighbours everywhere,
When he hits our Latin Quarter
He does things he shouldn't oughter:
It's a sort of,
Sort of kind of,
It's a sort of kind of something in the air.

3

Oh, Lady, Lady opened out of town in Wilmington, Delaware, three days before Christmas, and the authors thought highly of it.

The integration of book and music was better than in *Oh, Boy!*, the story – for a musical play – exceptionally strong, so much so that Plum was able later to use it for a full-length novel, *The Small Bachelor*, and the score one long succession of those Kern melodies of his early youthful days that were so gay and carefree compared with his maturer style. After *Show Boat* he turned to more serious things, and the light duets and trios of the Princess era were no more for him.

The Wednesday matinée fell on Christmas Eve, and the number of Wilmingtonians who preferred to finish their shopping was in considerable excess of those who visited the Dupont Theatre. Guy and Plum sat surrounded by a vast acreage of empty seats. What audience there was was in the first two rows, and the authors hardly knew they were there.

For the paying customers did little to draw attention to themselves. In theatre parlance they 'sat on their hands' and were pretty defiant towards any attempt to make them laugh. The best that could be said of them is that they were not the barking seal type. They were quiet.

So quiet that half-way through the first act Bolton, forgetting their existence, rose and addressed Harry Brown, who was playing his opening scene with Carroll McComas.

'That's wrong, Harry,' he said. 'You'll kill the laughs if you keep pointing to the settee. Carroll would be bound to know what you were talking about.'

His voice trailed off in silence as he became aware of thirty-six blank faces which had turned and were regarding him with astonishment from rows one and two. There was a long moment of silence. Plum came to the rescue.

'Ladies and gentlemen,' he said 'we must apologize. We're down here trying to get this show right for New York, and Mr Bolton has just spotted something that is wrong. Would you mind if we fixed it?'

Some civil person said, 'Not at all. Go ahead,' and Guy, encouraged, found his voice.

'There are so few of you,' he said, 'and you were keeping so quiet that I had quite forgotten you were there.'

This got a better laugh than any of the lines in the show, and Guy said, 'We're all a little dizzy these days, and I thought we were having a rehearsal. If you don't mind, we'll have one now.'

It was one of the most successful rehearsals in the history of the stage. The audience listened with rapt attention as the authors made their corrections. Many of them contributed suggestions. When the performance ended, the cast came down to the footlights and signed the programmes that were handed up to them.

'If only we could have you people with us for our first night in New York!' said Vivienne Segal.

'They certainly liked it,' said Plum, as he and Guy crossed the corridor that separates the theatre from the hotel. 'There was a delightful woman with a face like a weasel who called it a gem.'

'If they call this a gem,' said Guy, 'can you imagine what they'd say about *The Little Thing*?'

'You know what,' said Plum. 'I almost hope *The Little Thing* is never produced. Then you'll always have something to look forward to.'

The shaping-up tour of *Oh, Lady, Lady* was a long one, taking the play through eight one-week stands.

What happens in such cases is that you cosy-up and become one big happy family. The chorus of twelve girls, chosen less for their abilities – although of course they must be able to dance and sing – than their good looks, were about average. That is, all except one.

She was the youngest of the troupe with enchanting big blue eyes, a lovely, transparent skin inherited from an English mother, beautiful everything, figure, face, smile, speaking voice, a smile that bestows kindness on everyone, everyone but especially Plum, with whom she fell in love.

Guy called it Plum's 'one wild oat', but Plum insisted there was nothing sexual about it. Fleur – that was her name – Fleur Marsden had fallen in love with his books.

She has several copies of them and she'd marked things she didn't quite understand. She longed to have him help her, she was terribly badly educated. Her mother had married an explorer and she'd been moved about to all sorts of strange places and had actually never been to school at all. And Plum longed to help her.

It was fun and they laughed and chaffed and treated Plum's 'one wild oat' as a proper subject for banter. Fleur hadn't understood what it meant. Guy told her.

It was late when the train rolled into the Grand Central. Guy dropped Plum at his abode on the roof of an office building, 22nd Street and Madison Avenue. Ethel greeted him coolly.

'The show's a big hit,' he told her.

'Good,' Ethel said, 'perhaps it will pay for the expense of the tour.'

'What do you mean? The tour is paid for by the management even to the box of cigars for Guy and me.'

'I'm speaking about the diamond watch-bracelet you gave your girlfriend, the receipted bill for which arrived here yesterday morning.'

'It was her birthday, her nineteenth, and no one sent her anything, not even a card.'

'And you didn't know it's a racket. Six birthdays a year though she's not likely to meet up with another costing close on a thousand dollars.'

'Even if you think of it as an affair, which it wasn't. . . .'

Ethel broke in. 'Don't give me that! I'm not a fool.'

'No, you're an angry wife and if you won't believe what I say you'll just have to go on believing what you think. And now I suppose we might talk about the play. It's the best job any one of us three has done. Guy's story is both charming and terribly funny.'

'I hate the play and I hope it turns out a stinker. . . .' She turned away.

'You're the woman I work for. You are my inspiration. . . .'

He was following her as he spoke. She cut off his speech with a sharp bang of the door.

4

Oh, Lady, Lady turned out to be what Comstock had asked for – another *Oh, Boy!* All the New York critics – there were about twenty of them in those days – were enthusiastic and complimentary. One even burst into song:

This is the trio of musical fame,
  Bolton and Wodehouse and Kern:
Better than anyone else you can name,
  Bolton and Wodehouse and Kern.
Nobody knows what on earth they've been bitten by:
All I can say is I mean to get lit an' buy
Orchestra seats for the next one that's written by
  Bolton and Wodehouse and Kern.

And Dorothy Parker, never easy to please, wrote:

> Well, Bolton and Wodehouse and Kern have done it again. Every time these three gather together, the Princess Theatre is sold out for months in advance. You can get a seat for *Oh Lady, Lady* somewhere around the middle of August for just about the price of one on the Stock Exchange. Only moving-picture artists and food-profiteers will be able to attend for the first six months. After that, owners of munition-plants may be able to get a couple of standing-rooms.
>
> If you ask me, I will look you fearlessly in the eye and tell you in low, throbbing tones that it has it over any other musical comedy in town. I was completely sold on it. But then Bolton and Wodehouse and Kern are my favourite indoor sport, anyway. I like the way they go about musical comedy. I like the way the action slides casually into the songs. I like the deft rhyming of the song that is always sung in the last act by two comedians and a comedienne. And Oh, how I do like Jerome Kern's music! And all these things are even more so in *Oh, Lady, Lady* than they were in *Oh, Boy!*

All of which was as rare as refreshing fruit to two battered wrecks who had just groped their way out of the ruins of *The Riviera Girl*, *The Rose of China*, and *The Second Century Show*. Life began to animate the rigid limbs again, and Cain's Storehouse became once more merely a number in the telephone-book.

Oh, Lady had a very long run at the Princess, and was actually played simultaneously at the Casino by a second company. It also had the distinction of being put on at Sing-Sing with an all-convict cast.

One of the most popular numbers in it was the duet between Spike Hudkins, the ex-burglar, and Fainting Fanny, the shoplifter, which ran as follows:

SPIKE

Since first I was a burglar, I have saved in every way
Against the time when some nice girl should name the happy day.
When I retired from active work and ceased at nights to roam,
I meant to have enough nice things to furnish up the home.

And I achieved, as you will find,
The object that I had in mind.

Our home will be so bright and cherry
That you will bless your burglar boy:
I got some nifty silver, dearie,
When I cracked that crib in Troy:
And I got stuff enough in Yonkers
To fill a fairly good-sized chest,
And at a house in Mineola
I got away with their victrola,
So we'll have music in the evenings
When we are in our little nest.

FANNY

I've made a nice collection, too, to add, my love, to yours
Since I began professionally visiting the stores.
I've been a prudent little girl, and I have saved, like you:
I never started squandering as girls are apt to do:
Each time I stole a brush and comb,
I said 'There's something for the home'.

Our home will be so bright and cheery
With all the stuff I swiped from Stern's
And all the knick-knacks from McCreery
And from Bloomingdale's and Hearn's.
And I've got stacks from Saks and Macy's
Of all the things that you'll like best,
And when at night we're roasting peanuts
Upon the stove I pinched from Greenhut's,
Although it's humble, you won't grumble,
You'll love our cosy little nest.

This number was, as they say, 'well received' up Ossining way, where it must have brought nostalgic memories to many a first-nighter. Playwrights who nowadays console themselves for a flop on Broadway with the thought that 'They liked us in New Haven' know nothing of the thrill of being able to say, 'They liked us in Sing-Sing.'

One odd thing in connection with the piece was that the song 'My Bill', subsequently so popular when sung by Helen Morgan in *Show Boat*, was written for *Oh, Lady, Lady*, tried on the road and cut out before the New York opening.

8

EXPERIENCE brings wisdom. The two alumni of Cain's Storehouse had learned their lesson. The vital thing for brainworkers, they saw now, is to husband their energies and never attempt to do too much. That way disaster lies.

'We must have been crazy,' said Guy as they walked down Fifth Avenue one morning about a week after *Oh, Lady* had opened. 'We just said, Yes, yes, yes, to everything anybody offered us, forgetting that if the machine is not to break down it must have constant intervals for rest and repose. The reservoir needs to fill itself. But never again. At least six months must elapse before we consider writing another show. It will be embarrassing, of course. Managers will come pleading with us to accept contracts, but we shall be firm . . . resolute . . . and – what's the word?'

'Adamant?'

'Yes, adamant. We shall say, "Sorry, boys, but nothing doing. We are husbanding our energies and filling the reservoir. We hate to disappoint you, dear old chaps, but in a word—" '

'No!'

'No!'

It was at this point that Colonel Henry W. Savage suddenly appeared on the steps of a brownstone church which they were approaching.

'Just the boys I was looking for,' he said, beaming. 'Would you like to write a show for me starring W. C. Fields?'

'Yes!' said Plum.

'You betcher!' said Guy.

'Then what I would suggest is that you come for a few days' run in my boat, the *Dorinda*. A yacht is a perfect place for conferences.'

'A yachting trip? We'd love it.'

'Good. The *Dorinda* has been lucky for me as a workshop. It was aboard her that poor Browne and I laid out *Everywoman*.'

The reference to 'poor' Browne coupled with the ominous phrase 'laid out' cast a momentary chill, but the Colonel's pleasure at the prospect of having them as guests on his luxury yacht was so evident that the unfortunate allusion was soon forgotten. The following Friday – Friday the thirteenth, they realized later – was fixed for the start of the cruise.

'And now I must be getting back to my trustees' meeting,' said the Colonel. 'The church has had a handsome offer for its property, but they want me to see if I can't get a bit more. They seem to think I'm a pretty good bargainer.'

There was silence for some moments as the two authors continued on their way down the avenue.

'Yes, I know,' said Guy, speaking a little defensively. 'But one can't husband energies and fill reservoirs when one's offered W. C. Fields. And, anyway, you said "Yes" first.'

'And I'd say it again,' said Plum. 'W. C. Fields! The greatest comedian there is. And W. C. Fields plus a yachting cruise. . . .'

'Have you ever been on a yachting cruise?'

'No, but I know what it's like. I've seen it in the movies. Deep cushioned chairs on the after-deck, stewards in white coats handing round cocktails and canapés. . . . You realize what has happened, of course? Remorse has been gnawing old Hank because he did us down over that Billy Van thing. Quite possibly he heard an organ playing a hymn his mother used to play on the harmonium in his childhood, and it softened him. "I must atone," he said to himself, "I must atone," so regardless of expense he gives us this yachting trip. It does him credit, I say.'

'Great credit,' agreed Guy.

Friday was a spring-like day and the yachts at the Columbia anchorage made an attractive picture. They found the Colonel in the club house attired in an ancient serge suit and a yachting cap which the passage of time had changed from blue to green. He greeted them warmly, but seemed surprised by the spruceness of their appearance.

'You lads look rather dressed up,' he said, 'but I think I've some dungarees aboard that will fit you.'

'Dungarees?'

'You'll need dungarees,' said the Colonel, and he never spoke a truer word.

The *Dorinda* was a large boat – seventy-three feet six on the waterline, eighteen feet two beam, four master-cabins and two baths – but its crew consisted merely of an engineer called Peasemarch, a name Plum registered for future use, a cook called Palmer, quickly christened Palmer the Poisoner by the guests, and a captain, Henry W. Savage. The thing that struck Guy and Plum immediately was that what it needed was a couple of deck-hands to do the dirty work, and this, events were to prove, it got.

'I thought of asking Jerry along,' said the Colonel as he showed them to their cabins, 'but he's such a little chap.'

This puzzled the two pleasure-seekers. Why Jerry's delicate

physique should rule him out as a reveller aboard the *Dorinda* they were unable to understand.

'We thought we might have Bill Fields with us,' said Guy.

'Bill Fields?' The Colonel spoke the name a little blankly, as if it were new to him. 'Ah, yes,' he said. 'Bill Fields. No, no, too fat and lazy.'

The guests had rather expected that the course would lie north to Spuyten Duyvil and through that waterway to the Harlem and Long Island Sound. The northern shore of the Island with its charming harbours and the great houses of Morgan, Mackey, Otto Kahn and Mrs Belmont would make an ideal cruising ground, and then they could slip through the Shinnecock Canal to the romantic south shore lagoons or perhaps cross the Sound to Newport and Narragansett, then in the Indian Summer of their glory.

But the Colonel had other plans. Erect at the wheel, he steered down the bay passed Guttenberg and Weehawken and, hugging a shore lined with factories, foundries and coal yards, through the oily waters of Bayonne to the narrow inlet that separates Staten Island from the mainland.

'Afraid lunch will be a bit late,' he said. 'I want to hit the Raritan canal on the incoming tide. Tide's quite a help until you get to the locks.'

Locks! That magic word. Visions of Boulter's Lock on Jerome K. Jerome's Thames with its punts and skiffs, its girls with parasols and its young men in club blazers rose before the eyes.

When the locks on the Raritan and Delaware rose before the eyes, they proved to be somewhat different. The traffic consisted mostly of barges laden with gravel or coal. One that was preceding the *Dorinda* had a cargo of fish destined, the Colonel explained, for a glue factory on the Delaware River. Only the riper and more elderly fish are used for manufacturing glue, and those aboard the *Shirley B* were well stricken in years and almost excessively ripe.

As they approached the first lock they brought the matter up.

'Think we might slip past *Shirley*?' asked Plum.

'The barge ahead?'

'That's the one. It reminds me of Cleopatra's. "Purple the sails and so perfumed that the winds were love-sick with them".'

'We find *Shirley* a little on the niffy side,' said Guy.

The Colonel was unsympathetic.

'Come, come, you lads are a bit finicky, aren't you? You aren't here to sniff dead fish. You've work to do. There's a lot of handling needed in the locks.'

There was. Quite a lot. There were three boats swung outboard on davits, a launch, a dory for fishing and a dinghy, and these had to be swung inboard before the *Dorinda* was able to enter the lock.

'First get the boats stowed and then when we're in the lock go ashore and secure the hawsers. You'll have to remove a few sections of the rail first,' said the Colonel, and his guests at last realized what all that stuff about dungarees and Jerry Kern's lack of robustness had meant. The scales fell from their eyes. For all practical purposes, they saw, they might have been aboard the Savage grandfather's slave-ship.

'Morning, Cap'n,' said the Colonel genially to the mate of the *Shirley B*. 'Carrying fish, eh?'

'Ah.'

'I've got two dudes aboard who don't like the way you smell.'

'Sissies,' said the old salt briefly.

After an eternity of removing sections of rail, stowing boats and securing hawsers and trying not to inhale, they were past and the *Dorinda* drew away down the long straight waterway. Guy cautiously lowered the handkerchief from his nose.

'Good-bye, *Shirley*! Thank heaven we've seen the last of the lady.'

'Lock ahoy!' called the Colonel.

The work began again. The boats were hauled inboard, the lock gates opened, the amateur deck-hands seized the hawsers as Pease-march threw them and made the *Dorinda* fast. They stood waiting expectantly for the lock gates to close and the water to be poured in. Nothing happened.

'What's the matter, Colonel?'

'Lock master's waiting for the barge. He doesn't like to work the lock for one vessel.'

Presently the *Shirley B* bore slowly down on them, preceded by its noisome effluvium. There are – or were – eleven locks on the New Jersey canal system, and in every one of them *Shirley* snuggled in cosily beside the *Dorinda*.

'Got any fresh fish, Cap'n?' inquired the Colonel on their third encounter.

'My God, he wouldn't!' muttered Plum, aghast.

They were spared. The barge captain shook his head.

'Never eat it.'

'You should. Healthiest food in the world.'

'I guess maybe I'll try a piece sometime,' said the barge captain.

They tied up for the night at the side of the canal. When they sat down to dinner they noticed that the table was laid for four. The extra place, it appeared, was for Palmer.

'I always have him in for dinner,' said the Colonel.

'Like Cesare Borgia,' said Plum. 'He used to have the cook dine with him and always made him eat a bit of each course before he sailed into it himself. So if it was poisoned, all that happened was that he was a cook short.'

'Ha, ha!' laughed the Colonel merrily. Then, as Palmer entered bearing a dish of boiled potatoes and another of turnips, the smile faded from his lips. 'What, *two* vegetables?' he said frowning like someone austere contemplating one of those orgies that preceded the fall of Babylon. 'Oh, well,' he said resignedly. 'I suppose this *is* something of an occasion.'

Palmer was a weedy young man with a pale intellectual face and large horn-rimmed spectacles. He deposited the turnips and potatoes and went back for the *plat de jour*, a dish of brined herring. When this had been distributed, the two authors got down to business.

'We've roughed out a tentative idea for the Bill Fields play,' said Guy.

'Oh?' said the Colonel.

'Let's hear it,' said Palmer, closing his eyes and putting the tips of his fingers together.

'Well, Bill's a man who's lost his memory through overworking—'

'What at?' said Palmer.

'It doesn't matter what at. The point is, he's lost his memory. He ties bits of string round his fingers to remind him to do things, and then can't remember what they're to remind him to do.

'So his wife takes him to a psychiatrist.'

'I don't like it,' said Palmer.

'Nor did the man, because the psychiatrist fell in love with his wife and she with him. They start an affair.'

'I don't like it,' said Palmer.

'Well, of course, this makes the man unhappy, though for the life of him he can't remember what he's unhappy about. He ties a bit of string round his finger to remind him, but next day it holds no message for him. However, he knows he's unhappy, so he decides to end it all. He tells his wife he proposes to commit suicide. He goes into the kitchen, and she hears him dragging out a table. She hears him climb on to the table, and then there is a long silence. She is just wondering what is going on, when the man suddenly appears with the rope around his neck. He points at it and says, "Now what on earth was that to remind me to do?" '

Palmer shook his head.

'I don't like it,' he said. 'It seems to me to contain nothing that would make an appeal to the more advanced appreciators.'

'What do you mean, the more advanced appreciators?'

'The *avant garde*,' said Palmer. 'In writing a play the scale of values should be at once objective and rational, hence absolute and authentic. One aims to achieve in these days of mere impressionism a newness – if I may use the term – which is continually intended and essentially correct. One's explorations should be eruptive, vital and intense. How do you like the herring, Colonel?'

The Colonel said the herring was fine, which was a black lie. Palmer seemed gratified.

'It has nuances,' he agreed.

Guy tried again.

'Well, if that idea doesn't attract you, we have another.'

'Eruptive, I hope?' said Palmer.

'In this one Bill Fields is a pawnbroker, the last of a long line. His family have been pawnbrokers for centuries, and one of them was the fellow who loaned the money on Queen Isabella's pearls when she pawned them to finance Columbus. She signed a document to say that the pawnbroker was to get 10 per cent on whatever Columbus discovered. Well, he discovered America, and this old Spanish grant turns up, so there is Bill Fields in the position of having an iron-clad claim to 10 per cent of America. Then some crooks get hold of him—'

'Crooks!' said Palmer. 'Why must there always be crooks in these things? Thematic archaism. And just as I was beginning to think that you were groping for something esoteric and foreign to the debauched conception the public of today has of the theatre. I've made a steamed pudding,' he said, rising. 'I'll go and get it.'

He disappeared in the direction of the galley.

'That's an odd cook you've got, Colonel,' said Guy.

'Yes, not any great shakes at his job, I'm afraid, but what are you to do nowadays? You have to take what you can get. And it doesn't really matter to me. I was shipwrecked once and lived for three weeks on dog biscuits. Ever since then I find everything wonderful.'

Palmer returned with the pudding, a large glutinous lump that tasted not unlike a pair of old boiled slippers. The authors declined it and shortly afterwards went out on deck. The air was still vibrant with the scent of dead fish.

The next morning they were roused at daybreak. The moorings had to be dealt with and after that there were more locks ahead. They came out on deck to find rain falling in a manner which Palmer would no doubt have described as eruptive, vital and intense. They negotiated the last of the locks and the *Dorinda* sailed on down the Delaware, slipping into the Chesapeake and Delaware Canal and thence through the Elk River into Chesapeake Bay. As Guy and Plum sat huddled under a tattered and inadequate awning, Palmer popped out of the galley and bore down on them.

'Good morning,' he said. 'Lovely weather. Have you ever studied the dominant impulse of the unconscious as exemplified in the plays of Pirandello?'

The two stared at him.

'You seem to know a great deal about plays,' said Guy.

'Well, naturally. I'm a playwright.'

'I thought you were a cook – well, when I say a cook. . . .'

'Oh, no, I'm a playwright really. The Colonel's got a play of mine which he's going to do as soon as he finds the right star. It's called *Ophelia* – Hamlet from the woman's angle. Meanwhile, he's given me this job. He doesn't pay me anything, of course. But I must be getting back to my galley. I'm doing you a bouillabaisse for lunch. An experiment, but I think it will have significant form.'

'Hold on a moment,' said Guy. 'How long has the Colonel had this *Ophelia* of yours?'

Palmer considered. 'Let's see. This is my fifth trip to Florida on the *Dorinda*. . . .'

'Florida? You mean we're on our way to Florida?'

'Of course. Didn't the Colonel tell you?'

'He didn't say a word about it. He just suggested a cruise.'

'We haven't brought any clothes for Florida,' said Plum.

'Oh, *you're* not going to Florida,' said Palmer, reassuring him. 'He'll put you ashore somewhere round here. That's what he has always done before.'

'What do you mean, "before"?'

'With the other authors he's brought along to work the *Dorinda* through the locks. As we've passed the last of the locks, I should imagine he will be landing you shortly. Excuse me, I must be looking after that bouillabaisse. If all goes well, it should be an entertaining little *morceau*. I think you will be amused by its *naïveté*.'

The two authors made their way to where the Colonel, clad in glistening oilskins, stood at the wheel.

'You didn't tell us you were going to Florida, Colonel,' said Guy.

'Didn't I?' said the Colonel mildly. 'Stupid of me.'

'If you had warned us before we started—'

'Of course, yes, I ought to have done. It slipped my mind. I'm sorry. I'll land you boys after lunch. You can get a train from Annapolis. It will give you a chance to look around the Naval Academy.'

'You realize,' said Guy, 'that we haven't discussed the play yet?'

The Colonel looked at him a little vaguely. Then his face lit up.

'The play? Ah, yes, the play. I'm sorry about that. I didn't want to cloud your enjoyment of the trip by telling you before. That's off. I'm not doing it. Fields wants too much money.'

It was as they sat in the draughty station at Annapolis, waiting for their train to arrive, that Guy observed that Plum was scribbling on the back of an envelope.

'What's that?' he asked. 'A lyric?'

'No, just an idea I've had for a mystery thriller. It's a little out of my usual line – but I think it will be good. A corpse has been discovered with its head bashed in by a blunt instrument, and the police lieutenant has come with his sergeant to the scene of the crime.

' "A foul and brutal murder," he says. "Cost what it may, we must spare no effort to bring the perpetrator of this hideous outrage to justice." (You know how these police lieutenants talk.) "Has the identity of the deceased been ascertained?"

' "It has," says the sergeant. "The stiff is a theatrical manager – Colonel Henry W. Savage."

' "Oh, well," says the lieutenant, "in that case, let's not bother."

'And they go off to lunch. It will run a bit short, I suppose, but it should have a wide appeal.'

'Very wide,' said Guy. 'You've got a winner.'

9

1

ANOTHER result of the substantial clicking of *Oh, Lady, Lady* was that Abraham Lincoln Erlanger, who during the bleak *Riviera Girl* days had shown a tendency to be as aloof to the authors of that musical gumboil as in his incarnation as Napoleon he would have been to a couple of Marshals who had lost an important battle, abandoned his resolve to have them shot at sunrise and invited them to do a piece for the New Amsterdam with Ivan Caryll, the composer of a long list of shows at George Edwardes's London Gaiety Theatre and of that historic success of 1911, *The Pink Lady*, the 'Beautiful Lady' waltz from which is still sung even now in many bath-tubs both in England and America, mostly off key.

Caryll – he was a Belgian, and his real name was Felix Tilken – was widely known as 'Fabulous Felix'. He had made a great deal of money in the theatre and, whatever else you might say about him, you could not say that he did not do himself well. He lived *en prince*, as much *en prince* as if his first name had been Flo and his second Ziegfeld, having apartments in both London and Paris, as well as a villa containing five bathrooms, overlooking the Deauville racecourse. A man, as he sometimes said, or if he didn't, he should have done, needs plenty of elbow room and, if he has five children, as 'Fabulous Felix' had, how can he possibly do with fewer than five baths, one for each child to sing 'Beautiful Lady' in?

When visiting New York, he did not actually charter a private liner, but he took most of Deck C on whichever was the best boat crossing, and on arrival settled down with his five children, his wife Maud and a cohort of nurses, tutors, governesses, valets and ladies' maids in a vast suite at the Hotel Knickerbocker. Then, instead of calling on the managers like the rest of the *canaille*, he would send word to them that he was, so to speak, in residence, ready to receive them and consider offers. And they came trotting round like rabbits.

It has never been decided whether or not 'Fabulous Felix' did it with mirrors, but he had a hypnotic effect on all the big musical comedy impresarios of Broadway. Harry Kelly's dog Lizzie could have picked up some useful hints on technique from the way these normally hard-boiled characters rolled over with their paws in the air in this man's presence. Some authorities claim that it was his beard that did the trick, and it may be that they were right. It was one of those long, black, square-cut, bushy numbers, as worn by Ozymandias, King of Kings, and other prominent Assyrians, concealing the whole face with the exception of the eyes and lending to its proprietor's appearance a suggestion of some dangerous creature of the wild peering out through a jungle. It is not surprising that sensitive managers, accustomed from childhood to composers who shaved daily and pink-cheeked authors smelling of bay rum, should have been as wax in his hands.

What happened on these occasions was that 'Felix' would say he had found a wonderful play in Paris which would make an ideal musical and, being an impulsive sort of fellow who had taken a sudden fancy to the manager whom he had selected to be the goat, was prepared to let him have this and to write the score for the customary composer's royalty of 3 per cent. No need for you to read the thing, my dear boy – it was, he assured his dear boy, superb, and he had the contracts here, all ready to sign.

'You couldn't give me some idea of what it's about?' the manager would say timidly.

'It's about a man who's in love with a girl.'

'I see. Yes, that sounds fine.'

'And there's another man. He's in love with a girl, too. It's tremendous. There's just one point. The French author's royalties. These French authors come high. I doubt if I could beat them down below 7 per cent.'

And just as the manager was about to say 'ouch!' or 'Zowie!' or whatever managers say when they are asked to part with 7 per of the gross to a bunch of French authors, he would catch sight of that beard, quivering a little as though what was inside it was crouching for the spring, and his nerve would fail him. Quaking, he signed on the dotted line.

And what 'Felix' in the rush and bustle of the conversation had completely forgotten to mention was that, as he had bought the French authors out for a few thousand francs before leaving Paris and was sole owner of the property, the entire 7 per cent would be added to his personal take-home pay. No wonder he could afford to launch out a bit in the matter of bathrooms. He must have been astounded sometimes at his moderation in confining himself to five.

This time he had deviated from his normal routine. What he had sold to Erlanger was not a French play but a mere idea of his own which had occurred to him on the voyage over. It concerned the Parisian ladies who during the first world war had adopted army 'godsons' to whom they wrote letters and sent cigarettes and books and food. It seemed to 'Felix' that out of this pleasant custom there might grow a romance.

The thing presented possibilities. Guy and Plum felt that they could do something with it, making the lady a star of the Paris stage and the 'godson' a struggling playwright who had written a play and wanted to get acquainted with her in order to persuade her to act in it. With this end in view, he exchanges identity books with the star's actual 'godson', an army cook, and presents himself at her home in the country. Add a comic husband, whom the star has caught cheating and is determined to punish in kind; a rich uncle who, finding the star and the playwright in each other's arms, assumes the latter to be the husband; and bring the playwright's fiancée on the scene, she being a co-worker with the star in an army canteen; and you have something which, if not literature, is certainly a French farce. And it was a French farce on which 'Felix' insisted, for his *Pink Lady* had been founded on one and he believed in sticking to a formula.

So gradually *The Girl Behind the Gun* – it became *Kissing Time* when produced in London – took shape.

2

Rehearsals began in the middle of September and, one morning a week later, Plum, arriving at Guy's apartment, nearly collided with a strikingly handsome brunette in a very exotic costume who was coming out. She beamed upon him in friendly fashion.

'Are you Mr Wodehouse?'

Plum said he was.

'How do you do? I'm Marguerite Namara.'

'Of course, yes. I recognized you at once.'

Marguerite Namara was a well-known opera singer. She had appeared recently in a Schubert operetta, *Alone at Last*.

'I'm so glad to meet you,' she said. 'Guy has told me so much about you.' She looked at her wrist-watch. 'Oh, dear, is that really the time? I must rush. We shall be seeing one another again at dinner tonight.'

She hurried off, and Plum went in and found Guy settling down to work.

'Oh, there you are,' said Guy. 'Did you see Marguerite?'

'We met in the doorway. She says we're dining tonight.'

'Yes.'

'Will she be joining us in those Czechoslovak reach-me-downs?'

'That dress isn't Czechoslovak. It's Greek. She's wearing what is called a peplum.'

'Will she expect me to wear a peplum?'

'A peplum is a feminine garment. If you wore anything, it would be a *sakos* or possibly the *esorroko* or *palto*.'

'Does she always dress like that?'

'Generally.'

'Slightly cuckoo is she, by any chance?'

Guy stiffened.

'You are speaking of the woman I love.'

'I thought you loved them all.'

'Not as I love Marguerite. You're the one who has kept telling me I ought to find myself a wife. Well, now I've done it.'

'You aren't married?'

'We're going to be.'

'A thousand congratulations. This means that your lightest wish is law to her. Ask her not to wear that Greek costume tonight.'

'Why not?'

'I don't like it, as Palmer would say. It's too eruptive, vital and intense.'

'Very well. I think it's charming myself, but perhaps it is more suited for the privacy of the home.'

Marguerite, the soul of amiability, cheerfully consented to substitute for the Greek costume something simple and inconspicuous. When Guy called for her that night, she was wearing a bright scarlet dress trimmed with astrakhan and a matching *shlyapa*, or, as we would say, hat. Around her neck was a collar decorated with silver bells similar in design to those seen in paintings of *troikas* pursued through the Siberian woods by wolves. Short red Russian boots completed the costume, each having a large bell hanging where one would have expected a tassel. The *tout ensemble*, though perfect for Old Home Week at Nijni-Novgorod, was not so good, Guy felt, for the Ritz-Carlton, where he had been intending to dine. Didn't she think, he said, that the Ritz-Carlton was a bit stodgy, and wouldn't a Bohemian place be more fun?

'Oh, yes, let's go to Mouquin's. We'll see all the people from the Met.'

Guy could think of no reasonable excuse for avoiding an encounter with the Metropolitan Opera personnel. At any rate it was better than braving the stares of the aristocratic feeders at the Ritz-Carlton's Oval Room. He telephoned Plum to meet them there with a flask and to order some 'set-ups' if he got there first.

He did get there first and was seated sipping something that had been sold to him as bourbon, when he was startled by what sounded like a *troika* with a bevy of wolves after it. The jingling appeared to be coming from his immediate rear, and turning, he found himself confronted by what might have been The Spirit of the Volga in one of the twelve refrains of a number for the girls in *The Second Century Show*.

His imitation, a very close one, of the late Sir Henry Irving in his most famous role ('Eah! daun't you hear . . . the sund of bell-ll-s?') was interrupted by the converging on the table of a *maître d'hôtel*, an assistant head-waiter, two ordinary waiters and a bus-boy, for Marguerite was an established and popular patron at Mouquin's. Wine was brought – in a teapot – and the soup had just been served when several new arrivals came through the swing doors that faced Sixth Avenue.

'*Scotti!*' screamed Marguerite in that carrying voice of hers which had so often given the back rows of the Paris Opéra Comique their money's worth. 'Scotti, my *angel*!'

Guy and Plum, the latter a little unsteady on his feet, for he was feeling as if he had just been hit by something solid between the eyes, rose as the great Scarpia of the Met came over, and stood politely while an animated conversation took place in Italian. Finally, after Scotti had delivered a long speech, accompanied by passionate gestures, they were at liberty to resume the soup at which they had been looking longingly for the last ten minutes.

'What was all that excitement?' asked Guy.

'No excitement,' said Marguerite. 'Antonio was just saying he doesn't like the steam-heat in New York. I love Antonio.'

'Charming chap,' agreed Plum, 'but he made it a little difficult to concentrate on soup. I often say that it is fatal to let soup—'

'*Pavel!*' shrieked Marguerite. 'Pavel, my *dear*!'

The new arrival was Pavel Solokolov of the Ballet Russe. He had known Marguerite in Moscow when she had appeared at the Malenskia Theatre with Isadora Duncan and her troupe of dancers. Guy and Plum once more rose politely, but contributed little to the conversation. It was in Russian, and their Russian was a bit rusty. They were inclined to be peevish as they resumed their soup, and Guy was just saying that the next one that came along he was going to fix three of these straws together and get his standing up, when Marguerite interrupted him.

'*Feodor!* Feodor, my *pet*!'

This time it was something spectacular, the great Chaliapin in person, looking, as he always did, like a benevolent all-in wrestler. Both Guy and Plum had often admired him, but never more so than now, for his first act was to thrust them back into their seats with a ham-like hand and insist jovially that they get on with the serious business of the evening.

'Zoop is zoop,' he said, speaking in English with an accent in which a spoon would have stood upright, and they felt he could not have phrased it more neatly.

'These are two playwrights that I am dining with,' said Marguerite, performing a belated introduction.

'We do musical comedies,' said Guy, pegging away at his soup.

'A low form of art, of course,' said Plum, pegging away at his.

Chaliapin would have none of this self-deprecation.

'*Not* a low form of art,' he insisted vehemently. 'When I am a student at the gymnasium, I too write a musical comedy. In it there is a scene which I will give to you, Mr Bolton, as a present. It is a bum scene and very phoney.'

It seemed to Plum that the great man was too modest.

'Oh, I'm sure it isn't,' he said politely.

Marguerite interpreted.

'Bomb scene. Very funny.'

'Yes, so phoney you will laugh off your heads,' said Chaliapin. 'You are to imagine that I am a cruel Governor and you two are revolutionists who have come to blow me up with a bum. But I catch you, and my men they tie you to a bench and I put the bum beneath the bench. It is a time-bum and it goes tick-tock, tick-tock. I laugh. It tickles me like a horsehair undervest. Because it is a fine torture for you to hear that tick-tock, tick-tock, tick-tock.'

'Like someone reading the minutes at a meeting,' said Guy brightly. 'What happens then?'

'I tell you. The bum is going tick-tock, tick-tock, when a noise outside distracts my attention, and I turn my back for a moment. You have one hand free, and you take the bum and slip it into the pocket of my *palto*, my big overcoat. There are more noises outside and I go out to ask, "What the hell?", and the bum she goes with me.'

He illustrated this bit of action by turning away and squeezing past a party of two elderly ladies and a deaf old gentleman who were taking their places at the next table.

'But wait,' bellowed Chaliapin from a distance of several yards, his organ-tones ringing through the restaurant. 'You have not seen the last of me. I come back now to gloot over you.'

He began to creep back, his face wearing a hideous and menacing scowl. The two ladies at the next table stirred uneasily.

'Remember I have the bum in my pocket.' He patted his pocket. 'I am coming back to laugh, to gloot over you. The bum is ticking – any minute now she is going off – and I am glooting. Pigs! Children of pigs! In a little moment you will be sausage meat. You will be buttered all over the walls. It makes me laugh to think of it. Ha, ha, ha, ha.'

It was a good laugh, and it sent the two elderly ladies scurrying to the door, leaving their deaf escort to his fate. People were standing up, trying to see what the commotion was about. There was a sense of relief, mingled perhaps with a certain disappointment, when Chaliapin, reaching the table, sat down and helped himself to wine from the teapot, his face wreathed in smiles.

'Phoney?' he said.

'Very phoney,' agreed Guy faintly.

Chaliapin looked about him, inspecting the table closely. He seemed puzzled.

'Where is the other gentleman? There were two gentlemen, two musical comedy writers, drinking zoop. Now there is one gentleman.'

'Mr Wodehouse had to leave hurriedly,' Guy explained. 'A sudden seizure. He gets them sometimes. I understand he hears buzzing sounds—'

'Like a bum going tick-tock, tick-tock, tick-tock?'

'Exactly. Accompanied by an occasional cow-bell.'

As Guy was going to bed, the telephone rang.

'Sorry about running away like that,' said Plum.

'I don't blame you. Heaven deliver us from opera stars with comedy scenes.'

'How did it end?'

'The bum scene? I couldn't tell you.'

'You mean that ruddy basso left without giving you the finish?'

'He never mentioned it. He went on to speak of other things. Why, are you interested?'

'Interested! I shall dream about it for weeks. You and me tied to a bench and Chaliapin coming back and forth, glooting over us, and the bum going tick-tock, tick-tock.'

'I'll get Marguerite to call him up and ask him to tell us who blew up whom in the end. Oh, by the way. Marguerite. Charming, don't you think?'

'Very charming. And I'll tell you something else I think – something you probably know already. I think you're going to have a wonderfully exciting married life.'

3

The Girl Behind the Gun opened in New York in November, settling down at once to a long run, and the authors were able to concentrate on the next show for the Princess, on which they had been working for some time in their intervals of leisure.

It seemed to both Guy and Plum that these Princess shows were running too much to type and that the formula was becoming evident. They begged Ray to strike out in a new direction with *The Little Thing*, but he insisted that the pattern be followed just once more.

Even if this one were not so successful as its predecessors, there was, he argued, plenty of slack to take up.

This one – they called it *Oh, My Dear* – was certainly not another *Oh, Boy!* or *Oh, Lady*, but it did quite well when, a few weeks after *The Girl Behind the Gun* had opened at the New Amsterdam, it made its bow on 39th Street. It was a lively musical farce, the scene of which was a sanatorium in the country, where a young man who thought he had inadvertently committed a murder found it convenient to hide out. It was the first comedy to bring the psychiatrist to the stage and also the only Princess show to have a non-Kern score. Jerry was busy elsewhere, and Lou Hirsch, composer of 'The Love Nest', a song still heard after all these years, wrote the music but without – unfortunately – contributing another 'Love Nest'. It was one of those pieces which are quite all right – business excellent – nothing to complain of – but not sensational. It was the 'Ruddigore' of the series.

4

A couple of weeks after the *Oh, My Dear* opening the two authors met for lunch.

'I suppose you're spending your Christmas with Marguerite?' said Plum.

'No,' said Guy. 'On Christmas Day Marguerite will be appearing in the Bull Ring in Mexico City with Titta Ruffo.'

'Become a lady bullfighter, has she?'

'She's singing *Carmen*, ass.'

'I trust she won't wear that red dress.'

'There are no bulls in the Bull Ring while they are singing.'

'A pity. It would make the thing so much more exciting. So she's in Mexico City, eh? Your fiancée does get about, doesn't she? How's the romance going?'

'It's in a state of suspended animation.'

His partner asked him to elucidate. Had there been a lover's quarrel? No, nothing like that, only Marguerite had doubts as to whether their divergent tastes, their disparate careers could be welded into a workable marriage.

'It'll probably end in her going her way and you going hers.'

'It'll probably end where it is right now,' replied Guy pessimistically.

Plum looked at him.

'The thing you need is a holiday,' he said. 'You pack your traps and come off to Palm Beach with Ethel and me.'

'Don't you have to be a Rockefeller or something?'

'Not at all. Theatrical managers and other lower type Fauna Americana are migrating there in flocks.'

'You call consorting with managers a holiday?'

'There is other companionship. It is a spot favoured by members of the *Follies* ensemble to rest up after the ardours of a New York run.'

'I don't want *Follies* girls either.'

'That remark alone proves you are far from being yourself.'

At the moment they were comparatively idle. Plum had just published *A Damsel in Distress* and in his spare moments was at work on *The Indiscretions of Archie*. Guy was collaborating on two comedies, *The Five Million* with Frank Mandel and *Adam and Eva* with George Middleton. Still these things were not being written to order. There was no deadline to meet. Though Guy was still inclined to demur, Plum remained firm. They bought straw hats and pongee slacks. They bought bathing-suits. They bought tickets to Palm Beach.

10

1

ANYONE in those days arriving for the first time in America's number one winter playground would have had to be very blasé not to experience a thrill. There was magic in the place. Nowadays the visitor is deposited at a shabby station in the least glamorous section of Palm Beach's frowsy namesake on the wrong side of the tracks, but when Guy and Plum opened their eyes at eight o'clock that December morning they found their train crossing a blue lagoon fringed with royal palms and a little later were deposited in a shining, white-painted terminus festooned with scarlet bougainvillaea. Coloured bell-boys and porters, all in spotless uniforms, stood lined up, awaiting them. On the pathway that ran along the shore of Lake Worth the hansom cab of Palm Beach, the open basket-chair with the driver mounted behind, sped by, carrying a couple attired in, of all things, evening dress.

'Must have been some party,' commented Guy.

'Probably spent the night at Bradley's,' said a fellow-traveller who was sorting out his luggage beside him. He pointed to a large frame building on the opposite side of the palm-lined avenue, and they looked with interest at the most famous gambling casino in America. One of the unobtrusive corps of guards, armed with a sawn-off shotgun, was strolling round between the big flowering bushes that dotted the lawn.

Back in New York it had been snowing, but here the sun shone brightly. Little puffy white clouds like dabs of whipped cream moved lazily across a sky of the deepest blue. The two mounted the steps that led from the station through a covered way into the longest hotel in the world, the 1400 feet Royal Poinciana, with one employee for each foot. Shops lined the way, New York's top couturiers, Charvet of Paris, Beale and Inman of London, bag shops, flower shops, jewellery shops. Plum waved a hand at one of the last named.

'Remind me to tell you a story about Arch Selwyn.'

'Who's Arch Selwyn?' asked Ethel.

'New York manager.'

'Then don't tell me about him,' said Ethel. 'I'm trying to forget that there is such a place as New York. Why can't we stay for ever in this Paradise?'

Their rooms overlooked the golf course. To one side were a couple of spurs running from the railway. On these, packed closely together, stood the private cars which had brought the wealthy down from Manhattan. One of them, which had been attached to the back of their train, was being shunted into place. The owner strolled out on to the spacious lounging platform. There seemed something familiar about his appearance.

'Good Lord! It's Flo!'

'Gosh, so it is. What does it cost to travel in one of those?'

'I can tell you,' said Plum. 'I asked. Not because I was toying with the idea of booking one for the homeward journey. I wanted to use it in a story. The tariff is ninety fares.'

'You mean ninety times what we paid?'

'That's right. Flo must be feeling rich.'

'Flo Ziegfeld always feels rich. The trouble is, it's just a feeling. The most extravagant man of our time. The arch-squanderer. . . . That reminds me. What was that about Arch Selwyn?'

'Oh, that? It was something Ray told me. It seems that last year Arch made his first trip to Palm Beach, and the night of his arrival found him at Bradley's plunging with the best of them. Birdie tried her best to stop him—'

' "Birdie"?' queried Ethel.

'His wife – but when she saw him scooping in the counters—'

'Oh, he won?'

'A packet. Couldn't go wrong. He was so loaded with the stuff when he left that he had to lean on her all the way home. She said "My hero!" or words to that effect, and next day steered him into one of those shops downstairs. He bought her a gorgeous diamond clip costing about $2000.'

'Nice man.'

'Oh, yes, Arch is fine.'

'Well, the next night he went back to Bradley's, and you can guess what happened. First he lost the price of the clip and after that the price of his shirt and mesh-knit underwear. The next night it was the same, and the next and the next, and all the time Birdie was chirruping around showing her clip and saying what a thing it was to have a generous husband. And when Arch dropped hints about marriage being a partnership in which the loyal little comrade should share the downs as well as the ups, she didn't seem to get it.

'Finally Arch pleaded with her to put the clip away somewhere. He said he couldn't bear to look at it.

'Then one evening it disappeared. It wasn't insured, and Birdie kept the loss to herself. It was only when they were back in New York that Arch happened to ask her why she never wore that diamond clip he had bought her in Palm Beach. She explained what had happened.

'When Arch at last gathered that the clip had been stolen, he nearly had a fit. "Why in heaven's name didn't you notify the hotel detective, the police?"

' "How could I? It would have got into the papers. It would have looked terrible – ARCH SELWYN STEALS WIFE'S JEWELS."

'Arch tottered. "You thought *that* of me? You really supposed that I would stoop – My God!"

'Arch was properly indignant, but he admitted to Ray privately that the thing that made him really so sore was to think of all those weary hours he had spent hunting everywhere for the clip after Birdie was asleep, and all the while some dirty crook had beaten him to it.'

2

They swam and lay in the sun. They played a round of golf on that odd little course where the hazards were palm trees and the greens – in those days – were of sand.

That night they went to Bradley's and Sam Harris, of Cohan and Harris, who came in with Charlie Dillingham, took them into the office and introduced them to the Colonel and his brother.

'Two writin' fellers, Colonel,' said Charlie. 'They want membership cards.'

'Can they afford to lose?'

'Up to a point, and I guess you know what that is.'

The Colonel told his brother to make out the cards.

'I don't like to win money from people who can't afford it,' he said. 'I think that's pretty well known . . . too well known, perhaps. At any rate, I got caught nicely the other day. Man came in and started to play big. In less than an hour he'd dropped $17,000. I went myself and watched him at the end. Seemed to me he looked kind of upset, and it worried me. Then the next day his wife came in and asked to see me. She was terribly wrought up. Said her husband must have been crazy. What he'd lost, she said, was the money they had been saving up for years to buy a home in Florida. A real tear-jerker it was. Well, I did what I've done quite a few times when this sort of thing has happened: I gave her back half the money and told her to tell her old man that if he ever tried to come sneaking into my place again, I'd make it my business to kick him out personally. That woman was certainly grateful. Tears coursed down her cheeks. She grabbed my hand and kissed it. She said she wished there were more men like me in the world.'

'I'll bet she did,' said Sam Harris. 'I've known a lot of gamblers in my time, from Dick Canfield down, but you're the only one that would hand back $8500 just because a dame cried at you.'

'You haven't heard the pay-off,' said the Colonel, and his brother, sitting at the desk, started to laugh. 'Spite of my warning, darned if the husband didn't come in again that very same night, and sat down calm as a codfish on ice, and began to high-roll all over the board. I was hopping mad. I sent one of my table-men to fetch him to the office, and when he came in I started to lay him out. "Didn't your wife tell you I said you weren't to come here?" I yelled at him. He looked sort of surprised. "My wife, Colonel?" he said. "I haven't got a wife!" I said, "You mean you haven't got a wife who came in here this morning and told me you'd lost the money you had been saving for years to buy a home?" "Certainly not," said the fellow. "Why would I buy a home?" he said. "I'm lousy with homes. Homes are what I've got nothing else but. I own the biggest hotel chain on the West Coast." '

'Women aren't gentlemen,' said Charlie Dillingham.

'But Ed hasn't told you the real snapper,' said the Colonel's brother. 'The fellow he'd been so big-hearted about had a run of fool's luck that night. He nicked us for close on $80,000.'

They went into the gambling rooms, which were filled with men in dress-clothes and women laden down with jewels. Europe had not yet regained its pre-war popularity, and everyone was coming to Palm Beach. The recently established tax on income, crushing though it was – 4 per cent, if we remember rightly – had not removed any of the gilt from the gilded set. The two writers, who had but recently acquired the feeling of solvency, shrank back into the ranks of the under-privileged as they saw the walnut-sized diamonds and the piles of green $20 chips strewn across the roulette tables.

There were a few faces that they recognized . . . Otto Kahn with his neat white moustache . . . General Pershing accompanied by his friend Coleman Dupont . . . Willie K. Vanderbilt, Junior . . . Mrs O. H. P. Belmont . . . the impish-faced Margaret Lawrence with her husband, Orson Munn. Most of these they knew from having seen their photographs in papers and magazines, but there was a leavening of characters from their own bailiwick . . . Arch Selwyn, Condé Nast, Addison Mizner.

'Take a look round,' said Plum, 'and tell me – who, if you didn't know who any of them were, would you say was head man, most assured, most at home?'

Guy could answer that without a moment's hesitation.

'Ziegfeld.'

'That's right. He's got an air. You feel that $100 bills mean no more to him than paper matches to a cigar store.'

'And half the time he hasn't enough to buy a knitted waistcoat for a smallish gnat.'

Ziegfeld was standing by a table with a handful of the costly green chips, dropping them carelessly on the numbers and turning to talk to the woman next him without watching the wheel. He won, but went on talking, leaving the chips where they lay. He won again. It was quite a win, but only when his companion squealed excitedly and pointed to the piled-up counters did he motion languidly to the croupier to push them toward him.

'The lady seems more thrilled at his win than he is,' said Guy.

'So I notice. "Blasé" about sums it up.'

'Know who she is? I just heard someone say. Mrs Edward B. McLean of Washington.'

'Do you mean to say that that blue thing she's wearing round her neck is the Hope diamond?'

'That's it. The stone Tavernier stole from the idol Rama-Sita. Fifteen violent deaths laid to its account.'

'Is that really the score?'

'So far. You wouldn't catch me playing roulette with that thing alongside me.'

But the Hope diamond seemed to have lost its malignant power tonight. Ziegfeld continued to win. Then, apparently bored, he pushed his counters over to the table-man and received a slip of paper in exchange. Two famous beauties from the *Follies* came up to him, Helen Lee Worthing and Olive Thomas. He fished some loose chips from his pocket and handed them to the girls. He caught sight of Guy and Plum and came over to them. He asked them how long they had been in Palm Beach. They told him they had arrived that morning by the same train as himself.

'Why didn't you come in my car?' he said. 'It's a lot more comfortable than those stuffy drawing-rooms.'

They did not mention that they had travelled down in humble 'lowers'.

'You didn't bring Jerry with you?'

'No.'

'He's coming. I reserved a room for him at the Breakers. He and I have been talking about a show for Marilyn Miller.'

This was news. Presumably Jerry had not mentioned this because there was another librettist involved.

'You ought to have a huge success with her,' said Guy. 'She's got the same sort of quality Maud Adams had. A wistful charm that goes right to the heart.'

'Have you settled on a story?' asked Plum.

'Practically settled. It's a musical version of *Be Calm, Camilla*, that Clare Kummer comedy. Clare will do the book and lyrics.'

'Isn't that the play in which the heroine breaks her ankle in the first act?' inquired Plum innocently.

'That's it.'

'I shouldn't have thought it would be an ideal vehicle for a dancer.'

Ziegfeld stared at him for a moment, then he laughed.

'Jerry and I ought to have our heads examined.'

'However, that's the only objection.' Plum's smile was benevolent. 'It's a very charming play otherwise.'

Ziegfeld eyed them thoughtfully.

'Have you fellows got a story?'

'Guy has. Scheherazade had nothing on that boy. He's full of stories.'

'We must get together when Jerry arrives and have a talk,' said Ziegfeld. He turned away, but came back as if struck by an afterthought. 'You boys like yachting?'

With the hint of an *arrière pensée* the boys said they did.

'I've chartered the *Wench*, Len Replogle's boat. We might take a cruise through the Indian River and possibly run up the Loxahackie in one of the launches. You'll see alligators and orchids growing wild.'

'That should be quite a saving for you, gathering a few wild orchids,' said Plum. Ziegfeld was famous as an orchid-giver.

'Are there any locks?' asked Guy.

'Locks? No. Why?'

'I was just thinking of something. How many do you carry as crew?'

'Fourteen, including the Captain.'

Guy drew a deep breath.

'We'd love to come, wouldn't we, Plum?' he said.

An immediate conference seemed to be called for. Watching millionaires winning and losing fortunes had its thrills, but it was not so thrilling as the contemplation of a show for Ziegfeld with Marilyn Miller as star. They left Bradley's and climbed into one of the chairs lined up at the entrance. They told the coloured owner to take them where he pleased. A full moon was shining. The air was soft and balmy. Though wearing dinner-jackets without overcoats they had no sense of chill even when they turned down the broad cedar-lined way that led to the ocean.

No motor vehicles were allowed on the island in those days. Bicycles and the bicycle-chairs were the only means of transit on pathways that wound through the semi-tropical clusters of palm, cedar and banyan.

They agreed that a show for Ziegfeld would be the biggest thing that had happened to them. Quite aside from New York, his name on the road was dynamite. The *Ziegfeld Follies* were the top drawing-card of America. And a show for Ziegfeld *with* Marilyn Miller. . . . You couldn't beat that for a combination.

Inevitably Guy suggested *The Little Thing*. Plum was dubious. It seemed to him that the setting and costumes would strike Flo as giving insufficient opportunity for glamour.

The first scene of *The Little Thing* was the backyard of an actors' boarding-house, the heroine a little drudge who loathed washing dishes and longed to be a ballet dancer like the great Esmeralda, one of the boarders. Esmeralda, now an old woman with nothing left of her days of glory but an imperious temper, was certainly not a Ziegfeld type, nor was Mr Tolly, the old actor who had loved Esmeralda when she was the toast of Broadway and who had surreptitiously fastened a gold star to the door of her hall-bedroom. 'Not much there for Flo,' said Plum.

'But can't you just see Marilyn in that scene with the writer who'd do the article on the old-timers?'

'Which scene do you mean?'

'He says, "What's your last name, Sally?" "Rhinelander." "Oh, a society lady?" "No, that was just the telephone district. I was found in a telephone booth wrapped in an old shawl. I go and put flowers in it every Mother's Day." '

'Yes, yes.' Guy, once started on the subject of *The Little Thing*, was not easy to stop. 'Yes, I remember.'

' "The last time I saw Mother," ' Guy went on, ' "one of her hinges was broken and she had a sign on her 'Out of Order'. It's kinda sad, don't you think?" '

'What I remember most clearly about *The Little Thing*,' said Plum, 'is the lyrics. You secured a very gifted man to write those, some name beginning with W.'

'You are thinking of "Joan of Arc"?'

'No. Good, but not W at his best. "Church Round the Corner" was more up to the W mark. "Church Round the Corner" – did I ever tell you Ethel and I were married there?'

'No. Were you?' Guy sighed enviously.

'We had $126 between us in the world, and we were standing there waiting for the parson to appear and beginning to wonder if he had stood us up, when he came bounding in with a six-inch grin across his face.

' "Hello, folks!" he yodelled. "I've just made $10,000 on the Stock Exchange." I was as sick as mud. $10,000! There ought to be a law.'

They lapsed into silence as their chair turtled along beside a sea spread out like a dark-blue counterpane lace-edged with white where it touched the shore. Presently Plum spoke.

'By and large, not a bad world,' he said.

3

Jerry Kern arrived, and after a talk with Ziegfeld said, 'Well, boys, it looks as if you'd done Clare Kummer out of a job.'

Guy disagreed.

'All we did was point out that a play where the heroine spends the entire evening on crutches with a plaster cast on her leg might not be just right for Marilyn Miller. But Clare Kummer is so clever that I'm sure she will be able to think up something that will give a dancer more scope.'

'Come off it. You two hi-jackers are after the thing for yourselves.'

'Naturally we would like the job. But only if Clare Kummer turns it down.'

'She has turned it down. She's at work on a play called *A Successful Calamity*. She might have managed an adaptation, but isn't equal to inventing a new story, starting from scratch.'

'Well, tell Flo we are in residence, ready to receive him and consider offers.'

'Eh?'

'I was thinking of "Fabulous Felix",' said Guy.

But Ziegfeld, having raised their hopes, did nothing to sustain them. They ran into him every day, but on the subject of shows for Marilyn Miller he preserved a proud silence. His conversation was of golf, of gossip, of gambling. He talked quite a lot, but he did not talk turkey. One morning, meeting them pottering round the Country Club course, he told them that the yachting trip was set to start next Sunday morning.

'Do you boys like terrapin?' he asked in that curious, melancholy way of his.

Jerry Kern said he was crazy about terrapin. Plum and Guy, neither of whom had ever tasted it, said they were, too. (As he later admitted, Jerry had never tasted it, either.)

'Well, don't eat too much breakfast,' said Flo. 'We'll have terrapin for lunch that beats any you've ever eaten. The ship's cook has a special way of preparing it.'

The *Wench* was something very different from the *Dorinda* of evil memory, a real dream-boat with a cocktail shaker for every port-hole. Confident this time of finding a steward in a white coat deferentially serving refreshment, the visitors found three stewards in three white coats, each more deferential than the last. Everything capable of glistening glistened. Everything fashioned to glow glowed. The deck-chairs were lower, deeper and more luxuriously cushioned than those of any other vessel to be seen about the yacht-club pier. Each single item was the best money could buy, from the giant Havana Perfects to the three long-limbed young ladies stretched at their ease under an awning of the famous Ziegfeld rose pink. Their costumes were to the last degree what Palmer would have called *avant garde*. In a day when girls were arrested if they appeared on a bathing beach without stockings, the three nymphs justified Will Roger's famous crack, 'I never expected to see the day when girls would get sunburned in the places they do.'

The other men of the party were Messmore Kendall, a theatrical manager, Paul Block, the newspaper owner, and Walter Chrysler. Just before they were ready to sail, Arthur Somers Roche, the novelist, came aboard with his bride, Ethel Pettit, who had played the heroine of *Miss Springtime* in the Chicago company and later, when Sari Petrass, the Hungarian prima donna, retired from the New York company, had taken her place. In this gathering of millionaires and *Follies* girls it was pleasant to meet one of the gang.

The *Wench* turned through the inlet and headed up the coast past the tall red column of Jupiter Light standing at the end of the island which had been the home of Joseph Jefferson. Messmore Kendall had known one of the Jefferson sons – four of them, all actors – and this younger Jefferson had told him that, when his father had moved there, Jupiter Island had had only one other inhabitant, a hermit who had not exchanged a word with another human being for thirty years. The story ran that he had had his tongue cut out by a tribe of Seminoles, he having told a lie about one of them. (Seminoles are touchy.) He was held up as an awful warning to the younger Jeffersons.

The legend lost considerably in impressiveness when it was discovered that not only could he talk, but that once started it was impossible to stop him. Conversation, the accumulation of thirty years of silence, poured from him in an unending stream. He attached himself to the Jeffersons, and nothing they could do would rid them of him. Finally they accepted the inevitable and he became old Joe's constant companion on his fishing, hunting and painting expeditions. One day Joe asked him if it was true that he had remained silent for thirty years.

'Yeppy, that's right.'

'Why?'

'Weren't nobody worth talking to.'

Old Joe said he considered that one of the highest compliments ever paid him.

Jerry sat down at the little yacht piano that had been moved out of the saloon for the occasion, and began to play.

'What's that?' asked Olive Thomas.

'It's a delicious melody,' said Ethel Pettit. 'Are there any words?'

'You bet there are words and I'd love to hear you sing them. The song was written for *Oh, Lady* but we took it out.'

Jerry asked Plum to scribble down the lyric for Ethel and, while he did so, he told them something more of the song's origin. The melody was one of several that Jerry had assembled to play Charles Frohman back in 1906 or thereabouts. He wanted to get in on the writing of those extra numbers which were interpolated into the scores of the

Austrian composers. These at that time were always supplied by some member of the 'English school' – Lionel Monckton, Paul Rubens, Howard Talbot and the rest, Frohman having that odd passion of his for anything English.

Frohman refused to see Jerry, sending word that he bought all his material in England, and anybody but Jerry would have accepted the situation meekly and given up the struggle. But the fellow who said 'You can't keep a good man down' must have been thinking of Jerome D. Kern. He scraped together his few pennies and went to London. There he succeeded in selling a number called 'Won't You Come and Flirt with Me?' to George Edwardes, who put it into one of his productions. It had girls in swings that swung out over the audience displaying black-stockinged legs and frilly petticoats, and was the hit of the show.

On the second night, when Jerry was standing at the back of the circle glooting, as Chaliapin would have said, over his success, Charles Frohman came up. He told Jerry that he had been pointed out to him as the composer of the number. He was enthusiastic.

'When it comes to this sort of thing,' he said, 'you Englishmen are in a class by yourselves. We haven't anyone who can do it on the other side.'

He asked Jerry if he would consider coming to America. Jerry thought he might be able to fit in a trip – he had often wanted to see America – and they sailed back on the same ship. As the boat went up the bay, C. F. pointed out the various objects of interest to the bit of imported English talent at his side.

'The highest building of all is the Manhattan Life. The one with the gold dome is the World Building. This is the Hudson River, navigable by quite large vessels for 100 miles.'

'Coo!' said Jerry. 'Really? 100 miles? Lord-love-a-duck! Makes a chap think a bit, that sort of thing, what?'

At this point a lady, a poor sailor, who had remained in her state-room during the voyage, espied Jerry and came up to him.

'Why, Jerry Kern!' she cried, 'How did you like London? Weren't you homesick? After all, there's no place like dear old Newark, is there?'

'What did Frohman say?' asked Paul Block.

'He behaved like the sport he always was,' said Jerry. 'He laughed and laughed, and finally I was sufficiently reassured to join in. We became great friends, and the next time C. F. went abroad, he asked me to come with him. There were a couple of new musicals in London and he wanted my opinion on them. Well, naturally I jumped at the invitation, and the night before we were to sail a bunch of my friends gave me a farewell party, at which I did a thing I don't often do. I got pie-eyed. I was just sober enough to ask whoever it was that brought me home to set the alarm-clock for seven, and when seven came there was a little croak from the clock, but it was enough to wake me up, and I staggered out of bed and started getting dressed. The boat was sailing at ten, and I wanted to have plenty of time.

'I made myself a cup of coffee and got my clothes on. It was a miserable day, and all the time it kept getting darker, until I thought there must be a terrible storm coming up. By the time I got into a taxi, the sky was almost black. I said to the driver, "What on earth's happening? Is there going to be a thunderstorm?" He said he didn't think so. "Then what's making the sky so dark?" I said. "Why wouldn't the sky be dark?" he said. "It's close on eight-thirty."

'And suddenly I got it. It was eight-thirty at *night*. I'd slept right through the day. The alarm-clock hadn't wakened me, and that croaking sound which I had finally managed to hear had been the little bit of alarm left for the next time the hour it's set at comes round.'

'So of course you had missed the boat?' said Chrysler.

'Yes. And do you know what boat it was? The *Lusitania*, sailing 2nd May 1915.'

4

Plum handed the lyric he had been writing out to Ethel Pettit, but before she had a chance to sing it one of the stewards announced luncheon. They all filed through the big lounge into the dining-saloon. The meal started with grapefruit au Kirsch, caviar having already been served with the cocktails. Then came the terrapin.

'Wait till you taste this,' said Ziegfeld.

But after the first mouthfuls and the appreciative 'Ohs' and 'Ahs' he shook his head.

'There's something wrong,' he said. 'This isn't it. It's not bad, but nothing like what I promised you.' He turned to the steward. 'Did Shimo cook this?'

He was told that Shimo had not cooked it, having been fired by the Captain for impertinence. Ziegfeld nodded moodily, but said nothing.

While they were still at lunch, the *Wench* put into Port Pierce. A steward went ashore with a sheaf of Ziegfeld telegrams. This was routine. Few hours of the day passed without Ziegfeld sending a telegram to someone.

It was on the return journey, when the sky had begun to glow with one of those magical Florida sunsets, that Ethel Pettit sang the song that had been dropped from the score of *Oh, Lady, Lady:*

I used to dream that I would discover
    The perfect lover

Some day:
I knew I'd recognize him if ever
He came round my way:
He'd have hair of gold
And a noble head
Like the heroes bold
In the books I'd read.

Then along came Bill,
Who's not like that at all:
You'd pass him on the street and never notice him.
His form and face,
His manly grace,
Are not the sort that you
Would find in a statue:
I can't explain . . .
It's surely not his brain
That makes me thrill:
I love him because . . . oh, I don't know,
Because he's just my Bill.

'I've got to have that song,' said Ziegfeld. 'What do you boys want for it?'

'It's not for sale,' said Jerry. 'It's a valuable adjunct to a show.'

'I'll have Fanny Brice sing it and give it a big set-up – plenty of *schmaltz*.'

'It's no good for a revue, Flo. It needs a situation back of it. It needs a guy named Bill and the girl who loves him.'

He turned to Plum. 'Am I right or am I right?'

'Of course you're right. I wrote it for Molly to sing about Bill in *Oh, Lady*. The whole point is that the audience has seen Bill and has been wondering what a girl like her can find to love in a chap like that. . . . And she tells them. It's no good except for a book show.'

'Well, I'm going to do a book show – plenty of them before I'm through,' said Flo. 'I'm starting next season with one for Marilyn Miller.'

'Okay, we'll put it aside till we see who you offer us to sing it.'

'Ruth Etting suit you?'

'Yes, Ruth Etting would suit us fine. So would Ethel Pettit.'

'Sorry, I've retired,' said Ethel. 'Though I admit,' she added, 'if anything would tempt me back, it would be a song like that.'

'Nora Bayes, Elizabeth Brice, Fanny . . . there's plenty who could sing it,' said Jerry, 'but let's get the show first.'

'We'll get a show.'

'If that song is in it and Ollie Thomas, I'll back it,' said Chrysler.

'You'll have a little competition, Walter,' said Paul Block. 'I'm already elected to back Flo's show for Marilyn, and I may say I don't mind having Ollie in it either.'

That's how simple it was to get backing in those days when big musicals cost $50,000 to put on and not $300,000 . . . a well-staged party with a few pretty girls . . . Irving or Jerry, Lou Hirsch or Rudy Friml at the piano . . . and one lady guest carefully chosen for her voice.

When the *Wench* came into the yacht harbour, there was a Jap standing on the clubhouse pier. Ziegfeld went over to the Captain.

'I'm told you fired Shimo because he was fresh,' he said. 'You were quite right, but I wired him that he's hired again. He won't be the ship's cook. He'll live in a hotel and come aboard only when we're having terrapin. That's all he's for – just terrapin.'

Chrysler laughed.

'You and Paul and I,' he said, turning to Messmore Kendall, 'have quite a bit of money between us, but it takes a Ziegfeld to do a thing like that.'

5

The two partners had one more encounter with the Glorifier before they left. It was on the golf course that had been laid out between the Breakers and the Royal Poinciana. There were only nine holes, and though it was quite late in the afternoon Plum thought he would be able to make it before dark. Guy, who had blistered his hands in a country-club match the day before, was walking round with him. On the first tee they found Ziegfeld, who was likewise accompanied by a non-player, Freddie Zimmerman. It seemed only fitting that the two active members of the quartette should team up.

'What'll we play for?' asked Flo. '$5?'

'All right,' said Plum, getting ready to drive. 'And if it gets too dark to finish, we'll give the $10 to Freddie to hold for tomorrow.'

'I meant $5 a hole.'

Plum was actually swinging as Flo said it. He foozled his drive. Flo, however, following his almost invariable custom, foozled his, and Plum won the first two holes. As he addressed his ball on the third tee, Ziegfeld called out 'Double or quits', which caused his opponent to slice, and the ball, striking a palm tree, returned almost to the starting point. In these circumstances a protest regarding the wager would hardly have been sporting, so Plum agreed and Ziegfeld sent a topped shot a matter of eighty yards down the fairway. Once more Plum won the hole, and once more Ziegfeld said 'Double or quits'.

By the time they holed out at the seventh, Plum again winning, two things had begun to gather – darkness and a gallery. Guy and Freddie, working it out with pencils and bits of paper, announced that the contest for the short eighth would be for $640.

The eighth was a mashie-niblick shot on to a narrow green surrounded by bunkers.

'You shoot first,' said Plum. 'It may change your luck,' and Ziegfeld proceeded to make a shot Francis Ouimet might have been proud of. The ball rose in a beautiful arc against the still faintly glowing western sky. It dropped a yard from the hole, and there was a round of applause that was probably as gratifying to the master-manager's ear as any earned for him by his artists.

It was unnerving for Plum to have to follow such an effort, and he topped his shot badly. The ball took off on a flat trajectory, whizzed across the green, hit one of the private cars in the siding behind it, came whistling back, ricocheted off a caddy, soared into the air, fell ten inches from the cup and trickled in.

Plum was relieved. It had been a near thing.

'Thought for a moment I'd missed it,' he said.

'Double or quits,' said Ziegfeld.

'Or suppose we make it an even thousand?'

'Okay. Mind if I shoot first again?'

'Go ahead.'

The shades of night were falling fast now. There was just enough visibility for the spectators to be aware that this time Ziegfeld meant business. They could see him only vaguely, a dim form in the darkness, but even that glimpse was sufficient to tell them that there stood a man who intended that his stance should be right, his grip right, his body still, his head unmoved, and his eye on the ball; a man who proposed to come back slow, bring the arms well through, roll the wrists, let the club-head lead and pivot on the ball of the left foot, being careful not to duck the right knee. A man, in short, whose driver would travel from point A to point B along dotted line C, winding up at point D, as recommended in all the golf books.

And so it proved. It was a superb drive. It was unhurried. It had rhythm. The arms were straight, the wrists cocked at the top of the swing, the elbows close to the body, the weight shifting at precisely the right moment from leg to leg, the wrists uncocking to give the final snap, the whole winding up with a perfect follow-through. A ball hit by a man doing all that sort of thing has to go places. Ziegfeld's did. It shot from the tee as if Walter Hagen were behind it, and was immediately swallowed up by the night.

'Watch it!' yelled Flo, apparently crediting those present with the 'patent double million magnifyin' gas microscopes of hextra power' which Sam Weller claimed not to possess in place of eyes, and the caddies ran ahead, the gallery following. The hunt was up. Ziegfeld, his caddy, Freddy Zimmerman, Guy, Plum and perhaps twenty pleasure-loving followers of sport were searching hither and thither about the fairway, striking matches and lining up in arm-linked squads. They combed the ground in every direction, but the ball was nowhere to be found.

Plum, meanwhile, having given up the search, had holed out, using his mashie-niblick, not trying for distance but being content with smooth, wristy shots that travelled from eighteen inches to two feet. Ziegfeld, joining him on the ninth green, pulled out a roll of bills and extracted one. It was a beautiful thing with a yellow back on which was a portrait of President Garfield and a printed promise that it could be redeemed at the US Treasury for $1000. The two authors gazed at it respectfully. It was the first thing of the sort they had ever seen.

They walked back to the Poinciana.

'What I like about show business is that you meet such interesting people,' said Plum, taking out the $1000 bill and fondling it. 'Flo Ziegfeld, to name but one.'

'Yes, and "Felix", Ray, Arch Selwyn, Charlie Dillingham, Hank Savage and the rest of them. I suppose that's why the theatre draws one like a maggot, as Joe Urban would say.'

They came to the hotel. Inquiring at the desk for mail, they were handed a cablegram. It was from 'Fabulous Felix', urging them to come to London. *The Girl Behind the Gun*, its title changed to *Kissing Time*, was to go into rehearsal in a week or two with a cast of stars – George Grossmith, Leslie Henson, Phyllis Dare, Yvonne Arnaud, Tom Walls, Stanley Holloway . . . a breath-taking roster of talent.

'*Kissing Time*!' said Guy. 'My God, what a title! We'd better get over there quick and change it.'

'It may not be so bad for London. "Kissing Time" was the hit song of *Chu Chin Chow*.'

They cabled 'Felix' that they would come, but a few days later Guy had developed doubts.

'Suppose Flo suddenly comes through with the Miller show?'

'One of us could always jump on a boat and come back.'

'One of us, yes. I suppose one would also be able to look after things in London.'

Guy had personal reasons for not wanting to go to England at this time. He had hopes that he might be able to convince his prima donna that if Jack Sprat and his wife could make a go of it with such contrary tastes, why couldn't they? She was still in Mexico and there was no hint of an early return. Unless things were taken in hand their romance seemed destined to dwindle to extinction in a dismal and occasional exchange of picture-postcards.

'All right,' said Plum. 'You stay here. You can keep in touch with Flo, and I can do anything that needs to be done in London.'

A week later he and Ethel sailed for Southampton on the *Majestic*.

6

Guy went to see them off, joining the crowd at the end of the pier and waving as the queen of the White Star fleet turned from the pack of bustling tugs and moved slowly down stream. A couple unrecognizable at the distance were waving. They looked like Plum and Ethel. Guy waved back, then turned away disconsolately. When he returned to his 57th Street apartment he was conscious of a lost feeling. For the first time since he and Plum had met and formed their partnership, he faced the ups and downs of their strange theatre world alone, and he could not help feeling that it was the end of a phase – a period. Something told him that there would be no more Princess shows. Jerry had drifted away and was writing with other librettists, while Plum, he knew, was in the process of capturing a public with his books and short stories that would give him a more secure position, a more solid standing than the theatre ever could.

It depressed Guy to think that this separation might mean the end of a writing partnership which had been so pleasant and so successful. He knew that Plum had been feeling the need of refreshing his view of the English scene. England was the background of his stories, and he had said while they were waiting for the boat to sail that he might settle there for a while. How long was 'a while'?

However, there was work to do, as always, and Guy got down to it and finished *The Five Million* and *Adam and Eva* and went on to tinker a comedy George Middleton had written called *The Cave Girl*. He and George also wrote a rather strange play about Oberammergau Passion Players, *The Light of the World*. He was steering away from musical comedy. He started work on a serious play all his own with a wartime background, *The Dark Angel*.

Letters passed back and forth between him and Plum. *Kissing Time* – the London management had insisted on keeping the title – had opened at the Winter Garden and was the success it was bound to be with that galaxy of stars. It ran for nineteen months.

Several times during that period Guy was on the point of boarding a liner and joining Plum, who had settled down in Kensington, but something always happened to stop him. Marguerite was singing with the Chicago Opera, and he journeyed there and back between rehearsals and bouts of intensive writing at Atlantic City.

She still held off on their marriage, arguing that, for his own sake, he should find himself a wife who would fit into the pattern of his life without having any conflicting pattern of her own. It was on this note that they parted when, the Chicago Opera season ended, Marguerite started off on a tour with the St Louis Symphony Orchestra while Guy returned to New York for the *Adam and Eva* rehearsals.

Then, with the seeming inconsequence associated with feminine decisions, came a letter saying that she had changed her mind. She told Guy she was ready to get married as fast as he could get himself out to San Francisco where her tour was ending. They would be free then to buy a car and spend an enchanting honeymoon roving the Pacific coast. Only pausing on his way to the Grand Central to pay a quick visit to Tiffany's, Guy boarded the Twentieth Century.

The four-and-a-half-day journey seemed endless but the Overland Ltd, to which he had changed in Chicago, finally ambled through vast fields of artichokes into the delightful City of Hills. It was early and San Francisco was wrapped in its pearly morning mist. To Guy's surprise Marguerite was waiting on the platform.

'Come on,' she said. 'We've got time to go over to the Cliff House for breakfast.'

' "Got time"? What do you mean? Where are we going?'

'You're going back to New York on the noon train.'

'What are you talking about?'

'You've had a wire from Jerry Kern and heaven knows how many from Ziegfeld. They want you at once for the Marilyn Miller show.'

'Are you coming back with me?'

'I can't, darling. I've got two more concerts.'

'Well then, I shall chuck it.'

'Oh, no, you won't. I'm not going to have you looking at me some morning when I've a cold in the head and saying, "It was for that I turned down the biggest opportunity of my life." '

They took a taxi and breakfasted at a table looking down on the seal rocks. Guy saw in the seals a symbol of separation.

'Those aren't loving couples,' he explained in answer to her question. 'Those are all females. The males never bother with California. They are up in the Misty Islands where the fishing is better.'

'And don't these wives of theirs suffer from the same qualms as I do? Wondering whether the old boy isn't playing house with some little Misty Island chorus-seal?'

'Not a chance. The bull seals are sick to death of women once the mating season is over.' Marguerite laughed.

'There's an idea there,' she said.

She looked at the diamond wrist-watch that had occasioned the stop at Tiffany's. It was time to go back to the station.

A little later Guy was staring out of the train window wondering who it was that ate all those artichokes.

7

The Marilyn Miller show was to be called *Sally*. Ziegfeld had originally planned three shows, one for Marilyn, one for Leon Errol and the third for Walter Catlett, but after *Sally* was completed he decided to have Errol co-star with Marilyn. This necessitated a complete reconstruction, and not more than a week after it was finished he sent for Guy and asked him to 'put in' a part for Catlett which would be equal to Errol's but must take nothing away from it, as Errol had already seen the script. Just one of those simple little rewrite jobs that are so common in the world of musical comedy. Guy, as he toiled away, found himself thinking enviously of Plum, who about now was probably writing a serial for the *Saturday Evening Post* which would be accepted, paid for on the nail and printed without the change of a comma. These novelists, he felt, had it soft. It was some slight consolation to him, as he courted brain-fever in the effort to make the Catlett part screamingly funny but not so funny as to provoke growls of anger from his fellow-star, to reflect that it would hardly be possible not to reap a small fortune from a Miller-Errol-Catlett show with Kern's music, Ziegfeld's girls and Joe Urban's scenery to help it along. Ziegfeld authors might wind up sticking straws in their hair and cutting out paper dolls, but they could afford expensive nursing-homes in which to do it.

Plum having written that it was impossible for him to leave England at the moment, he was working alone. He shipped a script over to his partner in London, and a certain amount of long-distance collaboration took place. Plum wrote two or three lyrics, at the same time urging Guy to use 'Bill' and extract 'Church Round the Corner' from *The Little Thing*. He did use the latter, and the final scene was built around it, but Marilyn's voice was not suited to the singing of 'Bill', which needed – and finally got – a Helen Morgan. Two more lyrics were taken from a musical adaptation of *Brewster's Millions* which Jerry and Guy had started but abandoned. These – 'Whip-poor-will' and 'Look for the Silver Lining' – were by Buddy de Silva. Two other lyricists, Clifford Grey and Anne Caldwell, also had lyrics included. It was all pretty haphazard and very different from the Princess days.

The script called for a funny woman to play opposite Catlett. Guy suggested Ada Lewis. Flo wouldn't hear of it.

'Make her young and cute,' he said. 'I hate women comics.'

He gave the role to little Mary Hay, and again overruled the author in the matter of the casting of the elderly society matron who was mixed up with Sally's fortunes. Guy presented the names of several of the leading theatrical *grandes dames*, but Flo refused to consider them. He engaged Dolores, the lovely six-feet-one amazon who had been the central figure of the Ben Ali Hagan tableaux in the *Follies*.

'I don't want old people in my shows,' he said. 'What you look at is just as important as what you listen to.'

One argument, however, Guy did win. Ziegfeld wanted a 'star' entrance for Marilyn, and Guy had introduced her as one of the six orphan girls who came on early in Act One in a line, all dressed alike in cotton frocks and laced-up ankle-boots, to be inspected by the restaurant owner, who had applied to the orphanage for a dishwasher.

Ziegfeld hated the idea. So did Jerry Kern. But, of all people in the world, Guy found an ally in Marilyn, who might have been expected to be the first to recoil in horror at the suggestion that she should make an entrance like that.

'It's fine,' she said. 'Just right for my eccentric dance.'

'We'll try it together in Baltimore,' said Flo grudgingly. 'But be prepared to rewrite it for New York.'

It did not have to be rewritten. It was an immediate success. A delighted gasp went up all over the theatre when the last of the row of orphans was yanked out of the line by the restaurant owner and revealed herself as Marilyn. Charlie Case, the vaudeville comedian, used to tell a story in his act which culminated in the line 'He tore off his whiskers, and it was Jim!' Marilyn's entrance had much the same effect, not only in Baltimore but two weeks later when she made it at the New Amsterdam.

But Flo had been right about Dolores. Not only was she lovely to look at, she was the perfect foil for Errol, the Balkan Grand Duke who had been thrown out of his country by a revolution and was making a living as a waiter. When the pair emerged together from 'The Little Church Round the Corner' they were greeted with a storm of applause. The finale was the number that Plum had written for *The Little Thing*.

There's a church around the corner that's waiting for us:
  It's just above Madison Square.
I'll borrow a dollar and buy a clean collar,
  And then I'll be meeting you there.
There'll be crowds in the pews and excitement and fuss,
  For I mean to be married in style,
And the girls will go dizzy and whisper 'Who is he?'
  When I start to step up the aisle.

Dear little, dear little Church Round the Corner,
  Where so many lives have begun,
Where folks without money see nothing that's funny
  In two living cheaper than one.

Our hearts to each other we've trusted:
We're busted, but what do we care?
For a moderate price
You can start dodging rice
At the Church Round the Corner,
It's just round the corner,
The corner of Madison Square.

Few who were there on that opening night will ever forget the reception that was accorded the little star when she came down the steps of the church in the lovely lace bridal-robe that Ziegfeld had dressed her in. Many things contributed to the magic of that night – Jerry's wonderful score, the *Follies* beauties in their lovely costumes; the Urban scenery and still more the Urban lighting; the two comedians, each turning in the best performance of his career. But it was Marilyn that really mattered, Marilyn who gave to the play a curious enchantment that no reproduction in other lands or other mediums ever captured.

8

'Church Round the Corner' had a significance that carried beyond its role in *Sally*. It served as admonishment and happy omen for a real life wedding. Marguerite and Guy got married, with Jerry as best man in lieu of Plum.

'How are the mighty fallen!' said Jerry when he and Eva were sipping champagne with the newly married pair. ' "Marriage means giving up your comfort and your ideal of woman, in trying to be some woman's ideal of man." Line by Guy Bolton. "Marriage isn't a process for prolonging the life of love but for mummifying its corpse", a further comment on the institution from the same source. "Marriage is the net in which the jade snares the jaded." "Marriage—" '

'Listen,' said Guy. 'Just because I write of a cynical woman-hater is no reason I should subscribe to his views. My opinion of woman as the priceless pearl of creation is well known.'

'Let us trust,' said Marguerite, 'that I'm the last bead on the string.'

'I wish to propose a toast,' said Guy. 'Here's to the author of "Church Round the Corner".'

'You'll be seeing the old boy soon.'

'Let's hope,' said Guy. 'We're sailing for England next week.'

Actually it was five weeks later that they sailed for England on the *Olympic*, a delay occasioned by discussions with Max Marcin concerning a comedy melodrama which he and Guy were writing together. Among their fellow passengers were Charlie Chaplin and Eddie Knoblock, the author of *Kismet*.

At the ship's concert Marguerite sang and Chaplin did a pantomimic act in which he portrayed an out-of-work actor applying for a job. As the manager, played by Knoblock, described each aspect of the character, Chaplin became successively humble, aggressive, charming, ultra-aristocratic. Told he was too short for the role, he seemingly grew several inches taller. Questioned as to his romantic qualifications, he hurled himself into the manager's lap. Finally he is asked to run through a scene in which he is supposed to come home and find his wife in the arms of his best friend. In a frenzy of jealous rage he is called on to kill his betrayer. The manager shakes his head and says he fears Charlie can never be sufficiently convincing in the scene, whereupon the actor, determined to win the coveted role, seizes the manager by the throat. When he at last relaxes his grip and turns away to get his hat and stick, the manager is a corpse on the floor. Charlie, turning back with an ingratiating smile to receive his applause, was Chaplin at his best. His surprise on seeing the empty chair, his consternation on discovering the body that has slipped down under the desk were done as only Chaplin could do it. And then his famous shuffling exit, looking back over his shoulder and raising his hat to the corpse. It made a perfect finish.

9

The first thing Guy did on reaching London and depositing their bags at the Berkeley was to go in search of Plum. He was living in bachelor quarters in a tall, old-fashioned building in Queen Street. His flat was on the fourth floor. There was no lift and Guy, travel-tired, toiled up the long staircase to arrive somewhat breathless as he entered the already opened door. Plum had just finished a letter and he called out a cheery 'Hurray, you're here. Just a tick while I get this letter off.' So saying he walked to the half-open window and tossed it out.

'What on earth,' exclaimed Guy. 'Has the joy at seeing me brought on some sort of mental lapse?'

'You're referring to that letter? I throw all my letters out of the window. I can't be bothered to toil up and down stairs every time I post a letter. These are honest people, you know, each one is his brother's keeper, whoever picks it up will quicken his pace as he hurries it to the nearest letter-box.'

'Well, I wish you'd write me a letter while I'm here, I'd like to show it round in America. Quite a score for good old England.'

Guy turned from the window to Plum's battered old typewriter.

'The same old girl,' he said, 'I duly salute her. But what is that large affair with a great big roll of paper hitched up behind her?'

'That,' responded Plum, 'is the great Wodehouse invention.'

'You type directly on to that roll of paper?'

Plum explained. 'Nothing is more destructive,' he said, 'when the steam's up and ideas are tripping over each other to suddenly arrive at the bottom of the page. You have to take the page out, lay it on the pile, find another sheet, put it in, then find yourself uncertain what the last word was, find it, realize you've misspelt it. . . . But, with this Wodehouse invention you just type merrily on, words flowing like a purling stream.'

Guy took over, 'Witticism after witticism, yes, yes, brilliant, brilliant! What a man!'

'But,' resumed Plum, 'every silver lining has its cloud. Last Thursday I was having a wonderful day, I had typed a good seventy feet and I felt I could easily pass the hundred mark when a smouldering odour seemed to have come into the room. I leapt to my feet in the middle of a big laugh, the seventy-foot page had made its way across the floor, passing a pile of books, an old-fashioned spittoon, and had curled up round the little electric heater that I use to take the chill off the room. I rushed over and started stamping on some of the best comedy lines I had ever written.'

'What a tragedy!' Guy exclaimed sympathetically. 'Nothing you put in its place ever seems any good.'

It was two days later that Guy heard a timid knocking on his door. He opened it and a man said, 'Your name "Bolton"?' Guy said it was.

'I've got a letter for you, sir.'

Guy put his hand toward his trouser's pocket.

'Thank you, sir, but I'm not looking for any tip, I was coming this way.' He felt differently about a beer and Guy poured him one. While he was drinking it Guy went to the telephone and called Plum.

'I've got your letter,' he said.

Plum said, 'Are you sure it's mine?'

'Yes, of course I'm sure.'

'I only threw it out of the window twenty minutes ago.'

Guy said, 'The GPO had better look to their laurels.'

'And keep an eye on their laburnums,' Plum added. 'That sure beats everything if you want it to go fast.'

11

1

GUY was having a business honeymoon. He had hoped to be able to buy a car and tour the British Isles at his leisure, but a playwright's programme is always subject to changes without notice. Work fell on him out of the skies. Gilbert Miller was putting on *Polly With a Past* at the St James's, and he suddenly decided to advance the opening date and called on Guy to attend rehearsals.

Miller had assembled a brilliant cast for *Polly* – Edna Best, a newly arrived star who had made a great success in a play called *Brown Sugar*, Edith Evans, Claude Rains, Aubrey Smith, Henry Kendall, Helen Haye, Donald Calthrop and a young man named Noel Coward. Altogether quite an array of talent and one that would be on the expensive side today.

It led off the season on 2nd March. The following night Maugham's *The Circle* opened at that most delectable of theatres, the Haymarket. Then on the 14th came *A Bill of Divorcement*, followed by Cyril Maude's revival of *Grumpy* on the 26th, and *Bulldog Drummond* on the 29th. And the players – Gerald du Maurier, Marie Tempest, Meggie Albanesi, Allan Aynesworth, Lottie Venne. Marguerite and Guy had chosen a good month for their theatre-going.

'The London theatre is wonderful,' said Guy. He had dropped in to pay a morning call on Plum.

'Surely not as vital as New York?'

'I'm worried about New York – not the plays but the way the men up top are running things. Take this ticket-speculating. The managers could stop it in a minute if they wanted to, but half of them are getting rake-offs. They're driving people away from the theatre. That boy and his best girl that we used to talk about can't afford to come any more. We're getting the out-of-town buyers – tickets bought for them at inflated prices by the firms they do business with – and the new rich who sprang up during the war. And the kind of audience you get largely determines the kind of plays you get.'

'The musicals are better in New York.'

'Yes, but the costs are sky-rocketing. They tell me you have to have close on $50,000 in the kitty to put on a big musical today.'

'I wonder what our old friend Hank Savage would say to that.'

'Even an *Oh, Boy!* would cost between $30,000 and $35,000. In London things are reasonable. And the theatres look so much better here with everyone dressing and most of the men in white ties. It seems as if the audiences are out to enjoy themselves. They don't have that grim I-wonder-if-I'm-going-to-get-my-money's-worth attitude that paralyses you in New York.'

'Not the people in the stalls, perhaps, but how about the gallery boys?'

'Yes, they're tough, of course. I would hate to be booed.'

'There are worse things than booing. Did I ever tell you about the very first play I ever had produced?'

'I don't think so. In London?'

'At the Vaudeville. It was supposed to be funny, but you would never have thought it from the way the audience reacted. Not a laugh from start to finish, as I remember it. When the final curtain fell, there was a dead silence all over the house. Then a voice in the gallery said, "Well, good night, all," and they went home to bed. I would much have preferred the loudest booing. What a ghastly thing a real solid flop in the theatre is.'

'All the same, I'd sooner have one in London than on Broadway. And I still maintain that London audiences are better than New York audiences and London plays – most of them – better than New York plays.'

'Well, if you're so keen on them, you'd better come and lunch with me at the Dramatists' Club and meet some of the fellows who write them.'

'What's the Dramatists' Club?'

'It's . . . how shall I put it? . . . it's the Dramatists' Club.'

'I see. The Dramatists' Club.'

'That's right.'

The Dramatists' Club had no clubhouse. Its members met once a month in the private dining-room of a hotel in Northumberland Avenue, where they lunched and exchanged views. Its president at this time was Sir Arthur Pinero.

Today there was a distinguished gathering. Barrie was in the seat next to Pinero and on his other side the club's secretary, Ian Hay and, beside Ian, Edward Knoblock.

The man next to Knoblock was a rather colourless-looking little fellow with blondish, greying hair.

'Who's that?' whispered Guy.

'Jacobs.'

'Not W. W.?'

'There's only one Jacobs.'

'There certainly is,' said Guy reverently. He knew practically all

Jacobs by heart. Sam, Ginger, Bob Pretty and the rest of them were his familiar friends. If there had been a deliberate attempt to thrill him, they could not have done better. Louis Parker came in, and with him Clemence Dane, and shortly afterwards Cyril McNeile, who wrote under the name of Sapper. His *Bulldog Drummond*, with Gerald du Maurier starring, had just opened and was a tremendous success. Of those who had big hits running in London, only Willie Maugham was missing.

As they were sitting over coffee and cigars, Barrie rose, looking, even when standing, not much taller than his sitting neighbours.

'I know speeches are not in order,' he said with his faint Scottish burr, 'but I haven't been to one of these meetings for some time and I've got to tell you of the wee little thrill I always get when I come here. It's some years now since we founded this club, Arthur here and poor Haddon Chambers, whom we've just lost, and Harry Esmond and Kipling and Hornung and one or two more. We were all pretty young then and we talked a lot about the things we'd written and the things we were going to write. There was one fellow talked more than all the rest of us put together. A tall, Irish chap with a red beard . . . I've often wondered what became of him.'

Guy asked the man seated next to him, if it was true, as Barrie had seemed to imply, that Shaw never came to these lunches and, if so, why.

'There was a lot of unpleasantness during the war,' his neighbour told him. 'He wrote stuff praising the Germans and it infuriated a good many people, Kipling particularly. The atmosphere got so strained that Shaw finally resigned. Pinero announced it at the next meeting. "Mr Shaw has handed in his resignation," he said, then paused for a moment. "Mr Shaw's resignation," he added, "is as nothing compared to ours." '

2

Sally was to be presented at the Winter Garden in the autumn at the end of the long run of *Kissing Time*. The management was again that of Grossmith and Laurillard and discussions regarding book adjustments, casting and other matters called for daily meetings with George Grossmith, who thus took his place in the Bolton-Wodehouse gallery of theatrical managers.

'Tell me about Grossmith,' said Guy one morning.

'What do you want to know about him?'

'He's a strange bird compared with our New York gang.'

'George isn't only a manager, he's one of London's top musical comedy actors.'

'Yes, I know. He's a brilliant light comedian, but he can't have been so hot in the Donald Brian part in *Kissing Time*.'

'Hotter than he was as Prince Karl in an Austrian operetta I once caught him in. The trouble with George is that if there's a prince in the show you can't keep him away from it with an injunction. Show him a white uniform with gold frogs across the chest and a lot of medals, and he starts making mewing noises.'

'A snob, perchance?'

'A priceless snob, but the looking-up kind, not the looking-down. The looking-up snob longs to know a duke, the looking-down variety can't afford to know a dustman. George reads himself to sleep with Burke's *Peerage*, but he'll go pub-crawling with the stage-door man.'

'I like him.'

'Everybody likes him. Women especially.'

'Oh, he's a ladies' man?'

'Second to none. I heard a funny story about George the other day. I don't know if it's true or not, but it sounds just like him. He had gone to see the Grand National and, strolling through the paddock, met his friend Lord Lathom, who introduced him to a very pretty woman, Lady something – I can't quite remember – Mudge – that's not quite it.'

'Peeress?'

'No, wife of a baronet – but that would be enough to endear her to George. They got along together like ham and eggs and, when she said that racing bored her and that she couldn't bear seeing the horses fall at the jumps, he gallantly insisted on remaining with her in the paddock during the running of the race. The friendship ripened on the journey back to London and when they parted she invited George to come and spend the next weekend at the old home. She said her husband would be delighted. A touch of gout had kept him away from Aintree but she was sure George would brighten him up.

'George accepted but when he met the gentleman he had misgivings. If the Bart was delighted his manner didn't show it. He had heard about the meeting in the paddock and he started right in asking George why the devil he had gone halfway across England to see a race and then chosen to turn his back on it and talk to a woman instead. This had evidently aroused his worst suspicions.

'The dinner was a ghastly affair with the host whipping the carving-knife back and forth across the steel until his wife complained that he was setting her teeth on edge. George tried to talk about the house, which was ancient to the point of mouldering. Hosts are usually to be drawn out on the subject of the family manse. "Fascinating old place," he said.

' "A lot of people have died in it," said Bart darkly.

' "Probably from the damp," said his wife. "It's the dampest place I was ever in."

'This disturbed George. He has a horror of damp. However, he beamed as cheerfully as he could manage. He was glad when the time came for bed.

'But he wasn't glad long. It suddenly came back to him what his hostess had said about the place being damp. The room they had put him in smelled musty, and he was sure the sheets must be wringing.'

'I thought it was an established custom before getting into any bed in England to make a test for dampness by putting a hand-mirror between the sheets?'

'It is. And don't think old hypochondriac George didn't think of it, but unfortunately the only mirror in the room was a thing six feet by eight, fastened to the wall with brass nails. Then he remembered something. He was pretty sure he had seen a mirror in a carved frame standing on the piano in the drawing-room. And what could be simpler than to toddle downstairs and fetch it? With the Grossmiths, to think is to act. He set off in his white silk pyjamas with the gold frogs across the chest, got the mirror and started back again. As he reached the landing, a door was suddenly thrown open and there was the Bart, looking like Othello.

' "What the devil are you doing, prowling about the house at this time of night in your pyjamas?" he inquired, clenching and unclenching his fists, his eyes burning with a green flame.

' "I came to get this," said George, exhibiting the mirror.

'Only it wasn't a mirror, it was a photograph of Lady Mudge.'

'Good Lord! What happened then?'

'I don't know,' said Plum. 'That's where the story ends.'

3

The chief problem in casting *Sally* was, of course, to find a Sally. Leslie Henson and Grossmith could handle the Errol and Catlett parts, but there were no Marilyn Millers in England – only one in America. It was decided to engage Dorothy Dickson.

Dorothy was an old friend of Guy's and Plum's. Ray Comstock had discovered her dancing with her husband, Carl Hyson, at the College Inn in Chicago, and had signed them up as a speciality dance team for *Oh, Boy!* Their success had been sensational. Dorothy used to make up with a round spot of rouge on each cheek like a painted doll, and accentuated this effect by wearing a little Dutch cap. She was prettier than any of her rivals in the field of ballroom dancing and, good though Carl Hyson was, this was the only team – except the

Astaires – in which the female partner was the equal of the male. Vernon Castle, Maurice, De Marco and the others made it their business to show off the girl they were dancing with, but, had they wanted to, they could just as easily have shown her up. Not even the best of them could have done that to Dorothy.

She was ambitious to become something more than a ballroom dancer and took vocal and acting lessons, but the first two parts she played were in failures – *Girl o' Mine* and *Rock-a-bye-Baby*. She then went to London, rejoining Carl, and appeared in the Cochran revue, *London, Paris and New York*. It was not an impressive record, and both Ziegfeld and Kern were vehemently against entrusting her with such a vitally important role as Sally, Ziegfeld eclipsing himself in the matter of violent cables. Guy, however, remained firm and insisted on her playing the part.

He wanted to get the matter settled so that he could get over to Paris. He had had a letter from Marguerite in which she told of an offer from the Opéra Comique of an engagement that would assign her the top lyric soprano roles, Louise, Manon, Mimi and Butterfly. He knew such an opportunity was her dearest ambition.

'Are you going to say "Yes"?' Plum asked him.

'There's nothing else I can do. I can't help remembering what she said to me when I wanted to chuck *Sally* and stay in California. "I don't want you to be looking at me in years to come and saying – for that I gave up my biggest opportunity." '

'I was afraid it was going to be like that, two ambitious people.'

'Oh, well, I can pop back and forth – London, Paris and New York – not a bad life.'

'You've got to go to New York for that farce-melodrama, haven't you?'

'*The Nightcap*? Yes. I've only a week or two to spend with Marguerite.'

Guy raised the question of when they might hope to get together on another show. Plum suggested that they should reunite the old triumvirate, Bolton, Wodehouse and Kern. Guy said it couldn't be a Princess show. Jerry had set his face against writing again for the tiny playhouse.

'If we can't have Jerry, who else is there?'

'Irving.'

'Fine, but he wouldn't want me. He writes his own lyrics.'

'Do you remember that boy who was rehearsal pianist at the Century?'

'You mean the lad who could make a piano sound like a whole jazz orchestra?'

'That's the one. He said he'd like to play us some of his music.'

'Every rehearsal pianist wants to play you his music.'

'I know, but I was with some people not long ago and they talked about this chap and someone said he was a genius.'

'You're sure it was the same fellow?'

'Yes, I'd clean forgotten his name but when they said it I remembered it. I've written it down so I won't forget it again and when I get back I think I'll look him up.'

'What was the name?'

'George Gershwin.'

'That's right, I recall him now. Pink cheeks, nice smile, a terrifically strong beard that even the closest shave couldn't conceal.'

'If I decide he'll do, will you come over?'

'Yes, but try to get Jerry. After all there's only one Kern.'

'True. Still, who knows? Maybe there's only one George Gershwin.'

4

Guy went to Paris. The opera engagement offered to Marguerite was for the autumn. He saw how eager she was to do it and told her to accept. It was for a year with an option for a second one.

'You'll just have to commute,' she said.

'I know how you hate to leave the stage for more than a minute but you'll have to when the baby arrives.'

'Not necessarily. Tonelli told me he was born in a dressing-room at the Scala during a performance of *Traviata*.'

'Don't tell me the lady was playing Violetta?'

'I wouldn't be surprised, dear. Crinolines you know. It's *the* opera for expectant prima donnas.'

They went to Italy – Rome, Florence and Venice – returning to Paris where Marguerite was due for rehearsals. *The Nightcap* rehearsals were starting in New York. Guy phoned Plum to say good-bye, Plum again urging him to try and re-establish the Princess team. He sailed from Cherbourg on the *Olympic*, the ship that he and Marguerite called their honeymoon boat.

Meanwhile Plum had retreated to the charming village of Rogate in the Petersfield district and was embarked on that intensive programme of novel writing which turned out, in rapid succession, *The Girl on the Boat, The Adventures of Sally, The Inimitable Jeeves, Leave it to Psmith, The Heart of a Goof*, and *The Small Bachelor*, the last-named *Oh, Lady, Lady* in new guise.

Just to keep his hand in he wrote the lyrics for *The Golden Moth*, for which Fred Thompson supplied the book.

The Nightcap opened early and then Guy, who happened to be in Atlantic City, saw the first performance of a show called *Tangerine* which was written by the head of the New York Theatre Guild,

Lawrence Langner. Langner had received some help from Philip Bartholomæ but it wasn't sufficient. The show fell flat on its face. Carl Carleton, the husband of Edith Day, was the manager. He asked Guy if he thought the piece could be saved. Guy thought it could, and he was right. His revised version ran for more than 300 performances.

Guy barely waited for the opening night, then sailed for Europe. *Sally* was already in rehearsal in London so there was no time to travel via Paris. He wired Marguerite asking her to meet him in London but when he got there he found a letter saying that she was singing *Traviata.* The role sounded significant. She begged him to come over. He phoned and told her he must stick with rehearsals for at least a week or so.

Plum was back in London, living in a house in Onslow Square, next door to the one that had been the home of William Makepeace Thackeray. When Guy went to see him, the door was opened by a butler. Plum explained that this wasn't swank.

'It's business,' he said. 'This chap is an author's model.'

'A what?'

'Come, come, you've heard of artists' models. Audrey Munson was one, if you remember. Well, he's an author's model. I'm writing some stories about a butler. At least, he's not a butler, he's a valet, but the two species are almost identical. I study this bird and make copious notes. Do you like the name Jeeves?'

'Is that what he's called?'

'No, that's the name of the man in my stories. This one is Robinson. You couldn't sell a butler called Robinson to the public. Not box-office. For a long time I was stumped for a name, then I remembered a cricketer, in the years before the war, called Jeeves. Played for Gloucestershire, I think. Calling a character after a county cricketer is lucky. Sherlock and Holmes were both county cricketers. I believe Doyle had decided on Sherrinford Holmes, when he suddenly thought of Mordecai Sherlock, who used to keep wicket for Yorkshire. Jeeves seemed to me just right for the sort of bloke I wanted.'

'What sort of a bloke is this Jeeves of yours?'

'He's omniscient. And, what is more, as Abe Erlanger would say, he knows everything. Robinson's like that. You can't broach a subject he isn't up on. Think of one.'

'Spats.'

'Too easy.'

'Spiders.'

'Right.' Plum pressed the bell. 'Do you know anything about spiders?'

'If you wish to live and thrive, let the spider run alive.'

'Damned silly saying. You wouldn't thrive very long with a family of tarantulas running around. Oh, Robinson.'

'Sir?'

'Mr Bolton is writing a play with an entomologist in it and he wants some inside stuff about spiders.'

'From what aspect, sir?'

'Their domestic life and all that sort of thing.'

'The domestic life of the spider is something that does not bear a close scrutiny, sir.'

'Things not too good in the home?'

'No, sir. The spider's is a matriarchal society. The husband, if we may call him such, has but one function . . . if I may put it that way.'

'Carry on. Mr Bolton understands. I've told him all about the bees and flowers.'

'When this function is fulfilled, the lady has him for dinner.'

'Nothing formal, I suppose? Just a black tie?'

'I speak in a literal sense, sir.'

'You mean she eats him?'

'Precisely, sir. As Shakespeare so well put it, "Oh, curse of marriage, that we can call these delicate creatures ours, but not their appetites." '

'Would you say "delicate" was the—'

'*Mot juste*, sir? Possibly not, sir. One confesses that one is inclined to look askance at the female spider and to view her activities with concern. She deceives the male with a tenderness which, in the light of what is to follow, one cannot but regard as in dubious taste. She flirts and plays, inviting him to swing with her on a long thread, holding him gently in her arms.'

'And all the time she is planning—'

'Precisely, sir.'

'Good God! Women! . . . I hope you're listening, Guy.'

'Would there be anything further, sir?'

'No, that will be all. Thank you, Robinson.'

'Thank *you*, sir.'

The door closed.

'There you are,' said Plum. 'And it would have been just the same if I had asked him about anything else.'

'Useful chap to have around. But a bit on the sombre side, isn't he? Doesn't he ever smile?'

'Faintly, at times.'

'I can't imagine him laughing.'

Plum seemed shocked.

'I should say not. Butlers don't laugh. They aren't allowed to by the rules of their Guild. Though – yes – I did once see one convulsed with mirth. It is one of my most painful memories.'

'You didn't like him laughing?'

'I didn't like what led up to the laughter. It happened when I was very young and very shy and very hard up. So hard up that I relied for my clothing mostly on the leavings of other members of the family. Thus – if you're interested – I had a frockcoat and a topper discarded by my brother Armine, an overcoat discarded by my Uncle George and a suit of dress-clothes once the property of my Uncle Hugh. It was in this suit of dress-clothes that I went to dine one night at the house where this butler held office. Some people who had known my father in Hong Kong. Rich blokes. All very posh. I was the only one at the dinner table who was of the *canaille*.'

'Still, you were properly dressed.'

'It depends on what you mean by "properly". And I wasn't dressed so much as swathed. This uncle of mine, this Hugh, was a man who weighed close on seventeen stone, and he liked his clothes roomy, the trousers in particular. And they kept climbing up over my shirt-front. Well, that was all right so long as I had my hands free, because I could shove them down again. But came a moment when I was helping myself to some dish, and they shot clear up over my white tie. And it was at that moment that this butler gave way to his baser nature. There was a sound like a paper bag exploding and he rushed from the room. He squared himself with his Guild later, I believe, by saying that he had had a fit.'

'You should have had the things altered by a tailor.'

'Talk sense,' said Plum. 'It would have cost about a quid.'

5

Sally opened at the Winter Garden, and was an instantaneous success. The only mishap was that Dorothy's toe-slipper came off just as the ballet started. Twice she tried to slip it back on and the audience applauded. Up to that point she had turned in a charming performance. In the dressing-room scene that followed she was delightful.

The next morning, after a breakfast of excellent notices, supplemented by a little light refreshment, Guy took off for Paris. Marguerite had reluctantly left the stage, her last performance having taken place ten days previous.

'Even then you were taking chances on being a second Madame Tonelli.'

They dined in the seclusion of Marguerite's studio-apartment in the Val du Grâce. The phone rang. It was from London. Plum reported *Sally* a complete sell-out. The show had gone like a breeze, the only mishap was that Dot's toe-slipper had come off.

'But, good Lord,' said Guy. 'Is this going to happen every night?'

'Every night, old boy, and at matinées. But don't worry. That pathetic slipping slipper has become one of the high spots of the show.'

'She can stop the show with any other kind of dancing.'

'She'll stop it in the ballet spot, too, before she's through. Don't worry.'

'It's your birthday this week, isn't it?'

'Yes, this coming Sunday, why?'

'Nothing. I just had an idea.'

His idea was right, the baby was born on Sunday. He couldn't call it Pelham so they compromised on Pamela, Pamela Marguerite.

A week or two later Guy had a cable from Sam Harris. It asked him to get together with the Duncan Sisters. He commissioned Guy to write a show for them. Irving Berlin would supply the score. Guy wired back saying he would like to work with Plum – Sam cabled to go ahead, only Irving would do his own lyrics.

Guy was delighted. The young lady who had arrived on Plum's birthday seemed to have been a happy omen. He called Plum and told him the news.

'The Duncan Sisters? You can't miss with them. I saw them the other night. They're terrific.'

'I'm glad you're so enthusiastic. What about you coming in with me?'

'Good Lord! Do you want me?'

'I sure do.'

'Then I'm with you. We can write the show here and then sail.'

'But what about Jeeves?'

'Jeeves can wait,' said Plum.

12

1

THE Duncan Sisters, in case the present generation needs reminding of it, were two small girls who created the impression of being about twelve years old. Their names were Rosetta and Vivian, though their friends, and their friends were legion, called them Heim and Jake. Their forte was the delivery of numbers like 'The Bull-Frog Patrol' in close harmony, and they were – there is no other word – terrific. The revue they were starring in at the Royalty was called *Pins and Needles*, and was about London's biggest success, crowded at every performance.

Guy invited them to have supper with him at the Embassy Club. Plum warned him not to, saying that a formal business meeting in the afternoon with pencils and notebooks was the right approach, but Guy would make it the Embassy, a place he adored. Plum said he would not be present. Guy could have the talented artists all to himself.

Guy went to see their new show and after a due interval to permit them to change and remove their stage make-up presented himself at their dressing-room. He found them ready to leave, but they had not changed their revue costumes, nor had they removed their stage make-up. All they had done was stick huge bows in their hair, one pink, one blue. In the final scene of the revue they had worn short dresses and socks. They were still wearing short dresses and socks. They looked like something left over from a defunct kindergarten, and Guy was conscious of a sinking feeling. The Embassy Club in those days, when the great Luigi presided over it, was the smartest, most exclusive supper place in London, posh to the eyebrows. Dukes and duchesses jostled countesses and earls, and it was a very exceptional evening when you could throw a brick in it without beaning some member of the royal family. It seemed to Guy that in such surroundings the Sisters Duncan and their socks were likely to make something of a sensation.

Propped up against the wall of the dressing-room was a huge floral horseshoe. It was taller than the Duncan Sisters. It was taller than a Duncan Sister mounted on another Duncan Sister's shoulders, and he gazed at it with a wild surmise.

'What's all this?' he asked, and Heim explained that it was a present from their manager, Mr de Courville, tonight being the 200th performance of the show.

They were now ready to be escorted to the taxi which Guy had asked the stage-doorman to have in readiness. Heim spoke to this worthy as they came out, and he ducked back into the theatre, emerging a few moments later accompanied by the stage manager and the assistant stage manager. They were cautiously negotiating the horseshoe through the stage door.

'We're not taking that with us?' faltered Guy.

'Of course we're taking it with us. We're not leaving all those lovely flowers here to die.'

'But what will we do with it at the Embassy?'

'We'll have it at our table. It'll look cute.'

'And another thing,' said Jake. 'It's lucky. It's a lucky horseshoe. Seems like a good omen to have it there when we sit down to talk about the new show.'

Guy tottered on his base. If there was one thing from which his sensitive nature recoiled, it was looking conspicuous, and it was plain that he was scheduled to look even more conspicuous than when giving Marguerite a bite to eat in those Greek reach-me-downs of hers which had so intimidated Plum, the Athenian stole and the serpent armlets. Broodingly he helped Heim into the cab while the driver and the stage manager secured the horseshoe on the truck stand. He was able to have a brief word with the driver before they started off.

'Ten bob extra,' was what he said, and the driver nodded intelligently.

When the cab drew up at its destination, the girls gave a simultaneous cry of dismay.

'It's gone – the horsehoe!'

'My God!' cried Guy, shocked to the core.

The driver was apologetic.

'Sorry, gov'ner, it slipped off and another cab ran over it. Didn't think it was worth while stoppin' to pick it up.'

Guy gave the faithful fellow a pound note, and they went into the club.

'It's a bad omen for the new show,' said Jake Duncan as they took their seats.

'Yes,' agreed her sister. 'It's put me clean off it. When you've got a good luck horseshoe and it falls off the taxi, that means something.'

'Yessir,' echoed Jake. 'That sure means something. Maybe we'd best get busy on that Topsy and Eva thing.'

Guy was aware of a sinister foreboding. What, he wondered, was the Topsy and Eva thing? He did not like the sound of it.

2

Sitting Pretty was the title of the show. They wrote it in Plum's study in Onslow Square. Its central figures were two sisters in an orphan asylum, one of whom was adopted by a wealthy old man whose passion was eugenics. He had already adopted a boy, and it was his aim to marry these two, not knowing that Horace, the boy, was in partnership with an amiable burglar named Uncle Joe, who insinuated him into rich houses to prepare the way for him by leaving doors and windows open.

Irving Berlin had written that he had no objection to Plum contributing a lyric or two if he felt so inclined, and a comedy song being needed for Uncle Joe, Plum attended to it with a number called 'Tulip Time in Sing-Sing'.

In Broadway haunt of pleasure
Where they dine and tread the measure
A young burglar was becoming slowly fried.
When the waiter saw this mobster
Sitting sobbing in his lobster,
He stole up and asked him softly why he cried.
And the egg said with a quiver
'There's a college up the river
Which I yearn for. That's the reason of my gloom.
For the little birds each Spring sing
Aren't you coming back to Sing-Sing
Now it's April and the tulips are a-bloom?
When it's Tulip Time in Sing-Sing,
Oh, it's there that I would be:
There are gentle hearts in Sing-Sing
Watching and waiting for me:
Take me back, take me back,
Give me lots of rocks to crack
With my pals of the class of '99:
For I'd rather have neuralgia
Than be tortured by nostalgia
For that dear old-fashioned prison of mine.'

Early in the autumn Guy returned with Plum and Ethel to New York.

'Look,' said Sam Harris, when they reported at his office, 'I'm afraid there's been a hold-up. Irving hasn't been able to work on the score because this *Music Box Revue* has been taking up all his time. I'm going to do *Sitting Pretty* all right, but it will have to be next season.

The delay doesn't mean much to you boys, but it does to the Duncan girls, and they've asked me if I will consent to their filling in by doing a thing of their own on the Coast. I don't have to say yes, because I've got them under contract and I can put them in the *Music Box* till we're ready for them, but I don't see any harm in letting them do this thing of theirs if they want to, do you?'

Guy and Plum thought it would be a good idea. If the girls appeared in the *Music Box Revue*, it would take a lot of the freshness out of *Sitting Pretty*.

'What is this thing out on the Coast?' asked Guy.

'Oh, it's some idea of their own that they say they've had for quite a while. They've written the numbers themselves. It's a sort of half-amateur affair. *Topsy and Eva*! they're calling it. It's a sort of comic *Uncle Tom's Cabin*.'

Guy's head gave a side jerk as if he had suddenly received a left jab to the jaw. *Topsy and Eva*! He recalled the night at the Embassy with a dim foreboding.

'What's the matter?' asked Plum, noting his friend's silence.

'I was just thinking. *Uncle Tom's Cabin* – it's never missed yet.'

3

Some premonition of disaster seemed to be disturbing Irving Berlin when they dined with him two days after seeing Sam.

The dinner took place at Irving's apartment on West 46th Street. This was a novel duplex penthouse that had taken his fancy. He had had to buy the building in order to get it, but that sort of thing was a trifle to Irving. Like 'Fabulous Felix', he believed in doing himself well.

There was a broad corridor that descended in a series of steps, each step an eight-feet-square platform, to the big living-room that faced the street. Moulded glass panels by Lalique lighted this handsome passage. These were fringed with big potted plants, and standing in front of two of them were tall wooden stands on which stood a pair of brilliant-hued toucans. They added the final touch of magnificence, and it occurred to the authors that 'Felix' must be kicking himself for never having thought of toucans. Only 'Felix' would have had five.

As they came down from the dining-room, their host put out his hand to one of the birds, which immediately proceeded to strike like an offended rattlesnake, its terrifying bill missing the hand by the fraction of an inch.

'I'd be a bit more distant with those fowls, if I were you,' said Plum. 'They're liable to take your finger off.'

'Yes,' laughed Irving, quite unperturbed. 'And it might be the one I play the piano with.'

His piano playing was, of course, as exceptional as everything else about him. He could . . . but why are we using the past tense about Irving? If anyone is perpetually present-tense, it is the one-man Hit Parade. . . . He can play only in the key of F sharp. But of course, if you're a composer, you can't have everything in one key, so Irving's pianos have a transposing keyboard, equipped with a lever that can be set here and there at any key desired, while Irving goes blithely along hitting his black notes. Blithely and magically hit after hit.

After dinner Irving played a couple of tunes he had designed for the Duncan show, then swung round on the piano stool.

'This *Sitting Pretty* book,' he said. 'I've read it, and I think it's darned good. But—'

'But?'

'Well, as I figure it out, it's no use without the Duncans. The high spots come when the sisters, the rich one and the poor one, meet and do numbers together. With the Duncans these'll be smashes. We know what those babies can do with a number when they work together. But without the Duncans. . . .'

'You think we may not get them?'

'I'm wondering. My grapevine tells me this *Topsy and Eva* of theirs is pretty big. It may surprise us all.'

As they went down in the little push-button elevator, Guy was looking grave.

'I suppose you got that?' he said. 'Irving doesn't mean to write that score till he's sure we've got the Duncans. One show more or less means nothing to that bird. He can always make another million or so whenever he feels like it. Lucky devil!'

'Yes, he must have been born in a bed of horseshoes.'

'Don't speak of horseshoes, I'm superstitious about them.'

'I thought they were lucky.'

'Not to me,' said Guy.

A day or two later came a letter from George Grossmith saying that the end of the *Sally* run was in sight and that a new show would be needed at the Winter Garden. He proposed that this would be home-made and, indeed, indicated that he was nominating himself as part-author. Jerry was to write the score.

'You'd better go and do it with George,' said Guy gloomily. 'It looks like a long wait on *Sitting Pretty*.'

'Why don't you come too?'

'How can I? I've got *Polly Preferred* going into rehearsal and there's more than a chance that Gilbert will do *The Dark Angel* with Bart Marshall.'

So Plum sailed back and set to work with George Grossmith on a show called *The Cabaret Girl*, in which Dorothy Dickson was to co-star with Leslie Henson as the author-actor-manager, while Guy went to Paris and the Val du Grâce studio, where his infant daughter regarded the stranger with doubtful eyes.

4

While Jerry was working with Plum on *The Cabaret Girl*, he had read the *Sitting Pretty* book and had offered himself as composer if Irving Berlin was dropping out.

Irving was dropping out. *Topsy and Eva* was now in the twenty-seventh week of its Chicago run with no end in sight. Thus when Guy received a letter from Plum saying here was the old firm back together at last, he shot a wire to Ray Comstock and everything was fixed up. He crossed to England and settled down to fit the numbers Plum and Jerry were writing into the *Sitting Pretty* book.

Then one morning the letters that came up with his breakfast tray included one from Marguerite written in her most slapdash style. It seemed that a crisis had arisen, not in Marguerite's affairs but in those of a friend. Marguerite collected crises. She would gladly involve herself in one that was the property of people she hardly knew. Like a boy scout, she believed in doing her daily act of kindness.

A woman of prodigal generosity, she had one pet economy. She hated to waste writing-paper. In consequence it was her custom not merely to write on both sides of a piece of thin writing-paper but to turn the page sideways and write slap across the writing already there. A great deal of no doubt interesting gossip was thus lost to her friends.

In this letter she had really outdone herself. There was some talk of Robert Milton's wife who was in Paris, and there was some stuff about a child. Whether it was the Miltons' child or the child of a woman travelling with Mrs Milton was not clear. Guy, remembering somewhat vaguely that the Miltons had a child, inclined to the view that this was it. Anyhow the child was a problem – 'I don't mean a problem child,' Marguerite wrote in brackets. His name was Ben or possibly Hen – that was Marguerite's handwriting. And his mother was paying a flying visit to Geneva or Genoa where a hick (possibly sick) relative demanded her presence. Meanwhile Ben or Hen – now it looked more like Len – was coming over to spend a week with Guy in England. That part was painfully clear. His mother would collect him at the end of that time on her way back to America. In the meanwhile the little fellow would be entertained by visits to the Tower of London, Madame Tussaud's and the Black Museum at Scotland Yard.

Guy took the letter round to Plum. Bob Milton had staged the Princess musicals for both of them, and it seemed to Guy that they should share this burden that had been thrust upon him, standing shoulder to shoulder like the Boys of the Old Brigade. A partnership, as he pointed out to Plum after Robinson-Jeeves had conducted him to the latter's study, is a partnership.

'How old is this little excrescence?'

'Nine.'

'I know that American children are extremely precocious, but a child of nine who has his heart set on visiting the Black Museum at Scotland Yard should be given a wide berth. I'll bet that he has six toes on each foot and that his hairline starts one inch above his eyebrows.'

'Marguerite says he is extremely well-behaved. She goes into details though unfortunately a good deal of it is impossible to read. I did manage to make out that he does not flip butter-pats at the ceiling, a pastime all too prevalent in juvenile American circles.'

'That may be, but let me point out to you that people who regard their nine-year-old offspring as a treasure would hardly be shipping it from Paris to London unguarded. The fact that Mrs Milton is willing to do so is the tip-off.'

'Well anyway,' said Guy, 'the point is I can't put the child up in that mousehole I'm living in at the Mayfair. Here you have lots of space. You also have a butler who might well be a college professor did he not prefer the freer life and higher pay of domestic service. You can turn Ben over to Robinson without a qualm.'

'When is the little louse arriving?'

'Tonight on the Golden Arrow. I'm to meet him at Victoria.'

The notes of the conversation as given in the Wodehouse diary break off at this point. They are followed by a one-line entry: 'Went with G. to meet Ben. Biggest mistake of my life.'

The cryptic statement is not enlarged on. On the other hand the Bolton entry is extremely detailed, if somewhat incoherent. It was evidently written under the influence of strong emotion.

The basic trouble seems to have lain in the fact that trunks are frequently sent from France to England in bond, thus saving a hold-up in the Dover Customs shed. The owner of the trunk can, and usually does, proceed to the spot where these trunks are assembled immediately upon alighting in Victoria Station. Should such a person be travelling with a child, it is not unnatural – though perhaps unwise – to tell the little half-wit to take a seat on the platform and look at a picture-book of which he, she or it is sick to death after the seven-hour journey from Paris.

'Be a good little honey-cub and sit down there with the bags and the Mommer-bear will be back right away.'

Why should a poor, unsuspecting American mother imagine that, in orderly England, two kidnappers were on their way ready to pounce on her innocent offspring at this first moment of arrival? Plum and Guy were just a fraction late or they would have seen the Mommer-bear and not have found an unaccompanied child goggling vacantly amidst an assortment of hand-luggage.

'Sure that's the one?'

'Of course. See his stars and stripes buttons? Also he looks like Bob Milton, the same sort of puddingy face and red hair.'

'How'y'r, Ben?' said Guy holding out a hand to the youngster.

'I'm okay. How's yourself?'

The complaint, widely circulated, that American children are badly brought up is not necessarily true. This specimen had clearly been taught to be bright and friendly with strangers.

'Come along,' said Guy, taking the little fellow's arm. 'I bet I know someone who's ready for some ice-cream.' The chauffeur, who accompanied them, gathered up Ben's surprisingly voluminous hand-luggage and they all moved off to the car.

'I hear you want to see Madame Tussaud's?' said Plum chattily.

'Yes, and the Tower of London.'

After that the two writers may well be pardoned for believing they were in possession of the rightful Ben. It did not occur to them that all small boys are told when they visit London that they will be taken to Madame Tussaud's and the Tower.

During the journey to Onslow Square the child remained sunk in a gloomy silence. When the car drew up in front of the house he looked at it disparagingly.

'Rabbit hutch,' he said.

The remark wounded Plum who was rather proud of his little home. He had no notion that his guest was supposing this to be one of London's luxury hotels.

'This is your room,' he said, leading the way upstairs. 'The bathroom is the third door down the passage.'

'No bathroom?' rejoined Ben with a haughty stare. 'In America, hotels that don't have baths with every room is dumps.'

'Dinner will be in ten minutes.'

'Watcher mean dinner will be in ten minutes? Mom an' me eat dinner when we like.'

Plum went downstairs and joined Guy in the study.

'Correct me in a tendency to dislike this child,' he said. 'I don't mind a little healthy criticism but this blister treats my home as if it were a Bowery flop-joint.'

'He's certainly not what I expected from Marguerite's description.'

'I don't know why a man like Milton insists on propagating his species unless reasonably assured he can do a bit better than this.'

'Wait,' said Guy. He seemed agitated. 'Do you know what has just occurred to me? I'm pretty sure Bob has only one son.'

'One like this is plenty.'

'And that son, whose name as I recall it is Paul, not Ben, is editor of the *Dance Magazine* and, if I am not mistaken, has been married for some years.'

At this point the door was swung open by the Mystery Child.

'Where's my Mom?' he demanded.

'Your mother is on her way to Geneva – or Genoa.'

'You're a liar.'

'See here,' said Guy, 'if you go on like this, there'll be no Tower of London for you.'

'Phooey.'

'And you must be polite to Uncle Plum. He's being very kind to keep you here for a week.'

'A week my foot. We're going back home. My Grannie wants me. Me Pop wants me. My Auntie wants me. I guess most everybody wants me.'

'You guess wrong,' said Plum.

Ben surveyed them malevolently.

'You think 'cause they all want me they'll pay you money to get me back. My Mom'll fix you. She'll get the police after you. They'll get you under the lights. They'll beat you up with rubber hoses – that's what they'll do.' He turned abruptly and left the room.

'What on earth is the child talking about?'

There was a knock followed by the entrance of Robinson.

'Pardon me, sir, but what are your instructions regarding dinner? Master Breckenridge has informed me that under no circumstances will he eat boiled cod.'

' "Master Breckenridge"?'

'I gather from his observations that that is the young gentleman's name, sir.'

'If it is, I shall make it my business to present Mr Bolton's wife with a typewriter.'

Guy leapt to his feet.

'This isn't any question of spelling, of Milton or Wilson. We've got hold of the wrong child!'

'What? Do you think Mr Bolton is right, Robinson?'

'It seems a tenable theory, sir. It explains certain oddities in Master Breckenridge's behaviour.'

'Then for heaven's sake let's race this maverick back to the Lost Property Office.'

The car was summoned, the bags brought down and Master Breckenridge hustled into his coat.

'Where are we going?' he demanded.

'We're taking you back to your mother.'

On the chance that Mrs Breckenridge might have left Victoria in despair, they asked the youngster if he knew where his mother was planning to stay. He shook his head.

'With your approval, sir,' said Robinson, 'I will establish telephonic communication with all the leading hotels. The Breckenridges are, I believe, wealthy, and I fancy the lady will have booked rooms at the most expensive.'

As they were getting into the car Junior Breckenridge eyed them unpleasantly.

'Are you gorillas taking me for a ride?'

'Don't be crazy.'

'Then let me have your guns.'

He started to frisk them, rubbing his hands over their pockets. Plum pushed him into the car.

As they arrived at the station Junior nipped out of the car and rushed to where he saw a policeman standing.

'I bin kidnapped,' he said. 'I guess it's in the papers. I guess there's a reward – a mighty big reward. You take me to my Mom and you'll get it.'

The policeman turned to Plum and Guy.

'What's all this?' he asked. 'There's been some talk around here about a missing child. Are you the men who made off with him?'

'Sure. These are the ones,' said Junior. 'They know my Mom is rich. One of 'em said so. Get 'em under the lights!'

Speaking at once the two writers tried to explain. Guy pulled out Marguerite's letter and held it out waveringly to the policeman.

'I think you'd better come with me over to the station.'

'Must we? Can't you just take the little fellow and the bags? My man will drive you.'

The policeman was unrelenting. He insisted on taking them to the Westminster Police Station. There they found that a police call had been sent out asking for a report on two men seen leaving Victoria Station with a child and some purloined bags. They had, so the blotter read, joined an accomplice at the wheel of a battered car.

The Wodehouse Sunbeam was far from battered. Whoever had supplied the information was, doubtless, a devotee of crime literature. The sergeant in charge took their names. He had clearly never heard of either of them. Something in Guy's accent made him look up.

'You're an American, aren't you?'

'Yes.'

'Did you know these people in the States?'

'No.'

He eyed Guy keenly. 'Sure you didn't follow them over?'

Plum came to the rescue.

'Mr Bolton is a writer,' he said.

'He has no regular occupation?'

Plum, who might well have been expected to furnish a cutting reply merely faltered 'no'. It was not the stern-faced sergeant that made him go so suddenly jittery, it was Junior. The child had become fascinated by a notice on the station bulletin board headed 'Wanted for Murder', and depicting two thugs who had figured in a Thames warehouse crime. He was now switching his gaze back and forth from the printed portraits to the faces of the two writers. Plum's nerves, already so many tattered dish-rags, could stand no added strain.

'Well,' said the sergeant in a tone that suggested capitulation. 'It's unfortunate you men got hold of the wrong child. It was a piece of carelessness that caused this little lad's mother a lot of anxiety and distress. I have no doubt your excuse is that the other boy resembled this one. But still—'

'What other boy?' interrupted Junior.

'There was another little boy on the train with you that these gentlemen came to meet.'

This sounded better. They were now described as gentlemen.

'That's a lie,' said Junior. 'There was no kid on that train but me. I went through it and through it looking for someone to play with.'

The 'gentlemen' period was short-lived. They were now 'men' again and men in a most uncomfortable position. Junior Breckenridge was driven off to Claridge's with a policeman guarding him. Plum and Guy were still held answering questions regarding the non-existent Ben, their uncertainty as to his precise name, age or appearance imparting a quality of fishiness to their story.

It was on this intensely delicate situation that Robinson entered. He was looking his most dignified and ambassadorial. The sergeant was visibly impressed.

'Who are you?'

'My name is Eugene Robinson, sir. I am Mr Wodehouse's major-domo.'

'His what?'

'Butler,' said Plum.

'Your butler?' It was clear what was passing in the sergeant's mind. An employer of butlers, especially such a butler as this, must, like Cæsar's wife, be above suspicion.

'What about the child these gentlemen were supposed to meet?'

'That is precisely the point that I have come here to elucidate, sir. In the course of my inquiries regarding Mrs Breckenridge, I telephoned the Mayfair Hotel where Mr Bolton resides and was informed that there was a Continental telegram there addressed to him. I took the liberty of having it opened and the contents read to me. It was from Mrs Bolton and conveyed the information that the child Mr Bolton was desired to meet would not, after all, be visiting the

Metropolis, the young gentleman's mother having changed her plans. Might I ask, sir,' he added, addressing Plum, 'if you plan to return home shortly? When I left, the cook was expressing anxiety about the soufflé.'

On the way back to Onslow Square Robinson produced the telegram.

'I stopped at the Mayfair and collected this, sir,' he said. 'However, I feared that if I showed it to the sergeant, it might occasion further confusion.'

The telegram read: LITTLE NAN NOT COMING. HER MOTHER CANCELLING GERMANY VISIT. MRS NELSON THANKS YOU AND SENDS REGARDS.'

There was another wire, a cable. It was from Aarons and Freedley, a newly established management, asking Guy if he was prepared to write a show for the Astaires with a score by George Gershwin.

13

1

IT was a day or two after this shattering experience that Plum and Guy saw Gertrude Lawrence in a revue called *Rats* at the Vaudeville.

Plum had seen her before in *A to Z* and in the *Midnight Frolic* at the Hotel Metropole, an entertainment that was a close imitation of the one which Flo Ziegfeld had done on the New Amsterdam roof, but in *Rats* she had far greater scope than in either of those vehicles. Her performance affected Guy and Plum rather as his first perusal of Chapman's *Homer* affected the poet Keats. It seemed to them – a view that was to be shared later by the New York public – that she had everything. She could play sophisticated comedy, low comedy, sing every possible type of song, and she looked enchanting. When Guy got back to Mayfair, he wrote her an enthusiastic note in which he said that if she would come to New York he would guarantee to star her in a revue, a musical comedy or a straight comedy, whichever she preferred.

Getting the Ziegfeld spirit, she replied with a six-page telegram which could have been condensed into the words 'Right oh'. She was committed to play in a Charlot revue in New York, but after that she would be at his disposal. (The result of this exchange of civilities was *Oh, Kay*, the musical comedy which Guy and Plum wrote for her with music by George Gershwin and lyrics by his brother Ira when she was finally free to leave André Charlot's management.)

However, the immediate problem was the casting of *Sitting Pretty*. Letters passed back and forth with Ray and Jerry who was now back in New York. Frank McIntyre was engaged for the part of Uncle Joe, the sentimental burglar. The sole problem was the two girls who were to take the place of the Duncans. Queenie Smith was decided on for one, but who could play the other?

'I've just had a wire from Ray,' said Guy, bursting in on Plum at work in his study. If we cable "yes" Ray will book Gertrude Bryan.'

'Gertrude Bryan? You don't mean that Gertrude Bryan will come back to the stage?'

'I'm just telling you. All he's waiting for is "yes".'

'He'll get the loudest "yes" he's ever heard. Some cocktails, Robinson, and put your best effort into them. This is an occasion.'

'Oh yes, indeed, sir. In that brief visit I paid to New York with my late employer I had the privilege of seeing the young lady you refer to in *Little Boy Blue*. You have my warmest congratulations, sir.'

There are no doubt by this time a whole generation of voting age who will fail to see the significance of all this enthusiasm. Let them learn now that to have seen Gertrude Bryan in *Little Boy Blue* is to have wandered in a garden of enchantment. Her eyes were like the bluebirds in the spring, and her hair like finches' feathers a-wing. Gertrude Bryan, even more than Marilyn Miller, might well have worn the mantle of Maud Adams, had she not married at the very outset of her career and retired.

'I'll tell you what I think,' said Plum. 'I vote we board the first liner that's sailing and bend to the task of fitting this reborn star with the material that best suits her.'

'Yes, you're right, we mustn't waste a moment.'

'Your tone sounds a bit regretful.'

'Well, Marguerite and I had planned a little trip in the *roulotte*.'

'In the what?'

'Didn't I tell you about it? I suppose you'd call it a caravan, but the front part is a smart little car built by the Minerva people. You pull a lever and the *roulotte* is released and away you dash to do the family shopping.'

'Where did you acquire this monstrosity?'

'It was made for the King of the Belgians but he passed it up and I bought it for Marguerite. It sleeps four and has a bath, a kitchenette and a bar.'

'What, no ballroom?'

'However, I'll forget the *roulotte* until we've got *Sitting Pretty* on. Now where's *The Times*? Let's see what is the first boat going.'

'Don't bother. Robinson carries these matters in his head.'

Even as he spoke, Robinson had entered with the tray containing glasses and shaker.

'If I may be permitted to put two and two together, sir,' said Robinson, 'I fancy your remark indicates an immediate departure for New York.'

'Exactly.'

'The *Mauretania* on Wednesday, sir, the *Majestic* on Saturday.'

'We'll take the *Mauretania*,' said Plum. 'Ask Mrs Wodehouse if she's prepared to sail on such short notice, then book our passage.'

2

But, as Robinson might well have said, *surgit semper aliquid amari*. It is sad to have to record that the last effort of the Princess triumvirate, who had worked together so much and so happily, was their least successful, was in fact a flat failure. Jerry turned out a first-class score, the cast was excellent, the staging and mounting all that could be desired, but Irving, the lad who never made a mistake, had put his finger on it when he had insisted that the Duncans were, as Robinson would have said, of the essence. Charming Gertrude Bryan and clever Queenie Smith, brilliant individually, were not a team. When they met, when they performed together, the electric spark was missing, and the play was so written that these were the vital spots.

Poor *Sitting Pretty*, which had seemed to have so much to offer but which nobody wanted!

'We're like two flower-girls,' said Plum, waxing sentimental. 'Stretching out our small, grubby hands with a pathetic nose-gay which the passers-by – blister their insides – curtly ignore as they hurry past.'

'For heaven's sake don't talk about flowers,' said Guy. 'It reminds me of a certain floral horseshoe.'

Who knows? Perhaps it is because of that horseshoe – the Horseshoe of Fate it might be called – that *Sitting Pretty* is a name remembered only as that of a film in which Clifton Webb was baby-sitter to an infant Junior Breckenridge.

3

There was no time for the licking of wounds. Guy had signed contracts with Aarons and Freedley for two shows, one for the Astaires and one to follow Plum's *Beauty Prize* at the Winter Garden. Since the Astaires were in London, playing in *Stop Flirting*, and Aarons and Gershwin also there busily occupied with the preliminaries of the two shows, an immediate return was indicated. As to Plum there was Jeeves.

The new Winter Garden show, which Aarons and Freedley were presenting jointly with Grossmith and Laurillard, had been sketched out by Guy on the voyage to America and a scenario sent back, of which the combined management had approved. It was now at the casting-stage and, on arriving in London (he had travelled via Paris), Guy went to report at the Winter Garden, whose bar is the tiny Drury Lane Tavern frequented by Nell Gwyn in her orange-selling days. Plum's *Beauty Prize* was coming to the end of a successful run, and

George Grossmith was holding a chorus audition for *Primrose*, which was the name of the new show. He sat with George Gershwin and Alex Aarons, surrounded by pressmen, yesmen, vocal experts and beauty experts, testing applicants as to voice, diction and appearance.

George, though one of the boys in private life, was, in his managerial aspect, rather pompous – nay, even stuffy. He had issued a ukase to the effect that all members of the chorus of *The Beauty Prize* should appear and bring a bit of music with them. He had recently lost a girl to Charlie Cochran because her talent had passed unnoticed in the choruses of *Sally* and *The Cabaret Girl*, and he wasn't having that happen again.

As Guy entered the theatre, coming in through the Nell Gwyn tavern, George was having difficulty in persuading one of the showgirls to demonstrate her vocal powers. It seemed that here was a young lady who, while willing to accept £3 a week for decorating the stage of the Winter Garden for a season or two, very definitely had other fish to fry. She was, as a fryer of fish, to make quite a name for herself. Several names in fact, two of them those of peeresses of the realm.

'Must I sing, Mr Grossmith?'

'Yes, Sylvia, you must. All of you have to sing if you want jobs as showgirls in *Primrose*. The Gershwin score demands it.'

'Oh, very well,' she replied petulantly, and, going down to 'the floats', she handed over a piece of music to the pianist in the pit. The piano struck a chord.

> God save our gracious King,
> Long live our noble King,
> God save the King.

George, a strict observer of ritual, rose and stood at attention. His minions rose and stood at attention. Guy, on his way to announce his arrival, stood at attention.

As the anthem came to the normal stopping point, George started to sit down, but there is more, much more of the fine old choral than is generally known. James Carey is credited with a three-stanza version; in another version John Bull, composer, singer and organist at Antwerp cathedral, has expressed the same sentiment in his own way; while James Oswald, a Scot, who was chamber-music composer to George III, also got into the act. A printing is extant giving them all. Sylvia Hawkes sang them all. The pianist stopped playing but that didn't stop Sylvia. They wanted her to sing, did they? Well, sing she would. Of course no one dared to call a halt. The national anthem is sacrosanct – especially if you're an actor-manager clinging to the hope of a belated knighthood.

Sylvia Hawkes said afterwards that she expected to be fired then and there. Perhaps she would have been had she not been so deliciously pretty. There are, it is true, more pretty girls to the square foot in the USA than in the British Isles. But, when they're really trying, the parent race can turn out an article of highly exportable value. Witness Ziegfeld's Dolores, also his Kathleen Martin and his June McKay, witness the Jersey Lily, witness Connie Carpenter, Deborah Kerr and, as we say, Sylvia Hawkes.

Sylvia Hawkes was not only pretty, she had a pretty sense of humour. George Gershwin was swept off his feet by her, so was Lord Ashley, heir of the Earl of Shaftesbury, so was Douglas Fairbanks, Sr, so was Lord Stanley of Alderley and so, finally, was the very sure-footed Mr Clark Gable. All of these, except George Gershwin, laid their fortunes and/or coronets at Sylvia's feet. George might well have done the same had he possessed at the time either fortune or coronet. Nobody ever cut a wider swathe than Sylvia Hawkes. But then, if you have those looks, combined with those brains, not to mention that charm, you don't have to invent a new mouse-trap to have the world beat a path to your door.

Primrose did somewhat less well than the most decorative member of its cast. It managed to hang on for 255 performances, which was a shade better than its predecessor, *The Beauty Prize*, and definitely better than it deserved.

It had one engaging ditty in which Leslie Henson and Claude Hulbert were overcome with pity when recalling the fate of some of the heroines of history. One quatrain ran:

> Oh, isn't it terrible what they did to Mary-Queen-of-Scots?
> When playing at St Andrew's she would *not* replace div-ots,
> So, after quite a bothering day,
> They locked her up in Fotheringay,
> Oh, isn't it terrible what they did to Mary-Queen-of-Scots?

Though not by Wodehouse, it was written in the Wodehouse style with triple rhymes. It somehow made Guy feel more at home.

14

1

THAT 1924 season in London when the first two of the Gershwin series of shows were written was one of extraordinary gaiety. Was it because the Astaires were there to hobnob with – the Astaires, George Gershwin and his piano, George Grossmith who knew everyone in London?

Adele had the faculty of making any party from two to fifty-two into a success. Such words as enchanting, delicious, captivating did not seem like tired adjectives from a Hollywood pressbook when applied to her. How nice if she could have gone on and on with brother Fred. How nice if George Gershwin could have gone on and on writing for them. His music suited them to perfection.

One weekend Guy encountered Adele at Knole. Knole is one of the top great houses of England. For those who don't know it, or who have not read the books of Victoria Sackville-West, in which its atmosphere is wonderfully evoked, a thumbnail sketch might be in order.

Belonging to Elizabeth's reign, Knole is all of one style as so few great houses are, and so is generally conceded to be the finest example of domestic Tudor architecture in England. It is built on a chronological plan containing 365 rooms, fifty-two staircases, twelve courtyards, and twenty bathrooms – including one that is haunted. It is packed with art treasures, Vandycks, Reynolds, Gainsboroughs and Romneys elbowing each other for the spot on the wall with the best light. All in all, quite a lot of house.

At the time Adele and Guy were weekending there, the family were living in reduced circumstances. They were huddled into a corner of the cosy edifice, where their simple wants were tended by a staff of only twenty-two servants. The gardens, which had been laid out on a scale commensurate with that of the house, had fifteen gardeners hustling round to do the work which had once commanded the services of thirty.

What were Broadway characters doing in such surroundings? Well, Adele had already had several offers to supply her with some such setting of her own, but Guy—?

Guy was there because Lady Sackville had also been, but a few years before, a Broadway character. She had appeared in Guy's first play *The Rule of Three* and then again in *Polly With a Past* . . . Anne Meredith, a charming and talented actress.

A wonderful dinner, some extraordinary bridge, a little dancing – there was a fresh supply of American phonograph records, and Adele Astaire to dance with, if you could buck the line.

Then came the hour when whisky-and-sodas were at the nightcap stage and the company drifted into corners, breaking up into little groups of fours, threes and twos. Lord Sackville made announcement of what the doings would be on the morrow, church or golf, and an expedition, by invitation of the Astors, to visit nearby Hever, home of the Boleyns, where poor Anne had first met Henry. These suggestions were all on a take-it-or-leave-it basis. You could breakfast when you pleased from the row of hot-plates in the dining-room. You could lunch or not as you pleased, so long as you told the butler. The only 'must' was the cocktail-hour, dinner and a white tie. That was weekending in England as still surviving in 1924. Not much left of that sort of thing today, my masters, save only at Blandings Castle.

Guy was paddling round his bedroom in his pyjamas, inspecting the Rowlandsons on its panelled walls, when there was a knock at the door. He opened it to find Adele attired in a heady negligé.

'Come right in,' he said heartily. 'This is what I call good old-fashioned hospitality. I didn't know Anne made such charming provision for her guests.'

'It's a cute idea,' said Adele, 'but I'm holding out for a wedding ring and I understand the one your girlfriends used to rent their apartments with is gone.'

'Then to what do I owe the pleasure?'

'I want you to change rooms with me. I've got the haunted bathroom.'

'Haunted bathroom? Must be rather a modern ghost?'

'Yes, and the poor thing is very upset or nervous or something.'

'How do you know?'

'Well, every now and then you'll hear the johnny flush.'

'And there's nobody there?'

'No, but the eerie part of it is that this particular convenience is the difficult kind. You know how it is with English privies – there are the overheads, the buttons, the levers, the foot release and ye olde worlde pull-up. Then with the overheads with dangling handle, of which this specimen is one, for some smart, quick pull, with others a long, steady, slow one. This one's a devil – the coax-me-variety.'

'But yet the ghost?'

'Oh, the ghost has no trouble at all, just a gruesome rattle of the chain followed by an immediate "whoosh". Somehow it gives you a creepy feeling when a ghost seems to be more at home in your room than you are. I know I won't sleep a wink.'

'We'll change, of course. I'm rather keen on ghosts. A bit of an amateur psychic researcher.'

The shiftover was effected. The phenomenon continued at intervals and was certainly disturbing. Eventually Guy wriggled down under the covers so that hearing was sufficiently impeded for him to get to sleep. He was still in a state of concealment when a soft-footed lady's maid entered, drew the curtains, and then laid him out a pair of demi-tasse shorts, a lace brassière, a pair of stockings and a fetching sports-costume.

He wakened during this operation but, being by inclination a slow getter-up, he decided to remain doggo. As he had supposed would happen, the maid withdrew without disturbing him. He dozed again and this time was awakened by what he presumed to be the ghost taking a bath. He cocked an eye in the direction of the bathroom and was startled to see a feminine form, partly concealed by a towel, flit across the open doorway. He had evidently made some slight noise, for the nymph came to the bathroom door rubbing herself with the towel. She was not only very pleasant to look at but she was a lady whose name was one of the most honoured in Debrett.

'I thought you wouldn't mind my coming in here, dahling,' she said. 'George was barricaded in ours and you know what men are in a bathroom. They fall asleep in the tub, I believe.'

Guy made some inarticulate noise from under the covers, pitched in as high a key as he could manage. The lovely peeress donned her robe and started out. As she passed the bed, she gave Guy a hearty smack.

'Get up, you lazy girl,' she said. 'We're playing golf, remember?'

She went out into the hall and Guy heard a sharp cry. A moment later Adele appeared.

'For heaven's sake what's happened?' she said. 'I just ran into Alex and when she saw me she almost fainted dead away.'

Guy put on a scarf and dressing-gown and went down to breakfast. Although the custom for ladies was a bedroom tray there was no rule in the matter. Adele elected to go with him. They found one of Britain's forty marquises lifting the covers of a line of silver hot-plates, weighing his choice.

'Did you come into my room this morning and take a bath?' inquired Guy.

'Me? No, but—'

'Funny,' said Guy, 'I'd have sworn it was you. Of course I wasn't properly awake.'

The marquis replaced the lid on the kedgeree.

'Excuse me a minute. I must pop up and have a word with the better half. She was in a bit of a dither about something.'

He disappeared.

'Quite the gentleman, what?' laughed Adele. 'I suppose it's the influence of all those belted earls looking down on you from the walls.'

2

'So you've been hobnobbing with the upper-crusters, have you?' said Plum, meeting Guy on his return from Knole. 'I remember the last time I dined with Johnny Galsworthy—'

'When was that?'

'Two days ago. It was the first time, too. Ethel met Mrs Galsworthy at a garden party – the house we've taken for the summer is near his – and she invited us to dinner. A very charming woman, we thought her.'

'Did he know your books?'

'He'd just bought one.'

'How do you know he had "just" bought it?'

'Because there was a mark in it. It seems it's been his habit when he stops reading to make a pencil note in the margin, so he'll know where he was.'

'Which book was it?'

'*Right Ho, Jeeves*. The mark was on the side of page ten.'

'Did he say anything matey like, "I laughed my pants off at that chapter in which Gussie Fink-Nottle presents the prizes"?'

'I somehow gathered the impression that he found it more tactful not to broach the subject.'

'Just you and Ethel?'

'Good Lord, no. There were twelve or possibly fourteen guests. As we took our seats at the dinner-table Galsworthy immediately began to discuss the deteriorating effect of educational uniformity on the incidence and development of genius.'

'You don't mean that you had to talk about that?'

'Apparently it's a time-honoured custom. The woman next to me told me that Galsworthy abominates desultory conversation.'

'But what happened when the subject became exhausted?'

'It never did. If the conversation lagged, Galsworthy would rap on the table with the end of his knife and present a new aspect of the problem. "To what extent is genius influenced by the educational standards of parents; with special reference to the cases of Thomas Chatterton and Shakespeare?" '

'What a dinner!'

'I was punch drunk by the time we got to the sweet.'

3

Lady be Good was the new Bolton-Gershwin show for the Astaires, and as soon as the script was ready Guy sailed for New York to help with the staging. Aarons and Freedley's idea was to make *Lady be Good* the start of a new series of musical comedies like those at the old Princess only on a larger scale, and Guy, while he approved of the scheme, felt a certain melancholy at the thought that he would not be working with Plum. George Gershwin always stipulated that his brother Ira should do his lyrics, and Plum did not blame him, for he had a great admiration for Ira's work. Ira Gershwin was the man who wrote the immortal couplet:

> Let's sing to every citizen and for'ner
> 'Prosperity is just around the corner'.

The substitution of George for Jerry did not bother Guy. The young man who had played the piano at the rehearsals of *The Second Century Show* was beginning to look uncommonly like a genius. But it would seem all wrong, working without Plum. There would undoubtedly be a lot of success, but there wouldn't be the same fun. It was with a pang that Guy envisaged the end of the partnership which had begun on that Christmas Eve after the first performance of *Very Good Eddie*.

The opening of his *Grounds for Divorce* at the St James's did nothing to cheer him up. Madge Titheradge, Owen Nares, and Lawrence Grossmith were the featured players, and very good they were . . . till on the second night Lawrence collapsed and was taken to hospital, and almost simultaneously Madge Titheradge developed laryngitis and became practically inaudible for three weeks. It surprised Guy that Owen Nares did not fall a victim to some wasting sickness, for once bad luck hits a show, it seldom knows where to stop.

'You're on the right side of the fence,' he said to Plum. 'Novels don't give you the headaches plays do.'

Lady be Good was a success. The first scene of Act One showed the Astaires – playing brother and sister – thrown out with their few goods and chattels on the sidewalk. Adele, behaving as she unquestionably would have done in real life, arranged the furniture neatly about a lamp-post, hung up a 'God Bless Our Home' motto and with the help of a passing workman – destined to become the hero – attached the percolator and fixed the hydrant so that water would be constantly available.

After which, of course, it began to rain, and she and Fred did a number called 'Hang On To Me', dancing together under a big umbrella.

Given perfect artists like Fred and Adele, it was just the sort of charming little scene to start a musical comedy off with a bang and, this being so, Alex Aarons, being a manager, could see no virtue in it. Only Guy's proviso that this would have to be done over his dead body had saved it from being thrown into the discard after the dress rehearsal.

He was behind on the opening night when Alex Aarons suddenly appeared, pale and agitated and reproachful.

'I told you!' he cried. 'I told you how it would be if we kept that scene in. They're howling and booing!'

'Not so much howling and booing,' said Guy, 'as cheering their heads off. You don't often hear cheering like that in a theatre. The scene has knocked them cock-eyed. But of course you're the boss and what you say goes, so we'll cut it out tomorrow night.'

'Over my dead body,' said Alex.

Lady be Good was a smash-hit and was equally successful when eventually it arrived in London. There, after a long run, it closed the famous old Empire. The Astaires appeared in one more Gershwin show, *Funny Face*, after which Adele closed her career with a triumphant performance in *The Band Wagon*, by George S. Kaufman, Howard Dietz and Arthur Schwartz. She then married the Duke of Devonshire's second son and retired to Lismore Castle in Ireland, leaving a gap that can never be filled. Fred struggled on without her for a while, but finally threw his hand in and disappeared. There is a rumour that he turned up in Hollywood.

4

It was two years before Guy was able to leave America. He had done several shows there, among them the second of the Aarons and Freedley series – *Tiptoes*, written with Fred Thompson – and he came away with a couple of contracts in his pocket. Philip Goodman, an advertising man turned manager, wanted him to do a big musical for Clark and McCullough with score and lyrics by a new team named Kalmar and Ruby. This subsequently became the very successful *The Ramblers*. (In passing, it was to Philip Goodman that Jerry Kern, arriving in his office to discuss a new piece and meeting the manager for the first time, introduced himself with the historic words 'Good morning, Mr Goodman. I'm Kern. I hear you're a son of a bitch, and you probably aren't – and you've heard I'm a son of a bitch, and I most certainly am.')

The other contract was with Aarons and Freedley for a musical for

Gertrude Lawrence, who had written to Guy saying that she was now available. Guy had debated whether to take her to Aarons and Freedley or to Ziegfeld, and it was George Gershwin's connection with Alex and Vinton that tipped the scale in their favour (and eventually put several hundred thousand dollars in their bank accounts). The most attractive aspect of the thing to Guy was that the book was to be written in collaboration with Plum. The old firm was in being again.

Marguerite had returned to Paris and the Opéra Comique. She met Guy at Le Havre with the *roulotte* and Peggy, and they had their long-postponed trip through the château country. After ten days of perfect weather they rumbled back from Châlons to Paris in a torrential downpour, and then Guy had to go to London to start work with Plum on the Gertie Lawrence show.

'Why don't you come with me?' he said to Marguerite when they were back in the studio.

'How can I? They've given me *Thaïs*, the one role I've always wanted to sing. Besides,' said Marguerite, 'you're going to be terribly busy with those two shows to write. You won't want to be bothered with Peggy and me.'

Guy agreed that there was certainly no worse company than an author in the throes of composition.

'*L'absence est à l'amour ce qu'est au feu le vent. Il éteint le petit, il allume le grand.*'

'Since I recognize the word *vent*,' said Guy, 'I conclude that that is something about absence being like the wind. Or does *vent* mean stomach?'

'The wind puts out small flames but fans strong ones.'

'It's humiliating, this language thing,' said Guy. 'There's that daughter of ours – no ball of fire, as you must admit – and I'll bet she grabbed it right off the bat. At three years old!'

'It's your own fault. Why don't you learn French?'

'I've tried, but I don't seem to get anywhere. I decided to start by learning how to count, because, having had some experience with the French I thought that – next to being able to say, "*Où est le Messieurs?*" – that would come in most useful. And I got along fine till I stubbed my toe on "seventy". Apparently "*septante*" wouldn't do.'

'It's *soixante-dix*.'

'Exactly. "Sixty-ten". A fine way to say "seventy". And when you get to "eighty", it isn't "seventy-ten", it's "four-twenty". And they call the French logical!'

'As a matter of fact, the Belgians do say "*septante*". The Italians say "*Sessanta*, "*settanta*", "*ottanta*". And in Spanish it's "*sesenta*", "*ochenta*".'

'It must be great to be educated. How about this young woman goggling at me over there on the sofa? I suppose she's got the whole thing down cold?'

'Oh, yes, she's wonderful at languages. You understood what Daddy and Mummy were talking about, didn't you, darling?'

Peggy nodded.

'Well, say those figures for Daddy.'

'*Sechzig, siebzig, achtzig.*'

'Before she says it in Russian,' said Guy bitterly, 'I'll call up and get that reservation on the Golden Arrow.'

'Flèche d'Or,' said Peggy.

She danced away and her richly bedecked mother took her place.

'I want words with you, Mister,' she said.

'Alas, they must be brief.'

'As per usual.'

'Alas again. I have a ship to catch.'

'With sailings widely spaced this time of year.'

'The occasional marriage. I have a feeling we should be introduced before getting into bed together.'

'You said to me, you'll have to commute.'

'I well remember. I'm not blaming you in the least but what about calling it a day? You're a success in one continent, I'm a success in another.'

There was a pause.

'Before they make a joke of it,' she added.

'Call it a day, you said,' Guy repeated it thoughtfully. 'It's been a nice day.'

'A wonderful day!' she repeated and held out her arms to him. They went into an embrace.

'You mustn't miss your boat.'

Peggy reappeared as she spoke.

'I just came to kiss you good-bye, Daddy,' she said.

5

In London Guy found Plum finishing an adaptation of Molnar's *Spiel Im Schloss* – later produced in New York and London as *The Play's the Thing* – and in order to be able to give uninterrupted attention to *Oh, Kay*, the Gertie Lawrence show, they took the train at Paddington and settled in at the Impney Hotel outside what is, next to A. E. Housman's Clun, the quietest place under the sun – Droitwich in Worcestershire, where the brine-baths are.

In the long English twilights that last until ten at night – the faint western glow may continue even later – they paced the terrace of the Impney – it's hard to say the name without giving the impression that you have a hare-lip – and worked out their plot, pausing occasionally to listen to the nightingales which collect in these parts in gangs. It was probably at Droitwich that the conversation – recorded by *Punch* – between the romantic man and his deaf friend took place. 'Have you ever,' sighed the romantic man as they strolled through the lanes one summer night, 'heard anything so perfectly wonderful as these nightingales?' 'Eh?' said the deaf man. 'I said, "Aren't the nightingales simply marvellous"?' 'Huh?' 'The nightingales. They're superb, don't you think? The nightingales. The *nightingales.*' The deaf man shook his head regretfully. 'I'm sorry,' he said. 'I can't hear a word you're saying. These nightingales are kicking up such an infernal noise.'

Worcestershire is next door to Shropshire, and they drove there one day in the hope of finding Blandings Castle and catching a glimpse of Lord Emsworth's pig. In this they were unsuccessful, but they found the minute hamlet of Stableford, seven miles outside the town of Bridgnorth, where Plum had lived as a young man.

'Pretty remote sort of spot,' said Guy, studying the old home through the window of the car.

'Yes, quite remote,' Plum agreed. 'I loved it. I've never found a better place for work. At the age of twenty I once wrote fourteen short stories there in ten days. They were never printed, which was a break for the reading public, but I wrote 'em.'

'Had you any neighbours in this grim solitude?'

'One family about a mile away. We quarrelled with them two days after we arrived and never spoke to them again. It was milk that caused the rift. At least, they said it was milk when they sold it to us, and we said it was skim-milk. Harsh words and dirty looks passed to and fro, and the thing culminated in us cutting them or them cutting us, we never quite made out which. That always happens in rural England. It's pure routine. Directly you have moved in and got your trunks unpacked, you have a hell of a row with the nearest neighbours about milk. Make a note of that.'

'I will.'

'Father sorts out his things, has a wash and brush-up, and looks in on Mother. "All set?" he asks. "All set," says Mother. "Fine," says Father. "Then let's go and beat the stuffing out of those swindling crooks down the road who've been selling us that so-called milk." And off they go, Father with his Roget's *Thesaurus* under his arm in case he runs short of adjectives.'

'It sounds a jolly life.'

'Oh, it was. Though my mother didn't like it much. She found it a little on the lonely side. My father had seen this house advertised in one of the papers, and he and she went down to take a look at it. As they were driving away, my mother said, "Well, thank goodness I shall never see that awful place again." "Eh?" said my father. "I was saying that it was a relief to me to think I should never see that frightful house again." "Oh, the house?" said my father. "You are speaking of the house. I was meaning to tell you about that. I've signed a twenty-year lease on it." Victorian husbands were like that. Men of steel.'

'I'd like to see you springing that sort of surprise on Ethel.'

Plum shivered.

'Don't say such things, even in fun. But, as I was saying, I loved the place. Miles of smiling countryside, and not a Henry W. Savage to be seen as far as the eye could reach. The only thing I didn't like in my formative, or Stableford, period was the social stuff. Owners of big estates round about would keep inviting me for the weekend.'

'*You?*'

'I don't wonder you're surprised. Even today I'm about as pronounced an oaf as ever went around with his lower jaw drooping and a glassy look in his eyes, but you have literally no conception what I was like in my early twenties. Do you remember what Brichoux said about the chambermaid in the third act of *The Girl Behind the Gun*?'

' "She was a nice girl, but she had no conversation." '

'That was me. I was completely inarticulate. Picture to yourself a Trappist monk with large feet and a tendency to upset tables with priceless china on them, and you will have the young Wodehouse. The solution of the mystery of my mixing with the County is that my brother Armine was very popular. He played the piano like a Gershwin and could converse pleasantly on any subject you cared to bring up, and I suppose what happened was that one of these territorial magnates would run into Mother at a garden party or somewhere and say, "I do wish you would persuade your son to come to us for the weekend." "Why, of course," Mother would reply. "My sons will be there with their hair in a braid." The magnate would start like a man seeing a serpent in his path.

' "Did you say *sons*?"

' "Yes, I have two – Armine and Pelham."

' "Oh? . . . Well, of course, we were rather thinking of Armine, but if Pelham can come as well, we shall be charmed . . . that is to say . . . oh, yes, charmed."

'And he would totter off and tell his wife that the curse had come upon them and she had better put the best china away till I had blown over.'

6

Gertie Lawrence was back in England after playing in the second edition of *The Charlot Revue* on Broadway. Guy and Plum felt that it would be advisable to see her and discuss her part in *Oh, Kay*. They telephoned her and arranged a meeting at her flat and drove back to

London through those delicious Cotswold villages, Moreton-in-the-Marsh, Stow-on-the-Wold, Lower Slaughter, Weston-sub-Edge and possibly those hamlets of which Plum had written in his Mulliner stories, Chickenham-infra-Mud, Lower Smattering-on-the-Wissel and Higgleford-cum-Wortlebury-beneath-the-Hill! There was time to do some straying. They were not seeing Gertie till teatime.

On the piano in her sitting-room there was a photograph of a child dancing. It caught the eye immediately as they came in.

'Is that you?' inquired Plum.

'Yes, dearies, that's me at the time of my début in the Brixton Pantomime.'

'You took to the stage early?'

'For a good year before that photo was taken I'd been learning the ABC of my trade from dear old Italia Conti.'

'What a lot of distinguished pupils she had!'

'I'll tell you a little tale about one of them. It was the annual show that was put on for friends and relatives every June. I was just under ten – my birthday's 4th July – so you can imagine my surprise when, at the first rehearsal, Madame Conti's assistant handed me a part. Most of the children were "pixies" or "villagers" but I was to be a character. I was going to see my name on the programme: "*Jane* . . . Gertrude Lawrence." The theatre has given me a lot of thrills but never one quite as big as that moment when I held my first part in my hand.

' "Jane" it said on the cover. Jane was one of a party of children who steal out into the garden on Midsummer Night and find the flowers have changed into Little People and are giving a ball, a crafty lead into "The Dance of the Flowers", chief feature of this juvenile turkey. I delayed before turning the slightly battered blue cover, savouring the great moment. I opened it. There was a single line: "Oh, look, children! Pansy has turned into a Pierrot and he's dancing with Columbine!"

'I was standing there weighing the problem of how best to characterize Jane when I heard Madame Conti's voice say: "That's your cue, Gertie." Good God! I had missed my first cue. Properly flustered, I went charging on to the stage and said, "Jane pants."

' "Jane pants? You don't *say* that, dear. That's the stage direction. You've been running and you're excited."

' "Of course. I was upset at being late on cue, I just read it without thinking."

' "Well, you *must* think. Never do anything on the stage without thinking. Now make the entrance again and say the line."

' "Oh, look, children! Pansy has changed into a Pierrot and he's dancing with Concubine."

'The brats sniggered. Madame Conti explained patiently that the name was "Columbine", adding that if I said "Concubine" on the afternoon of the performance some of the parents might not think this was a very nice school to send their child to.

' "Whenever you're flustered, take a long, deep breath and pause. Always remember a slight pause never hurts." I paused. I took a long, deep breath. As I did so I heard a childish treble voice repeat my line, reading it beautifully, with wonder and excitement and just that little catch in the breath that was indicated by "Jane pants". "Don't you think, Madame Conti," the voice went on, and it had now changed to a budding baritone, "don't you think it would be *safer* if *I* said the line?"

'I was stunned, speechless, unable to find words in which to protest.

' "Yes, dear," I heard Madame Conti say. "I think perhaps it would be, I'm sure Gertie won't mind. Give Noel the part, will you, dear?" '

'It wasn't—?' exclaimed Guy.

'Yes, it was, duckie. Noel Coward, the little ham. If I had had a blunt instrument in my hand at the time the English-speaking stage would have lost one of its most brilliant talents.'

'He calmly walked off with your first part?'

'Darned unprofessional, I call it,' laughed Plum.

'Yes, but wait, boys. For years I've had a dream. In it I'm playing opposite him and, on opening night, just as we're coming to his favourite line, his most amusing *bon mot*, I say it myself and then give him the cue. Then, when he's left flat on his bumpty, I whisper, "Come on, Jane, old girl. Let's hear you pant."

'And let me tell you something – it's coming, Gertie's Revenge!' She waved a hand at her desk where stood a photograph of this distinguished author-actor-composer, lovingly inscribed. 'He's writing a play in which I'm to be with him. He calls it *Private Lives* and it's to be ready by the time I'm finished with your show.'

'Well, much as I look forward to that opening night, I trust it's a long way off,' said Plum.

'So do I,' said Gertie. 'And now you boys help yourselves to drinks and tell me about this *Oh, Kay*.'

7

Oh, Kay was a musical comedy about bootleggers. It was 1926 and the noble experiment had been in operation for seven years. People had learned to cope with it at least to the extent of having their liquor analysed or, in an emergency, of pouring some into a saucer in a darkened room, setting fire to it, and, if it burned with a reddish flame, changing their bootlegger.

It was the 'Hooch Age', and the spirit that made bath-tub gin (the human spirit, not the stuff you bought at the druggist with a doctor's prescription) was the same devil-may-care quality that accounted for flagpole-sitters, marathon dancing and the bull market.

It is hard to imagine two worlds more different than the one the authors said good-bye to as they left the Impney and that into which they plunged upon disembarking from the *Aquitania*.

It was not only missing the wine card from which they could select, even in that unfashionable retreat, a Chambertin or a Pouilly, as well as the bottle of crusted 'Taylor '96' that would supply the accompaniment to their after-dinner savoury. The whole tempo of life was different. People walked faster, laughed louder and became nervously excited – lost their tempers more readily.

The pace had, seemingly, quickened since the *Sitting Pretty* period of two years ago, the last time the two writers had been in New York together. When they dropped in at the Ritz barber shop on the afternoon of their arrival, the barbers of their adjacent chairs both got immediately on to the subject of stocks as if that were the one thing that anybody would want to talk about. The market had taken another upward spurt, it seemed, and each of the lads manipulating the razors had come appreciably nearer to East Street that everyone seemed bent on moving into.

'Have-a you gotta the Alice Charmers?' inquired Plum's barber.

' "Alice Charmers"? Never met the lady.'

The barber laughed.

'Lady! It sure acta like a lady. De mosta sweet stock on de board.'

'You watcha your foot with thatta Alice,' said the other barber. ' "Like a lady," you say. Sure, a lady you no canna trust.'

The coloured boy shining Guy's shoes looked up.

'I got a friend uptown made $400 last week. Beds it was. He bought beds an' sold 'em again. $400 he made.'

'$400!' said the barber disparagingly. 'Whatsa $400?'

'It ain't hay,' said the coloured boy. 'He's gwine back in again an' he's buying a couple for me.'

'Coupla beds?'

'No, couple of shares.'

'Oh, it's Simmons's beds?'

'That's right. Mr Simmons's beds.'

'There's a new bed company started,' said the manicurist, who was sitting at her small table reading the paper. 'It'll put Simmons clean out of business.'

'Howsa dat, Elsie?' inquired one of the barbers.

'One of my customers was telling me about it. He's in on the ground floor. They got wonderful improvements – buttons you press. One closes the window, another turns on the bath water. They're in the head of the bed. Then there's a radio that you listen to while you go to sleep. It's under your pillow. No one can hear it but you. And if there's someone in bed with you, they can listen to a different programme under their pillow.'

The barber removed the towel from Plum's face and pushed the chair into an erect position.

'What you tink, boss? You tink datta bed business is good thing for to putta de money?'

Plum didn't know.

'I'd like to get the name of the company,' said Guy. 'I've a theme song for them to play on those radios of theirs.'

He started to chant:

Bed, bed, beautiful bed,
Pull it all over your head
Wrap up your heels in it
Have all your meals in it
Make a hotel of your bed.

'What's that?' inquired Plum.

'A relic of my pre-Wodehouse days.'

Though your wife may desert you
Don't let that fact hurt you
So long as she leaves you the bed.

'There's a lot more, four verses and four refrains if you'd care to hear them?'

'Some other time,' said Plum, stepping out of the chair.

'I might have made a lyric writer,' said Guy, 'if I'd stuck to it.'

Plum wasn't listening. The barber was reciting a list of good stock-buys based on information gleaned from customers. He wasn't listening to that either.

'This country's gone nuts,' he said, as they made their way down the stair.

'Shall we have dinner in the Oak Room or the Oval Room?'

'I never like the Oak Room at night. It's depressing.'

'On the other hand in the Oval Room you will have to listen to Vecsey playing *The Rose of China* – and that is even more depressing.'

They were greeted at the door of the Oak Room by the younger of the Ritz's two 'Theodores'.

'What about a drink, Theodore?'

'Certainly, Mr Bolton. Two old customers, of course.'

When the drinks arrived with a long lemon twist disguising them as 'horse-necks', Guy asked Theodore if the essential ingredient was of unquestioned reliability. Theodore reassured him.

'But I heard that two Detroit millionaires woke up dead after drinking some bootleg hooch in this hotel.'

Theodore explained that if the story were true (it was) the thing had nothing to do with the hotel.

The gentlemen in question, if they ever existed (he was admitting nothing), had sent a bell-boy to a bootlegger they knew of and he had given them a bottle of whisky made from alcohol that the government had poisoned.

'You don't mean to tell us that the government are running a poisoning department?'

'Oh, yes, Mr Wodehouse. You've got to be very careful today. They're putting formaldehyde in it.'

'Embalming fluid?'

'Yes, sir, and wood alcohol. The enforcement people think it's the best way to stop drinking.'

'It stopped those two Detroit boys, all right.'

'One would think that even Andy Volstead might consider death a somewhat severe punishment for infraction of his famous Act.'

Theodore shook his head. Under the Baumes Law a woman had, only last week, been sent to prison for life for selling a pint of gin. Rum-runners were frequently shot down by government officers when crossing the Canadian border. The figure of 197 persons killed by prohibition agents had just been published.

They asked Theodore for the names of some reliable speakeasies. He recommended The Hyena Club, The Ha! Ha!, The Jail Club and The Day Breakers.

'We're interested in the subject because we're writing a play in which bootlegging is the main theme,' explained Plum.

It was a few minutes later that Bob Benchley strolled in.

'Well, as I live and attempt to breathe,' said Bob. 'If it isn't "Book and Lyrics". How are you, lads, and when does it open?'

They invited him to join them for dinner, and he said he would try to peck a bit, though not having much appetite. He was feeling a little down at the moment, he explained, as he had not yet shaken off the hangover caused by attending a party on the previous night.

'Was it a pleasant party?'

'I can't remember, but I think so. Bob Barbour was our host. Do you know Bob?'

'Yes, quite well.' Robert Barbour, the brother of the New Jersey Senator, was an old friend.

'Did you ever hear the story about him and his private stock?'

'No.'

'Thank God. Now it can be told. He kept it in an old family manse which was next door to the old family plant at Paterson, New Jersey, where I fancy, from the fact that they have so much of it, they print money, and came a day when he decided to move in to his apartment in New York.'

'He was taking a risk, wasn't he?'

'A grave risk. The one thing that wakes the fiend that sleeps in the authorities is someone conveying potables across a state line. In some of the more tolerable communities you are given the benefit of a trial, but the general view is that this is a bit sissy.'

'We live in stirring times.'

'We do, indeed. Well, Bob, knowing this, decided not to risk any minion's hide but to carry through the operation himself. So he loaded the stuff into his station-wagon, covered it over with some rugs and started to wend his way to Gomorrah-on-Hudson. And hardly had he wended a couple of parasangs when he heard that most unpleasant of all noises, the whine of a following motor-cycle.'

'Golly!'

'You may well say "Golly!" It was late. The road was empty. There could be no doubt that it was he who was the object of the attention of the hellhound of the law. He tried turning a corner quickly and doubling back on his tracks, but nothing could shake off the pursuer. Just clear of the town the state trooper rolled up beside him and signalled to him to stop.

'Mr Barbour?'

'Y-y-y-yes.'

'Look, Mr Barbour,' said the state trooper. 'You're a drinking man, aren't you? Could I interest you in some of our stock? We've got the best line of wet goods in Bergen County.'

Guy was impressed.

'Is that a true story?'

'You bet it's true. I could tell you a dozen more of a similar nature, if you like your stories by the dozen. I'll tell you what you two ought to do, if, as I understand it, you are writing about rum-running on Long Island. You should get this R. Barbour of whom I have been speaking to take you on that floating café of his that he calls a yacht to view the liquor fleet off Montauk. Scores of launches and fishing boats darting back and forth like nesting swallows. It's a heartening sight for those of a convivial kidney. I use the word playfully. Most of us old-timers have only half a kidney left after a seven-years' bout with prohibition.'

Guy and Plum thought of the Impney and George, the head waiter, leaning over with the wine-card.

'Since it is so warm this evening, sir, perhaps a glass of Château Yquem instead of the port? We still have a little of the '92. A very engaging wine, sir.'

'Everything ends in "– est" over here,' said Guy. 'When this country makes a bloomer, it's a beaut.'

8

Oh, Kay was a great success and so was Gertie Lawrence after which the play went to England, where Gertie, in sole command, pinched the good lines out of other people's parts and put them in her own.

Plum too went to Europe, choosing the French Riviera as his domicile, while Guy went to Hollywood where he wrote *The Love Parade* for Maurice Chevalier, making the transition from writing for the stage to writing for films with astonishing ease, but only because he had the helpful tutelage of that great Austrian director, Ernst Lubitsch. He went on to write *The Love Doctor* and collaborated on *The Yellow Ticket* for Elissa Landi and Laurence Olivier.

All this covered quite a lengthy period in which Guy and 'the little thing' bought them a charming house in Beverly Hills and settled down with a dog, a cat and a parrot that had an astonishing range of the English language at its lowest.

And then came a day in which Ethel Wodehouse appeared with the news that she had just signed a contract for Plum with Metro-Goldwyn-Meyer to give them his services for the length of a year.

After the longest lapse there was to be in their joint lives, the two were once more together.

'What is to happen to the wonderful stream of books about Jeeves and Bertie, Blandings, Uncle Henry and the rest?' Guy asked her.

'He can keep on with those as well,' Ethel replied. 'You know how easy writing is for him.'

'I know how easy it looks,' Guy responded.

They were in a beautiful Cadillac that Ethel had just bought, on their way to meet Plum in Pasadena. The train was the famed Santa Fe wonder, The Chief. Guy was thrilled as the familiar figure came down the steps.

The two old friends embraced. Guy noticed that Plum's hand was trembling slightly.

'Let's get going,' he said. 'These two bags are all I've got on me.' He added, 'And I want to have a look at the grand new car.'

Guy reflected that he still knew Plum better than anyone else did. There was someone on that train that he didn't want to meet.

In the car Guy said, 'You still need me to tie your bow ties for you,' and they both laughed. Plum knew that Guy knew there had been some happening that had shaken him.

Arrived at the Beverly Hills Hotel, there were cordial greetings, hearty handshakes, someone took a couple of snap-shots of the two writers and then Guy whisked Plum away to what was to be his writing room until he and Ethel took possession of the big Spanish-roofed hacienda with the gorgeous swimming-pool that Ethel had taken for the coming year.

There was a momentary silence and then Plum said, 'Can you put your mind back to *Oh, Lady, Lady*?'

'To the greatest of our Princess Theatre's triumphs, when the doyen of New York critics wrote a tribute in verse and Dorothy Parker proclaimed. . . .'

Plum interrupted him. 'And you can put your mind back to the five weeks we spent touring various cities working to get the show in shape for New York?'

'When we were like one cosy little family the world forgot.'

'And where we shared a giant hotel suite with Marion Davies which her boyfriend was paying for,' said Plum.

'And where P. G. Wodehouse sowed his one wild oat,' said Guy.

'I've told you that wasn't true.'

'But you told Ethel it was.'

'I was tired of arguing and thought if I said yes it would end the thing and we could get to talking about something else.'

'I hope Ethel appreciates the wonderful compliments you pay her.'

'Look, let's get down to modern times, shall we? When the mighty Chief pulled out of Chicago, who do you think suddenly appeared?'

'Who?'

'That beautiful little lady from the past. Fleur by name, straight out of *Oh, Lady, Lady*!'

There was a stunned silence.

'It isn't true!'

'It's true all right.'

'You mean to tell me that adorable pussycat with the matchless English complexion and the lovely long legs, and the beautiful lips always held partly open, the luscious . . . [breaking off] what does the poor old girl look like today?'

'She hasn't changed the veriest fraction from the description you've just given of her. Oh, of course she's changed in some ways, as she says she's "learned to read" and she adores my books.'

'Did she know you were going to be on the train?'

'Yes, she'd read it in the papers, so she booked to go on the same, she had some business in Hollywood. She's to appear as the leader at some big function.'

'Was it a touch?'

'What do you mean?'

'I mean getting on the same train and. . . .'

'You mean money? She's loaded, married a Texan and, as she herself expressed it, she's up to her nose in cattle ranches.'

'Thank heaven I'm anchored to My Little Thing,' said Guy.

'Yes, four wives should be enough even for you.'

'Go on with your story.'

'We dined together. She'd brought along a rare wine. She said I'd find it better than the champagne that was also from her cellars.' He paused.

'And then?'

'The train was halted for what seemed a long stop, the porters were down on the platform. I was sitting up, reading, when a lady came to me and said "your lady friend wants you to come. It seems something has happened. It's urgent." '

'I went with her. The curtains that lined the way were all drawn but, as I heard my name spoken, a pair parted. . . . Fleur was lying with a transparent something affording a slight cover for her nudity. She said, "Get on. The porters are down on the platform. Get in quick." '

'And did you?'

Plum paused before answering.

'No,' he said, 'no, I didn't.'

'What did you do – or say, for that matter?'

'I don't quite know. I remember hearing myself repeating the words "my wife" – and, I also seem to remember being swept into an outburst on how ravishingly lovely Fleur was without her clothes, I also asked her what the magic perfume was – if it wasn't just her, herself, that was wafted to me, an intoxicating fragrance – and I then became suddenly aware that the train was moving, the porter was at my elbow and I turned and fled back to "Cactus Flower". The door was closed but I opened it. And there, to my bewilderment, instead of "Cactus Flower", was the giant locomotive.

' "Youse belong on de 'Scenic Route'," the porter was telling me the train split in half and wouldn't unite again until we were at Pasadena. "An' everybody's wonderin' what's kep you back here." '

'A great story,' Guy said, 'with a splendid climax, but the one thing we must do is keep it out of the papers.'

'More important still,' said Plum, 'is to keep Fleur from meeting Ethel. She's longing to. She thinks Ethel must be such a very wonderful woman.'

And just at that moment Ethel arrived and said, 'How did you enjoy your trip through the Grand Canyon?'

15

1

OH, KAY opened in Philadelphia. On the third night of the engagement Guy and Plum were leaning on the barrier behind the last row of the stalls, happy in the fact that in the whole of the capacious Shubert Theatre there was not a seat for them to sit in.

The comedian – Victor Moore – had just gone off to a rousing hand. Gertie Lawrence and Oscar Shaw were in the midst of a romantic passage, and anyone looking at Guy would have realized that here at least was one man who found the scene utterly captivating. Plum, while perhaps equally enchanted, could mask his feelings more readily, nor had he the habit of repeating the lines in unison with the actors, a Bolton practice which he, not infrequently supported by members of the audience, had tried vainly to correct.

A more unfortunate moment for a dog to select for making his appearance on the stage could hardly have been thought of. Long windows stood half open on a moonlit beach; the door to the library was unclosed; there was also a stair. None of these appealed to the canine visitor. He preferred instead to come in through the fireplace, where a log fire was flickering realistically. He paid no attention to the actors but walked straight to the footlights and stared at the audience from under shaggy brows like a Scottish elder rebuking sin from the pulpit.

He then walked over to the proscenium arch, cocked his leg, then scuffled with his feet and made his exit – through the fireplace.

Guy was outraged.

'What are you laughing at?' he said. 'The love story has gone clean out of the window.'

'Out of the fireplace, you mean, don't you?'

The actors had stumbled through the buzzing and the ripples of laughter to the duet.

I remember the bliss
Of that wonderful kiss . . .
Oh, how I'd adore it
If you would encore it.

The dog made a second appearance, pausing this time while still in the fireplace, his paws resting on the log as he glanced archly from side to side of the room. He jumped the log and came in wagging his tail. He was a grey, rough-coated animal something like an oversize Cairn but, if such was his mother's stock, it seemed certain that her pride of race had been tried beyond the breaking point by a lop-eared hound.

> Oh, do, do, do what you done, done, done
> before, baby

sang the lovers.

The storm of laughter drowned the orchestra and, when the wretched animal, as if in response to the repeated admonitions, made his way again to the proscenium arch, there was no continuing with the number.

The pair on the stage were not as badly shaken as was Victor Moore, waiting, on the side opposite the fireplace, to make his re-entrance. He knew the authors had been busy writing in some new stuff for Gertie and Oscar. He knew that Oscar was an accomplished light comedian and he was further aware that, given encouragement, Gertie revelled in 'hoke'.

But, dash it all, if the so-called 'straight' people were going to get laughs like this he would have to pull up his socks. Then, shattering him completely, came a terrific 'scene-call' from the audience far in excess of the hand he had received. He could hardly have been expected to guess that a dog had decided that a stage fireplace was an excellent substitute for a kennel.

'I should have left Bugs at his club,' said Betty Compton afterwards.

'His club?' queried Plum.

'Oh, yes there are dogs' clubs in all the big cities. The top one in New York is The Blue Ribbon but poor Buggsie could never get into *that*. You have to have been shown before you're eligible, so of course Buggsie hasn't a hope. Jimmy pulled some wires and got him into The Beefsteak. The food is wonderful but it's full of mutts.'

Plum, an old-time dog-lover, was interested. Betty explained that there were some single-breed clubs and in those pets of both sexes were catered for. Then should there be any 'romances', as Betty termed them, the result would not be too disastrous. There was one for poodles called Colonie Caniche, and another exclusively for police dogs known as The Sentinel. The clubs were, she explained, a great convenience, especially for hotel dwellers.

'A car calls for Buggsie in the morning and he comes home at cocktail-time.'

'What do the dogs do at these clubs?' asked Guy.

Betty gave him rather a blank look.

'What does anyone do at a club? They eat lunch and play games.'

'Of course.'

2

'They're getting pretty nutty in this adopted land of mine,' said Guy a few days later when they were sitting over the Great Neck breakfast-table. 'I'm just reading about the funeral yesterday of the Chicago gangster, Dion O'Bannion. The casket with handles of solid gold, cost $10,000 and on top of it lay a wreath inscribed "From Al", sent by the man who had had him murdered.'

'Yes, I've been reading about it, too. There were twenty-six truckloads of flowers. Also three widows in weeds so heavy that they couldn't be identified.'

'But life even over here isn't all murders,' said Guy. 'Turn to the sporting page. "The Dixmoor Country Club has installed loudspeakers round the courses so that Sunday morning golfers can listen to the church services and still get their game".'

'Some game, too, if they play the latest style of golf match which a writer here says is growing in popularity. You're allowed to cheat in any way you like, but if caught cheating you lose the hole.'

'The crossword puzzle craze is now at such a pitch, my paper informs me, that a Pittsburgh pastor is handing out crossword slips which, when solved, give the text of his sermon. They're all loony.'

'The particular type of looniness that has sprung up in Florida seems to have been given a sharp lesson.'

'The hurricane? Yes, pretty ghastly, isn't it?'

'It says that the streets of Miami are littered with yachts – not one of them Hank Savage's, unfortunately – and that a five-masted steel schooner is standing in the garden of one of the new hotels.'

'400 dead, 5000 homeless. Even Nature goes a bit screwball in America.'

'But show business is booming.'

'Yes, it's never been better.'

'How's your *Ramblers* doing?'

'All the Lyric Theatre will hold.'

Plum's adaptation of *The Play's the Thing* opened at the Henry Miller on 3rd November and *Oh, Kay* at the Imperial five days later. They were both instantaneous successes. The old firm was doing all right.

Immediately after the first night of *Oh, Kay* Guy rushed over to London, where a show he had written, with a score by Rodgers and

Hart, was already in rehearsal and due to open at the London Gaiety on 1st December. It was for Cicely Courtneidge, Jack Hulbert and Phyllis Dare and was called *Lido Lady*.

Plum was at Rogate in Sussex writing a novel called *The Small Bachelor*, an amplified version of *Oh Lady, Lady*. Guy journeyed down there and found the Wodehouse family settled in at Rogate Lodge in that delightful region of hill and woodland. Plum was in his study. The windows looked over a long slope of garden to a valley at the far end of which lay Winchester, but Guy had no eyes for scenery; his attention was occupied with the long coil of paper on the floor, curling its way past chairs and tables and finally doubling over when it reached the wall.

'At the end of the day's work, I suppose you snip the thing up into pages with the scissors?' asked Guy.

'Exactly. Did you notice the walls?'

Yes, Guy had noticed the walls. Always observant, he had seen that they were covered with typewritten sheets.

'I pin them up, and when they first go up, they're all at the same level. Then I walk round, scanning them, and when I find one where the story seems to drop, I put that sheet on a lower level. The gaps are where there are holes in the story that need filling.'

'And when the sheet's hanging crooked?'

'That means that a twist is required at that spot.'

'Rather a good idea,' said Guy.

'What do you mean, "rather a good idea"?' said Plum. 'It's genius.'

Gertie Lawrence was arriving from America the next week to start preparations for the London presentation of *Oh, Kay*, and they went up to London to welcome her and discuss with her the possibility of making changes in the book. It had occurred to them that a musical comedy about bootleggers might not appeal to a British audience, and in their gloomier moments they had even felt that it might be necessary to construct a completely new story and fit the Gershwin numbers into it.

They were at Waterloo when the boat train rolled in, but found that they had not reckoned for Gertie's popularity. A dense crowd of friends and admirers were on the platform. André Charlot was there, so were Jack Buchanan, Ivor Novello and, so it seemed, half the population of London.

Clearly there was no hope of getting her attention now, and, when Ivor invited them to a party in her honour that night at his flat, they accepted gratefully, hoping that they might get a minute or two with her alone in the course of the evening.

It was very much wishful thinking. In the Novello flat above the Strand Theatre Gertie was always the centre of a group except when she stepped out to sing a song or give her impersonation of her cockney dresser, Clarrie, famous in the profession. Clarrie had an old grandmother who, too, had been a dresser, and the dialogue between them, as rendered by Gertie, ran thus:

'Grannie,' I says, 'I want your advice about sailors, Grannie.'

'Sailors?' she says. 'Listen, my girl. Cheer for the Navy every chance you get, but don't go round with it. A bunch of scamps, all of them, that's what sailors are.'

'How about actors?' I says.

'Must it be one or the other?' she says.

'As things are at present,' I says.

'Well, it's a 'ell of a choice,' says Grannie, 'but speakin' as a woman as was born in a wardrobe hamper, I'd say take the sailor.'

Having finished her act, Gertie became the centre of a crowd again, and to her intense indignation Clara Novello Davies, Ivor's mother, found herself deserted and standing alone with none to pay her reverence, a thing to which she was by no means accustomed. She was a woman whose powerful voice, dominating manner and majestically flowing robes made her seem like a blend of the Cumaean Sybil and the Statue of Liberty, and she was wont to hold court, not to be left in solitude.

'Well!' she said, giving the word the full force of that voice of hers.

A hush fell on the assembly. Clara Novello Davies strode to the door and, flinging it open, turned.

'I have been grossly insulted,' she boomed, 'and I am leaving my son's home for ever. I shall never again cross this threshold.' And she strode through the door, slamming it behind her.

Most unfortunately, it was the door of the coats and hats cupboard, and she emerged a moment later in floods of tears. Ivor rushed to console her, and the incident ended with the whole company singing 'For She's a Jolly Novello'.

On 15th December rehearsals of *Rio Rita* were to begin in New York, so Guy's visit to London was necessarily a brief one.

Rio Rita opened the new Ziegfeld Theatre on 2nd February. It had a most effective score by Tierney and McCarthy, the team which had written *Kid Boots* for Ziegfeld as well as the record-breaking *Irene*.

Ziegfeld drew Guy aside after the opening and told him that he had signed Marilyn Miller and Jack Donahue for the following season. Would Guy write a show for them and, if so, did he want a partner? He said he did and of course named Plum.

The two set to work immediately and turned out a scenario. The play, tentatively entitled *The Gibson Girl*, was in complete scenario form inside of ten days. They read it to both the stars and both approved. Ziegfeld was in Palm Beach so they decided to go down there and close the deal.

16

1

IT was in 1918 that they had paid their previous visit to the Florida resort – now it was 1927. The real-estate boom had come in the interval and, having reached its climax in the previous year, was in a state of recession. It had not yet, however, by any means collapsed.

Plum bought a paper when their train stopped at Fort Pierce and regaled his companion with a joint proclamation by the mayors of the East coast littoral announcing 'The Fiesta of the American Tropics' – 'Our Season of Mardi Gras when Love, Merrymaking and Wholesome Sport shall prevail throughout Our Domains'. They promised unitedly, 'Parades in which a Glorious Pageantry of Sublime Beauty shall depict in Floral Loveliness the Blessing Bestowed upon us by Friendly Sun, Gracious Rain and Soothing Tropic Winds'.

'I wonder,' said Guy, 'how the 1600 people injured in the great September hurricane feel about those "Soothing Tropic Winds".'

Ziegfeld was staying with Leonard Replogle, the financier, and wasn't in when they phoned. They spent the day swimming and playing a round of golf on the new Everglades course. They returned to the hotel expecting to find a message from the manager but there was none. They dressed, dined and went to Bradley's. There the Colonel told them that Ziegfeld was upstairs in the Chemin-de-Fer room. He said he was afraid Flo had had a bad night.

'Lucky that *Rio Rita* of his is such a hit,' he said. 'He's had nothing but bad luck down here.'

A man with a shock of pale straw-coloured hair standing nearby turned to them.

'You're talking about Flo?' he said. 'Did you ever see anybody like him? He was flat-broke before this new show of his went on, with a grocery bill up at Hastings that a greyhound couldn't jump over. But a week after the Ziegfeld opened he came down here in a private car.'

'There never was such extravagance,' agreed Bradley.

'I knew him out in Chicago when we were both knee-high to a grasshopper,' said the light-haired man. 'The first thing I remember about him was he'd buy an all-day sucker at six o'clock at night.' Everybody laughed.

'Suckers he had even then, had he?' commented a man who had been standing near them listening to the conversation.

As they turned to him he placed a finger on his chest.

'When I say "suckers" I'm pointing right at the biggest one. Believe me, gentlemen, that loafer still owes me for the costumes of the *Follies* of 1923. And then he had the nerve to ask for me to dress the Spanish Shawl number in *Rio Rita*. Real Spanish shawls he wants and, what you think? I am damn fool enough to get them for him.'

'Who was the chap who said he'd known Flo as a kid?' asked Guy as the Colonel escorted them to the stair.

'Jesse Livermore.'

'The Wolf of Wall Street!'

'Yes, I don't know why he wastes his time coming in here.'

'Shemmy' was an innovation since Guy and Plum had last visited Bradley's. When they were there in 1918 there had been only Roulette and 'Hazard', or 'Birdcage' as it is sometimes called. Now Bradley's 'Shemmy' game had the reputation of being the steepest in the world.

Ziegfeld was seated at the table. He greeted them gaily.

'Hello boys, what are you doing down here? Bad place, bad game.' He addressed the dealer. 'Card, please.'

'I never learned to play "Shemmy",' said Guy.

'Seems like I never did either,' said Ziegfeld, turning over a ten. 'You boys got some money on you?'

'Yes.' Guy, who was acting as the team's treasurer, pulled out his wallet.

'Give me $1000.'

'That's all we've got.'

'It's all I asked for.'

Guy handed him a small sheaf of crisp, new hundreds. Ziegfeld tossed them all on the table and pulled the 'shoe' toward him.

'That's pretty rich, isn't it?' protested one of the players.

'That's what the bank opens for, gentlemen, $1000.'

As the punters placed their bets, Flo conversed with the two writers standing beside him.

He turned his cards as he spoke. He had eight. The money was raked into the bank. They watched the play for a few minutes, then: 'We've brought down the lay-out of the Miller show,' Guy told him.

'Oh, good. I want it to be the biggest thing I've ever done. Incidentally Erlanger won't come in. He says $100,000 is too much to risk on any show.' He turned back to the table.

Ziegfeld continued to win steadily. The croupier announced that there was $24,000 in the bank. A voice said '*banco*.' Ziegfeld looked up and saw Jesse Livermore.

'Hello, Pinkie.' Livermore, a virtual albino, had that characteristic pink look about the eyes. 'Don't come round here with that hot streak of yours.'

Ziegfeld dealt the cards with the same careless flip.

' "Shooting for the stick", eh? That's always been your style.'

He turned over a natural.

'The Magoo, Pinkie. Looks like you aren't wearing your horseshoes tonight.'

Jesse Livermore laughed and threw in a wad of bills.

'Seems as if you boys have brought me luck,' said Ziegfeld.

'You're not going to leave that money in the bank, are you?'

'Why not? I'm doing all right.'

'You've run the bank for fourteen coups,' said Plum. 'You don't think it's going on for ever, do you?'

'I'll run it one more.'

'Well, I won't watch.'

'You stay right where you are. Maybe it's you that's the mascot.'

He won again.

'All right, boys, the bank passes. I'm going to go on gambling with this money,' he told the table. 'I'm going to use it to produce a show by these two gentlemen. What's it called, boys?'

'*The Gibson Girl*.'

'Yes, not bad. Come on, let's go down and have a drink.'

But Ziegfeld seemed lukewarm. He listened, nodded and said nothing. A day or two later Guy learned the reason. Flo produced a rough outline for a show which had been sent to him by Bill McGuire. It was 'timely', having to do with the recent visit to the US of Queen Marie of Romania and her daughter. The Princess was in love with a West Point cadet who, somewhat improbably, had flown the Atlantic with a cadet pal (Donahue). Still more improbably they had landed in Romania.

Neither Bill nor Ziegfeld was strong on geography, nor were they acquainted with the regulations covering West Point cadets. Guy had, in his architectural youth, spent two years at the Point, and he thought this might give him some advantage in dealing with the cuckoo about to lay its egg (a prophetic phrase he fancied) in the cosy nest that Plum and he were building.

But McGuire had done one thing which, for Ziegfeld, had a subtle appeal. He had telegraphed his story. As has been pointed out before, Ziggy was the telegraph-kid. He handled the forty-two yellow sheets, with Bill's name on the last one, with loving care.

So it was that *Rosalie* came into being. Flo told Guy he wanted him to team with McGuire. 'I know Bill,' he said. 'This telegram is about all I'll ever get from him.'

'But what about Plum?'

'He can write the lyrics.'

'How can he? You're getting Gershwin. He'll only work with Ira.'

'I'm having Romberg as well. He knows Romania. He's been there. Plum knows Europe too. It's a good combination.'

'Two book writers, two lyric writers, two composers?'

'Why not?'

'It's all right if you can pay for it.'

'If I can't pay for it, you won't get paid.'

This simple axiom summed up the principle on which all Ziegfeld undertakings were based. He had one disciple who adhered to this philosophy as strictly as he did, his pet author, William Anthony McGuire. Bill had his own way of putting it: 'If I haven't got it, they can't get it,' was his phrase, and the fact that he so frequently didn't have it because, like Ziegfeld, he'd bought what he couldn't pay for, seemingly troubled him as little as it did the manager.

Once when a scene that Bill had written in *Whoopee* was dubbed 'old-fashioned', he refuted it hotly.

'Damn it all, Flo and I are ahead of the times. Look at the way we both live on next year's income.'

He was constantly just one jump ahead of the sheriff. Once indeed the sheriff was one jump ahead of him. Guy was expecting Bill to come and spend a week at a shore cottage he had taken at Westhampton. Together they were going to put the finishing touches to *Rosalie*. Half an hour before the train was due, three men, one of whom wore a large silver star, tramped up the wooden path and displayed to the Bolton factotum a body-warrant that called for Bill's arrest and incarceration.

Though clad in a wet bathing-suit, Guy flew to his car and drove to Speonk, where he told his collaborator what was awaiting him at Westhampton. Bill and his bag were then driven back to Patchogue so that he could catch a train for New York. All there was of the polishing process took place during the drive.

It was a few days after that that Bill disappeared. He was living at the Hotel Warwick, but when Guy and Plum, who were working together on a spot where a new number was needed, phoned him, they were told he was no longer there. They called Flo.

'That's where he was last night. I'll see what I can find out. You boys had better come on over to the Ziegfeld.'

'I don't know where the man's got to,' were the words he greeted them with when they entered the office. 'His things are still at the Warwick. They're holding them for the rent.'

'I hope the revised script of *Rosalie* isn't impounded.'

'Holy cats! If he's got the script, God help us! That fellow is a crackpot. You know what he did to me once? Sold me a sketch – I bought it outright for $1500. He put the money in his pocket but forgot to leave the sketch. The *Follies* was already in rehearsal so I combed the town for him. His wife didn't know where he was – but it wasn't often she did. Then *The Passing Show* opened and there was my sketch. The stinker had sold it to Lee Shubert two days before he did to me. And all he'd charged Lee was $1000!'

The phone rang. It was Bill. Ziegfeld told him to beat it over as fast as he could come and to bring the script.

'He's got it,' Ziegfeld told them as he hung up. 'The Warwick people wouldn't let him take a thing but he sneaked *Rosalie* out tucked under his waistband. Then what do you think he did? He moved into the Plaza. He says he likes it better there, he's got a nice view of the park.'

Bill arrived, cheerful as usual.

'So you're at the Plaza now?'

'Yes, only trouble is it's a bit grand. You have to have a shave before you'd venture into the barber shop.'

'What did you do for luggage?'

'Oh, I always keep a bag at the club with a couple of old telephone books in it. Then I go and buy what I need and have it paid for at the desk.'

The phone rang again. Ziegfeld answered it. 'That was the box-office,' he said. 'They say there's a sheriff waiting for you downstairs, Bill.'

'Jeez! That what I get for coming here.'

'Look,' said Flo, 'I tell you what. I'll go down and say you've gone. Turn out the lights. I'll tell them there's nobody up here.'

It was about seven-thirty. They turned out the lights and sat in the dark discussing the show in whispers. A strange sort of story-conference, but then things were apt to be strange around Bill McGuire.

Then the door was opened and Ziegfeld switched on the lights. He held a folded paper in his hands.

'You son-of-a-bitch,' he said. 'He wasn't after you, he was after me.'

McGuire clicked his tongue disapprovingly.

'Why don't you pay your bills, Flo?' he said.

2

To compensate Plum for substituting McGuire as Guy's collaborator, Flo engaged him to write *The Three Musketeers*, a musical designed to serve as a twin starring vehicle for Dennis King and Vivienne Segal. The composer was Rudy Friml, whom Plum had worked with before on the lyrics of a dead and gone turkey of 1916 called *Kitty Darlin'*. On the book he, in turn, was teamed with McGuire.

About the same time he was commissioned by Gilbert Miller to adapt *Her Cardboard Lover* for Jeanne Eagles and Leslie Howard. He had, further, a comedy he had written for an English management called *Good Morning Bill.* All four of these, including *Rosalie*, were produced within the space of four months.

At the same time Guy was engaged with Fred Thompson on a new Astaire show, *Funny Face*, another Philip Goodman musical, *The Five O'Clock Girl, Rosalie* and *She's My Baby*, a Dillingham show written in collaboration with Kalmar and Ruby and with a score by Rodgers and Hart.

Guy, finding conflicting demands too much for him, bowed out of *Funny Face* after the play had passed its scenario stage. He suggested Bob Benchley to take his place. Bob took over.

Altogether Plum and Guy had, singly or together, nineteen opening nights in the three years 1926-7-8. Fourteen of these were new shows, five productions in one country of plays first presented in the other.

Looking through the diaries, every day seems to have been given to either writing or rehearsing. The protracted tours of the Princess days had given place to a more or less standard two weeks' try-out. This was a period of intensive effort, of re-writing, of early and late rehearsals, of the continual watching of performances in an effort to gauge audience reactions.

Four shows a year meant two months of this, the hardest and most exacting work of all. The chief intervals of rest were those spent on ocean liner – though even there you would most likely have found the team, rug-wrapped in adjoining deckchairs, busy with pad and pencil.

3

Although Plum was deeply preoccupied with his books – *The Small Bachelor, Meet Mr Mulliner* and *Money for Nothing* all published in the year, with *Summer Lightning* and *Carry On, Jeeves* coming along in the next – he still found time to do a little dramatic work. With Ian Hay he wrote *A Damsel in Distress*, based on an earlier novel, and he accepted a commission from Gilbert Miller to adapt the German play, *By Candlelight.* The fact that Gertie Lawrence was to be the heroine of the last-named was too great a temptation to be resisted.

This particular chore took Plum to America in the early summer of '29. He and Guy had not met for exactly a year.

'You're looking a little drawn,' said Plum. 'I know it can't be overdrawn, ha, ha, so there must be some other reason. Are you worried about anything? Which reminds me of a story about Eva Kern. Do you remember a play called *Six-Cylinder Love*?'

'Vaguely. Ernie Truex starred in it. He was a little clerk—'

'That's right. Well, Eva came to Jerry one day and said, "I'm terribly anxious about poor Ernie Truex. I've just seen him and he looked awful, as if he had got something dreadful on his mind. Honestly, I was afraid he might be going to commit suicide." So Jerry trotted off to investigate. It seemed to him, when he met him, that Ernie was looking reasonably cheerful, but he started making inquiries. "Are you all right, Ernie?" he asked. Ernie said he was fine. "No money troubles? Nothing wrong with your home life? Doctor hasn't told you you've got an incurable disease?" "No," said Ernie. "Plenty of money, home life terrific, and I haven't gone to a doctor for years." "Then what on earth was Eva talking about?" said Jerry. "She told me she had seen you and you were in a frightful state, contemplating suicide and all that sort of thing." "But I haven't met Eva for quite a while," said Ernie. "When did she see me?" "At the Thursday matinée." "Ah," said Ernie, enlightened. "Well, at the Thursday matinée and the Saturday matinée and also six times a week nightly I lose my job, I have my life's savings stolen, my wife tells me she's going to leave me, and I am expecting every moment to be arrested. Maybe I did look a little worried when Eva saw me." After which digression, is anything the matter with you?'

'Just the rat-race. I don't quite know why I've been doing it.'

'I don't quite know why either of us have. Youth's been knocking at the door for some time now.'

'Yes . . . only what do you do when you stop working? Just sit there listening to the hardening of your arteries.'

'It's not as bad as all that. We're still quite young.'

'Yes, quite.'

'Quite.'

'I hate that word "quite".'

Plum regarded him speculatively.

'The only symptom of approaching age I detect in you is that you don't talk about *The Little Thing*, as much as you used to.'

'I'm still as keen about it as ever.'

'Are you? They why don't we put in on ourselves?'

'Become managers?'

'Don't say it in that awed voice. There's no trick to being a manager.'

'Are you sure there isn't? All my life – my theatrical life – I've mentally been saying "sir" to them. They may be "Ray" and "Flo" and "Charlie" to talk to, but in my innermost soul they are Mr Comstock, Mr Ziegfeld and Mr Dillingham. I find myself waiting for them to ask me to sit down.'

The conversation was taking place in the Ritz where they were both staying. Guy's Great Neck home was rented. In answer to a question he said that Marguerite had been in America but was now in Italy.

'Let's talk over this *Little Thing* thing at lunch.'

'Where shall we go?'

'The Algonquin?'

'The Round Table? I'm never comfortable there. I feel like one does when one's trying to think up a funny opening-night telegram to the comic, which you know will be pasted on his mirror for the run of the show.'

'You seem to be in a very diminished state. What's happened to you?'

'Oh, a bit of this and that – nothing.'

'I suspect woman trouble – that old complaint of yours.'

'Nonsense. I nailed my flag to the masthead years ago. "Women are wonderful." It's still there, a bit tattered and battle-scarred but flying just the same.'

They went downstairs to the Japanese Garden where, ironically enough after their decision not to go to the Algonquin Round Table, Theodore (the big one this time) put them next a table where Alec Woollcott was seated with Bob Benchley, Arthur Richman and Phil Barry. Plum received a warm welcome and he and Guy were told to move over.

'Don't tell me you two fellows are planning another assault on Broadway,' said Phil. 'You're a menace.'

'Speak to those men respectfully, young fellow,' said Bob. 'They've written more musical comedies than any other four men in the world. I wrote *one* – that chap Guy landed me with it – and oh, boy, was that something. I always keep saying "Oh, boy" whenever these two are around,' he added. 'I like to see those nostalgic smiles steal across their faces.'

'What *are* you up to, Plum?' said Woollcott. 'If it's rude to ask.'

'I'm here to see Gilbert Miller about an adaptation I'm doing for him.'

'Gilbert Miller?' echoed Woollcott and, rising, he held up his coffee cup in a toast. 'Gentlemen, I give you Gilbert Miller. I give him to you freely. All I ask in exchange is a 5¢ cigar-butt and a Coolidge campaign button.'

'Come, come now,' said Plum. 'After all he is our most literate manager.'

'True,' agreed Woollcott resuming his seat. 'To quote one of his lady stars, "The man has his faults but, after all, he does speak our language." '

Everyone laughed, but this time Guy rushed to Gilbert's defence.

'It's the old story,' he said. 'When it's someone you like and admire, their faults are of moment to you. You notice a blemish in your sweetheart that would pass unchallenged in another woman.'

'Gilbert may be your sweetheart,' said Woollcott. 'He isn't mine.'

'But you must admit—'

'Yes, yes, yes,' interrupted the critic testily. 'I admit everything. I admit his impeccable taste in stage décor, his shrewdness in casting, his enterprise, his courage. . . . His stories have both pith and point, and I pay tribute to his admirable restraint when, with far more justification than have others who do, he does not attempt to rewrite his authors' plays. It is on a matter, not of sense, but of sensibility that I arraign him. . . . Mr Arthur Richman has the floor.'

'Oh, no you don't!' laughed Arthur. 'I'm not telling that story!'

'Are you not the author of the famous line: "You have to know Gilbert really well in order to dislike him"?'

'That was just a crack – not to be taken seriously.'

'Very well, if you won't tell the story, I will.' He turned to the table:

'The talented gentleman on my right recently received a dinner invitation from the Millers, and, in response to its instructions, presented himself at the door of the Bache-Miller residence, 814 Fifth Avenue, attired in white tie and with dark red carnation in buttonhole.

'Ushered into one of the sumptuous reception rooms where Fragonards and Watteaus rub shoulders, and where bergères, encased in lovely Oudry Tapestries, implore you not to sit on them, our author was set to wondering why he had been invited. It was clearly one of the fancier Miller occasions and he realized that all save himself enjoyed high rating by either social or cash-register standards, if not by both.

'In an effort to make him feel more at ease, or possibly because he was tired, Gilbert came and leaned on his shoulder, a rather favourite habit of the most literate of our managers.

' "Come with me," he said suddenly and rather abruptly, and, turning, he led the way to the elevator. . . . Oh, yes there is an elevator, known, because of its being hung with Gobelins, as the *ascenseur*. There are also solid gold fittings on the plumbing fixtures. Kitty maintains they are economical – they never have to be cleaned.

'Little Arthur, following in the wake of big Gilbert, thought to himself hopefully, "Ha, a business chat . . . Ina Claire . . . that comedy of mine that would have been collecting dust on Gilbert's desk this past twelvemonth, were not Gilbert's desk so constantly dusted."

'But no, it was not that. Gilbert shot the *ascenseur* upwards and stopped it between floors. He turned to Arthur with that, as always, ominous phrase: "Arthur, we've known each other a long time, so I think I may speak freely."

' "Go ahead," said Arthur.

' "You have a terrible case of halitosis."

' "Oh, no," protested Arthur, as perspiration beaded his forehead. "It can't be true. I'm a very healthy man with an excellent digestion and—"

' "Blow at me," said Gilbert.

'Arthur blew.

' "Blow again."

'Arthur blew again.

' "No, it isn't you," said Gilbert, and shot the *ascenseur* down again. To describe Arthur as shattered would be an understatement. His collar had wilted, two damp spots showed on his shirt-front, he felt that if Gilbert came and leant on him again he would collapse.

'But Gilbert was leaning on other shoulders. Arthur was free to stand there alone and try to recover his shattered morale. He, naturally, realized the reason for the mistake. Gilbert had not supposed that anyone who had their name in the Social Register could possibly have halitosis – well, now he had learned his lesson. Arthur watched as the host ambled off once again to the *ascenseur* with a prominent young upper-cruster in tow.

'When he returned Arthur could not resist an inquiry.

' "Yes, he's the one," said Gilbert, "but I think I've got him pretty well fixed up with some of Kitty's mouth-wash." '

Woollcott paused.

'If I was a pitiful object,' said Arthur, 'you should have seen this other poor wretch. Whenever one of the women on either side of him spoke to him, he never turned his head by the fraction of an inch. He spoke straight . . . out . . . front.'

'An engaging story,' said Plum, 'but still, reverting from sensibility to sense, isn't it better to know if you've got halitosis? Personally I find it comforting to reflect that, if your best friends won't tell you, Gilbert Miller will.'

4

The idea of turning manager and putting on *The Little Thing* themselves burgeoned as a bud in May. Guy, seemingly dubious when Plum first suggested it, grew daily more enthusiastic. Even when investigation revealed that costs had pyramided so that they must budget for close to $100,000 he was not discouraged – what was $100,000? Plenty of smart lads were making that every other day down in Wall Street.

The script was hauled out and completely revised. Some of the scenes had the 'colour' of *Sally*. These were eliminated. Bits of the material that they had designed for *The Gibson Girl* were fitted in. They chose Vincent Youmans as composer. Plum and he set to work on the score.

They took offices in the Brill Building. They interviewed Marilyn, miraculously free. She read the script and liked it.

'Why was this never done before?' she asked. 'You say you wrote it some time ago.'

'I'd hate to tell you how long.'

'It's a shame Jack can't play the comedy part but he's going into something he's written with Fred Thompson.'

'*Sons of Guns*? Yes, we know about that. How do you like that new chap they're all talking about who's playing in a thing at the Shubert called *Ups-a-Daisy*?'

'Lester Hope?'

'He's changing his name to "Bob" – "Bob Hope".'

'I think he'd be just right.'

'We'll get him.' It was said with confidence. Not, 'We'll get him if Mr Freedley agrees.' No nonsense about the management not being willing to pay the salary – the thing Savage had pulled when they asked for Billy Van.

'You're right,' said Guy, 'there's no trick to being a manager. It's like trying the handle of a door that you'd always imagined was locked and bolted, and finding it's been open all the time.'

'I suppose we ought to sell some securities and deposit that hundred grand in the bank?'

'Oh, we don't need it yet. My broker says the bull market's good for another six months. Seems a shame to pull the money out when every day you leave it there it keeps getting more.'

They hired a company manager, Jim O'Leary, an old-timer who knew the ropes and had costs at his fingertips. They had an excellent secretary, Lillian Hartman, who had worked for Guy years before. Everything seemed set. The only annoyance was what they always referred to as the *ascenseurs*. There never was a building whose elevators were so jammed. People seemed to pour in and out of the Brill Building in waves. Frequently three of four elevators would go by their floor as they were waiting to go to lunch. A little thing, but, when you want to go to lunch, you want to go to lunch.

'Let's move before we produce our next show,' said Plum.

Guy nodded. 'This is an anniversary,' he said, 'and I suggest that, for good and practical reasons, we go somewhere where they know us.'

'What's it an anniversary of?'

'Just thirteen years ago today we walked into Ray Comstock's office. *Go To It* had laid an egg the night before.'

'The *Oh, Boy!* contract.'

'That's right the *Oh, Boy!* contract. 8th October.'

'Good old 8th October!'

5

It was the following day that the roof started to fall in, but it wasn't until 24th October that the floor gave way and the two authors began to wonder how far down bottom was. Each hour the seismographs registered a further shock. Auburn Auto, in which they both had holdings, dropped sixty points in one day. After that bit of news came through, things got blurred and there seemed to be a general impression that Judgment Day had set in with unusual severity. Looking over one's shoulder one would not have been surprised to see a brace of those peculiar beasts with an unnecessary number of heads, as described in the Book of Revelation, flexing their muscles before starting in to do their stuff.

Plum and Guy closed the door of their Brill Building office with the knowledge that they would never have need to return. They pressed the 'down' button. The elevator that stopped at their floor was miraculously empty.

'That's funny,' said Guy.

'Not at all,' said Plum. 'Everybody is using the windows.'

Guy's reception of the witticism was not hearty.

'Where shall we go to lunch?' It was Plum who asked the question. 'Ever try the Automat? The food's darn good. I used to go there when I was writing *Polly Preferred*.'

'No,' said Plum firmly, 'I'm damned if we will. We'll take a leaf out of the Ziegfeld-Maguire book and go to the Ritz.'

'What smart fellows those two were: they *spent* their money.'

'Yes, I bet they're busy right now popping champagne corks and patting each other on the back.'

'Wise guys, eh?' I can hear them jeering. 'Now these smart Alecs will be coming round to us for some tips on sheriff dodging.'

They went to the Ritz and Theodore produced two smashing horses' necks that were not horses' necks. They didn't even mind when Vecsey struck up with *The Rose of China*.

'Funny, the failures don't matter any more. If we'd cleaned up with *The Rose of China*, today it would be alleesamee bottomside.'

'For heaven's sake don't start talking pidgin. That'll finish me.'

'How do you actually stand?'

'The books balance exactly – the red and the black. They did a thorough job on me.'

'They didn't get quite all of mine, thanks to Ethel.'

'Well, that's fine.'

'What about you taking a bit of it till the tide starts coming in again?'

'No, thanks a lot, but I'm all right. I've got enough for car fare.'

Guy took a letter from his pocket and extracted an oblong green slip from it.

'The three sweetest words in the language,' said Plum. ' "Enclosed find cheque." Remember which show that was from?'

'*Very Good Eddie*.'

'Right. Is it a big cheque?'

'Quite big. I'm sending it back.'

'You doing *what*?'

'Sending it back . . . to Marguerite. She heard about what's happened and sold all the bits and pieces I ever gave her. She even sold her beloved *roulotte*.'

'She's a wonderful wife.'

'Yes . . . but not mine.'

'What on earth do you mean?'

'The divorce was made final that day sixteen months ago . . . the day we lunched with Alec Woollcott and the others at the Ritz. It didn't work, you see. She needed someone who would be on hand to talk to and have a bit of fun with . . . what's the phrase . . .? "Turn out the pocketful of daily doings." '

'I'm terribly sorry.'

'Oh, I'm all right now. I've found a girl.'

'I'm glad to hear that.'

'And I've got a job.'

'That's odd. *I've* got a job.'

'I'm off to Hollywood.'

'I'm off to Hollywood.'

'Well, that's wonderful. I thought this time really had broken up the old firm. I'm with MGM.'

'*I'm* with MGM. They're putting me on a picture for W. C. Fields.'

Guy drew a deep breath.

'Do you think,' he said, 'the clientele would object if I sang a few bars?'

'MGM are putting *me* on that Fields picture, too.'

Plum gaped.

'You're kidding me.'

'It's the truth.'

'You mean we'll be working together?'

'But this is terrific!'

'Pretty good, I agree.'

'I think this calls for another one, don't you?'

'I certainly do.'

'Do you realize,' said Plum, 'that we've been working together for thirteen years and not a dirty look from start to finish? Most collaborators hate each other's guts after the first couple of shows. It's extraordinary.'

'Amazing.'

'Twin souls about sums it up, in my opinion.'

'In mine, too.'

They drank to Hollywood, to MGM, to W. C. Fields and to the further prosperity of the partnership.

'And now,' said Plum, when this ritual was concluded, 'tell me about this girl of yours.'

'I'd rather wait till you see her.'

'When will that be?'

'She'll be meeting me at Pasadena.'

'What's her name?'

'No, I'm not even going to tell you that. I'll tell you her nickname though. And she had it before I met her.'

'Yes?'

'The Little Thing,' said Guy.

17

1

THE train to the coast – the famous Chief – was rolling along through the wide open spaces where men are men. It was the second day out from Chicago and Guy and Plum were finishing their lunch in the diner. Ethel was to come on later after they had settled in.

The exodus from the East, which had begun with the coming of sound to the motion pictures, was at its height. Already on the train the two had met a number of authors, composers, directors and other Broadway fauna with whom they had worked in the days before the big crash. Rudolf Friml was there and Vincent Youmans and Arthur Richman and a dozen more. It was like one of those great race movements of the middle ages.

'Well,' said Guy, 'California, here we come! How do you feel?'

'I feel,' said Plum, 'as I should think Alice must have felt when, after mixing with all those weird creatures in Wonderland, she knelt on the mantelpiece preparatory to climbing through the looking-glass.'

'I see what you mean – wondering what kind of freaks she was going to meet this time. Still, maybe it won't be so bad. Hollywood can't have many terrors for two men who have survived Erlanger, Savage, a little Plymouth, junior Breckenridge, the Sisters Duncan – not to mention "Fabulous Felix" and Palmer.'

'Palmer?'

'Hank Savage's private poisoner.'

'Good Lord, I haven't thought of him for years. I wonder what became of him.'

'I hope he perished of his own cooking. I've never forgiven that bird for the supercilious way he sneered at that really excellent plot of ours about the pawnbroker.'

'I remember dimly something about a pawnbroker—'

'Good heavens, man, it was a superb plot and we might do worse than spring it on W. C. Fields when we get to Hollywood. You can't have forgotten. About a fellow who was the last of a long line of pawnbrokers and his ancestor had loaned the money to Queen Isabella to finance Columbus. . . .'

'I remember! The contract turned up, and he found that he owned 10 per cent of America. It was a darned good idea.'

'It was a terrific idea, and that hash-slinging sea cook crabbed it with a lot of stuff about thematic archaism.'

At this moment a man in horn-rimmed spectacles paused at their table.

'Oh, there you are,' he said. 'I'll come and have a chat in a minute or two. Can't stop now. See you later.'

He passed on, and they looked after him, puzzled.

'Now who on earth was that?' said Guy. 'He seemed to know us.'

'Probably somebody who was in one of our shows. The train's stiff with actors.'

They dismissed the man from their thoughts and returned to the subject of Hollywood.

'Have you talked to anyone who's been there?' asked Guy.

'Only Bob Benchley, and you know the sort of information you would get from him. He said I mustn't believe the stories I had heard about ill-treatment of inmates at the studios, for there was very little actual brutality. Most of the big executives, he said, were kindly men, and he had often seen Louis B. Mayer stop outside some nodder's hutch and push a piece of lettuce through the bars.'

'What's a nodder?'

'Bob explained that. A sort of Yes-man, only lower in the social scale. When there is a story conference and the supervisor throws out some suggestion or idea, the Yes-men all say "Yes". After they have finished saying "Yes", the nodders nod. Bob said there is also a sub-species known as nodders' assistants, but he didn't want to get too technical.'

'What else? Is it true that they're all lunatics out in Hollywood?'

'Bob says no. He says he knows fully half a dozen people there who are practically sane – except of course at the time of the full moon. . . . Good Lord!'

'What's the matter?'

'I've remembered who that chap was who spoke to us.'

'Who?'

'Palmer.'

'It can't have been.'

'It was. Palmer in person.'

Guy considered.

'I believe you're right. But we shall soon know. He's coming this way.'

It was Palmer – older and with a new and rather horrible briskness about him, but still Palmer. He reached their table and sat down, looking snappy and efficient.

'Well, well,' said Guy.

'Well, well,' said Plum. 'It's a long time since that yacht cruise. How's *Ophelia*?'

Palmer cocked a puzzled eyebrow.

'Ophelia?'

'Your play?'

'Oh, that?' Palmer's face cleared. 'I got tired of waiting for the Colonel to do something about it – he kept changing the subject to corned beef hash whenever I mentioned it – so I threw up my job as cook on the *Dorinda* and came out here. Do you know something?'

'What?'

Palmer's voice was grave.

'I don't want to wrong him, but I've sometimes thought that Colonel Savage may have been stringing me along all the time.'

'Colonel *Savage*?' cried Guy and Plum, horrified.

'I know the idea sounds bizarre, but it has occasionally crossed my mind that he encouraged me to think that he was going to produce my play simply in order to get a free cook on that boat of his. We shall never know, I suppose. Well, as I was saying, after the seventh – or was it the eighth? – trip to Florida I got tired of waiting and came out here. I had a hard time of it for a year or two, but I won through in the end and am now doing extremely well. I'm a cousin by marriage.'

'A . . . what was that?'

'I married the cousin of one of the top executives and from that moment never looked back. Of course, cousins are fairly small fry, but I happen to know that there's a lot of talk going around the front office of giving me brevet rank as a brother-in-law before very long.'

'A brother-in-law is good, is it?'

Palmer stared.

'My dear fellow! Practically as high up as a nephew.'

The two authors offered congratulations.

'Well, now we're all going to be in Hollywood together,' said Guy, 'I hope we shall see something of one another.'

'We shall. I'm your supervisor.'

'Eh?'

'On this W. C. Fields picture. If you've finished your lunch, I'll take you along to meet him. What's the time?'

'Two-thirty.'

'Ah, then he may be sober.'

They made their way along the train to the Fields drawing-room, Guy and Plum a little dubious and inclined to shake their heads. They were not at all sure how they were going to like being supervised by a man who thought that in writing a play – and presumably a talking-picture – the scale of values should be at once objective and rational, hence absolute and authentic. And their uneasiness was increased when their overlord said graciously that he hoped they would come to dinner at his Beverly Hills home on the following Saturday, adding that for the sake of old times he would cook the meal himself.

'I'm as good a cook as I ever was,' he said.

Just about, they imagined, and shivered a little.

2

In the semi-darkness of the drawing-room the first thing the authors heard was a hollow groan and the first thing they saw was a vast something bulging beneath the bed-clothes. It stirred as they entered and there rose from the pillow a face rendered impressive by what must have been one of the largest and most incandescent nasal jobs ever issued to a human being. It reminded Plum – who had read his Edward Lear – of the hero of one of that eminent Victorian's best known poems.

> And all who watch at the midnight hour
> From hall or terrace or lofty tower
> Cry, as they trace the meteor bright
> Moving along through the dreary night
> 'This is the hour when forth he goes,
> The Dong With The Luminous Nose'.

They were to learn later that the comedian was very sensitive about what he considered the only flaw in an otherwise classic countenance and permitted no facetious allusions to it even from his closest friends.

He switched on the light and regarded the visitors with aversion.

'And to what, my merry buzzards, do I owe this intrusion at daybreak?' he asked coldly.

Palmer explained that Mr Bolton and Mr Wodehouse were the two authors to whom had been assigned the task of assembling – under his supervision – the next Fields picture, and the great man softened visibly. He was fond of authors – being, as he often said, an author himself.

'Sit down, my little chickadees,' he said, 'and pass the aspirin. Are you in possession of aspirin?'

Palmer – who no doubt had foreseen this query – produced a small tin box.

'Thank you, thank you. Don't slam the lid. What I need this morning is kindness and understanding, for I am a little nervous. I was up late last night, seeing the new year in. Yes, I am aware,' proceeded Fields, 'that the general consensus of informed opinion in these degenerate days is that the year begins on 1st January – but what reason have we for supposing so? One only . . . that the ancient Romans said it did. But what ancient Romans? Probably a bunch of souses who were well into their fifth bottle of Falernian wine. The Phoenicians held that it began on 21st November. The medieval Christians threw celluloid balls at one another on the night of 15th March. The Greeks were broadminded. Some of them thought New Year's Day came on 20th September, while others voted for 10th June. This was good for the restaurateurs – who could count on two big nights in the year – but confusing for the Income Tax authorities, who couldn't decide when to send in their demands.'

'I never knew that before, Mr Fields,' said Palmer respectfully. There was that about the majestic comedian that made even supervisors respectful.

'Stick around me and you'll learn a lot. Well, you can readily appreciate the result of this confusion of thought, my dream-princes. It makes it difficult for a conscientious man to do the right thing. He starts out simply and straightforwardly by booking a reserved table for the last night in December, and feels that that is that. But mark the sequel. As March approaches, doubts begin to assail him. "Those medieval Christians were shrewd fellows," he says to himself. "Who knows whether they may not have had the right idea?"

'The only way he can square his conscience is by going out and investing heavily in squeakers and rattles and paper caps on the night of 15th March. And scarcely has the doctor left his bedside next morning, when he starts to brood on the fact that the Phoenicians, who were nobody's fools, were convinced that 21st November was New Year's Eve. Many a young man in the springtime of life has developed cirrhosis of the liver simply by overdoing his researches into New Year's Eve. Last night I was pure Phoenician, and I would appreciate the loan of that aspirin once more.'

He mused in silence for a moment.

'So you're coming out to Dottyville-on-the-Pacific, are you, boys?' he said, changing the subject. 'Poor lads, poor lads! Well, let me give you a word of advice. Don't try to escape. They'll chase you across the ice with bloodhounds. And even if the bloodhounds miss you, the pitiless Californian climate drives you back. The only thing to do is to stick it out. But you'll suffer, my unhappy tenderfeet, you'll suffer. Conditions were appalling enough B.S., but they're far worse now.'

'B.S.?'

'Before Sound – sometimes called the Stereoptician Age, rich in fossils. Picture first learned to walk. Now they've learned to talk. But the thing they've always managed to do is smell. In this year A.S. confusion is rife. Not a soul at the studios but is clutching its head and walking around in circles, saying, "Where am I?" And can you blame them? Think how they must have felt at MGM when they found that Jack Gilbert could only talk soprano.

'Yes,' Fields went on, 'confusion is rife. I was out to Pathé in Culver City last month and found the place in an uproar. One of their most popular vice-presidents had just been carted off to the loony-bin, strong men sitting on his head while others rushed off to fetch strait waistcoats and ambulances. It came about thus. As you doubtless know, the Pathé trademark is a handsome white rooster. For years he's been popping up on the screen ahead of their pictures and newsreels, flapping his wings and a-gaping open his beak. And when Sound came in, of course the directors held a meeting and it was duly resolved that from now on he had got to crow right out loud.

'Well, they set to work and brought out all the fancy sound equipment into the front yard. The countryside had been scoured for the biggest, all-firedest rooster the sovereign state of California could provide. It was a beaut – pure white with a great red comb on him – and they had a swell background fixed up behind him and the sound machines all waiting to catch that mighty cock-a-doodle-do – and – what do you know? – not a yip could they get out of him. He'd strut about, he'd flap his wings, he'd scrabble with his feet, but he wouldn't crow.

'Well, sir, they tried everything. They even went back to the first principle of show business – they brought on the girls. But he wasn't interested, and they began to wonder if it wouldn't be best to send for a psychiatrist. Then one of their top idea men told them that the sure way to make a rooster crow was to get another rooster to crow. He remembered that the second vice-president was pretty good at barnyard imitations, though his crow wasn't his best number. His quack was better and his sow-with-a-litter-of-baby-pigs was his topper. But they thought his crow might get by, so they fetched him out of his office.

' "Crow," they said.

' "Crow?" said he.

' "That's right. Crow."

' "Oh, you mean *crow*?" said the vice-president, getting it. "Like a rooster?"

'And they all said that the more like a rooster he was the better they'd be pleased.

'Well, these vice-presidents don't spare themselves when duty calls. He crowed and crowed and crowed until he rasped his larynx, but not a sign of audience reaction. The rooster just looked at him and went on scrabbling his feet.

' "Now let's all be very calm and rational about this," said the director who had been assigned to shoot the scene. "I'll tell you what's wrong, Adolf. This bird's no fool. He sees you in those yellow slacks and that rainbow shirt and the crimson tie and he's on to it right away that you're no rooster. 'Something wrong here,' he says to himself, and your act don't get over."

' "So here's what you do, Adolf," said the president. "You go out in the street round behind the studio wall where the bird can't see you and start crowing out there. That ought to do it."

'So the vice-president went out on the street and began to crow, and at last the old rooster started to perk up and take notice. He jumped on the perch they had built for him and cleared his throat, and it looked like they were all set to go, when darned if Adolf didn't stop crowing.

' "What's the matter with the fellow?" said the director, and the president yells over the wall:

' "Crow, Adolf, crow!"

'But not a yip out of Adolf, and then someone goes outside to see what's wrong, and there's two cops pushing him into the wagon. They're talking to him kinda soft and soothing.

' "Take it easy," they're saying. "Yes, yes, *sure* we understand why you were crowing. You're a rooster, aren't you? So you come with us, pal, and we'll take you back to the henhouse." '

3

It was only after they had left the drawing-room that Guy remembered that they had not told the comedian their pawnbroker plot. They had not, of course, had much opportunity, and they consoled themselves with the thought that later on there would no doubt be a formal story conference where only business would be talked.

The long journey was coming to an end. They breakfasted next morning as the train was pulling out of San Bernadino. There was a strong scent of orange-blossoms in the air, turning Guy's mind to thoughts of marriage. He mentioned this to Plum, as they sat in the diner gazing out at the mountains, at snow-capped Old Baldy and the distant shimmering peak of Mt Wilson.

'When are you getting married?' Plum asked.

'As soon as possible, now that we are both out here.'

'You'll probably settle down in Hollywood and spend the rest of your life there.'

Guy shook his head.

'Not if they paid me!'

'Well, they would pay you. Bob Benchley says that's the one redeeming feature of the place – the little man in the cage who hands you out the $100 bills each Thursday.'

'I mean, not if they paid me untold gold. Hollywood may turn out all right for a visit, but—'

'You wouldn't live there if they gave you the place?'

'Exactly. Not even if they made me a brother-in-law, like Palmer. I'm going to get back into the theatre again.'

'Me, too.'

'Venton Freedley said he liked that story of ours about the fellow who's such a hit with women and the millionaire father who hires him to stop his daughter marrying a titled half-wit.'

'You mean *Anything Goes*?'

'Yes. You still like that title?'

'I think it's great.'

'Vinton says Cole Porter would write the score.'

'Cole does his own lyrics.'

'Yes.'

'That means I'm out. What pests these lyric-writing composers are! Taking the bread out of a man's mouth.'

'You would do the book with me.'

'Do you want me to?'

'Of course I do. You had an idea about a crook escaping on the boat from New York dressed as a clergyman.'

'Public Enemy Number Thirteen.'

'A superstitious crook. Never had any luck when he was Thirteen, so wants to murder one of the top dozen and get promoted to Twelve. We ought to start jotting down some of these ideas before we get all tangled up with Hollywood.'

'Write on the back of the menu.'

Cups and plates were pushed aside. They paid no further attention to the orange groves, the mountains, the advertisements of the secondhand-car dealers, the flaming twenty-four sheets of the picture-houses. They were working.

'I see the whole of the action taking place on a transatlantic liner.'

'Giving the hero six days to disentangle the girl.'

'There'll be another girl – a comic – who's mixed up with the hero. He was out with her on a supper-date when the heroine's father gave him the job, and she follows him aboard. You never saw *Girl Crazy*, did you?'

'No, I was in England.'

'There was a girl called Ethel Merman in it. It was her first job and she made a terrific hit, singing that "I've Got Rhythm" thing of Gershwin's. She puts a song over better than anybody and is great on comedy.'

'She sounds right for this part.'

'Exactly right. We're rolling!'

'Yes, we're rolling.'

But they were also rolling into Pasadena. They had to hurry back to their compartment for their things.

Held on the car platform while suit-cases, golf-bags and typewriters were handed down by the porters, they looked out at the strange new land that was to be their home. Tall eucalyptus . . . blue-flowered jacarandas, feathery pepper trees dotted with red. . . . And what looked like a thousand shiny new cars, one of which, they felt, must unquestionably belong to Palmer.

Guy saw all these things without really seeing them. His eyes were on a girl farther down the platform who was searching the faces of the passengers waiting to alight. She turned and saw him . . . smiled and waved.

'Journey's End,' felt Guy.

Palmer came bustling up.

'I wanted to see you two boys,' he said briskly. 'I've had an idea for the Bill Fields picture. Just an outline at present, but something for you to be mulling over. Bill's a pawnbroker, the last of a long line of pawnbrokers. His family have been pawnbrokers for centuries. They started originally in Spain and – get this – it was an ancestor of Bill's who loaned Queen Isabella the money to finance Columbus. She signed a regular contract—'

Guy drew a deep breath. His eyes had glazed a little. So had Plum's.

'—giving this ancestor 10 per cent of anything Columbus discovered,' continued Palmer. 'Well, what he discovered – see what I mean – was America. So – this is going to slay you – there's good old Bill with a legal claim to 10 per cent of America. Take it from there. Isn't that great?' said Palmer, his horn-rimmed spectacles flashing. 'Isn't that terrific? Isn't that the most colossal idea for a comedian's picture anyone ever heard?'

There was a long silence. The two authors struggled for words. Then they found them.

'Yes, Mr Palmer,' said Guy.

'Oh, *yes*, Mr Palmer,' said Plum.

And they knew they were really in Hollywood.

Acknowledgements

The authors wish to extend their sincere thanks to Messrs Chappell & Co. for permission granted them to reprint lyrics from a number of musical comedies. Those lyrics are copyright as follows:

From *Very Good Eddie*, copyright, 1916, by T. B. Harms Co.
From *Have a Heart*, copyright, 1916, by T. B. Harms Co.
From *Miss Springtime*, copyright, 1916, by T. B. Harms Co.
From *Oh, Boy!* copyright, 1917, by T. B. Harms Co.
From *The Riviera Girl*, copyright, 1917, by T. B. Harms Co.
From *Oh, Lady, Lady*, copyright, 1918, by T. B. Harms Co.
From *The Rose of China*, copyright, 1919, by T. B. Harms Co.
From *Sally*, copyright, 1920, by T. B. Harms Co.
From *Sitting Pretty*, copyright, 1924, by T. B. Harms Co.
From *Show Boat* (the song 'Bill'), copyright, 1927, by T. B. Harms Co.

BARMY IN WONDERLAND

1

J. G. ANDERSON took up the telephone.

'Give me the desk,' he said.

They gave him the desk.

'Hello?' said the desk.

'Phipps? This is Mr Anderson.'

'Well, well, well,' cried the desk, baying like a pleased bloodhound on the trail of aniseed. 'Good old Anderson! Splendid old Anderson! The top of the morning to you, my bright and bounding J. G. But this isn't Phipps. Phipps has stepped out to put ice on his head. He is sick of a fever. This is Potter, old pal. P. with an O., O. with a T., T. with an E., E. with an R. Potter.'

'Potter!' muttered Mr Anderson gratingly, as if the name had hurt him in a sensitive spot. He replaced the receiver and sat back in his chair. His eyes had closed. He seemed to be praying.

Each year when Summer came with flower and bee, turning the thoughts of red-blooded American men to vermilion slacks and parti-coloured sports shorts and those of their wives to one-piece bathing suits, it was the practice of Mr J. G. Anderson, owner of the Hotel Washington in Bessemer, Ohio, to migrate to the State of Maine and devote his trained talents to the conduct of a more recent purchase of his, the Lakeside Inn some five miles distant from the town of Skeewassett. To assist him in his task he had brought with him this season, among others of the home staff, his courteous and popular desk clerk, Cyril ('Barmy') Fotheringay-Phipps, the young man who was out looking for ice to put on an aching head.

A discerning bird, flying over the grounds of the Lakeside Inn and subjecting them to a bird's-eye scrutiny, would have drawn in its breath with a sharp whistle of approval at the sight of them, feeling that in investing his cash in this desirable property Mr Anderson had acted with sturdy good sense. 'His lines are cast in pleasant places,' it would have said to itself. 'Yea, he has a goodly heritage.' The lake, spacious and picturesque, was unquestionably value for money, and in addition there were lawns, trees, flowers, tennis courts, clock-golf courses and a Summer theatre, the whole interspersed with cosy bungalows for the convenience of such guests as might prefer seclusion to the camaraderie of hotel life. One of these last, the bird would have noted with regret, appeared to have burned down recently, for where it should have stood there was now a mere charred scenario still giving out little puffs of smoke.

With the sun shining, the lake glittering, the trees rustling, the flowers blooming their heads off and every room in his establishment occupied at a high rental, it might have been expected that Mr Anderson, though short of a bungalow, would have been gay and carefree, counting his blessings one by one. But as he sat in his office this morning in late August, his brow was dark and his aspect gloomy. Even on his good days he looked a little like something thrown off by Epstein in a particularly sombre mood, and this was not one of his good days. He had had a disturbed night and he could not shake off the depressing thought that he was sharing the same planet with Mervyn Potter and Cyril Fotheringay-Phipps. As far as it is possible for one upright Christian gentleman to dislike the intestines of two other upright Christian gentlemen, J. G. Anderson disliked those of Mervyn Potter and Cyril Fotheringay-Phipps. If you had tried to cheer him up by pointing out that there was only one Mervyn Potter and only one Cyril Fotheringay-Phipps, he would have replied that that was a great deal too many.

A knock on the door broke in on his reverie, one of those cheery, exuberant knocks which are practically bangs. It was followed, even before he could say 'Come in', by the entrance of a figure at the sight of which, had his conscience been less clear, Mr Anderson might have started apprehensively. He blinked and took another look, but still saw what he thought he had seen. His visitor was wearing a policeman's uniform, complete with cap, belt and pistol.

The face beneath the cap was one of singular beauty, lean, keen and finely chiselled, with eyes, slightly bloodshot at the moment, which over a period of years had shaken more women to their foundations than any pair of eyes since those of the late Valentino. For this was Mervyn Potter, the world-famous star of the silver screen, beloved by all except J. G. Anderson. Deserting Hollywood, it being his intention to appear shortly in a play on Broadway, he had been a guest at the Lakeside Inn for the past two weeks, though to Mr Anderson it seemed longer. It was the latter's considered opinion that of all the crazy, irresponsible pests ever sent by an inscrutable Providence to bleach the hair of a respectable hotel proprietor, this finely chiselled mummer was the worst.

A female Mervyn Potter fan, seeing her idol face to face like this, would probably have blown bubbles at the mouth and collapsed in a swoon. At the least, she would have gazed at him with ecstasy. From Mr Anderson's gaze ecstasy was conspicuously absent. His manner was bleak, bordering on the austere. We have mentioned that his night had been disturbed. What had disturbed it had been the entry into his bedroom at about 3 a.m. of this Mervyn Potter and Cyril Fotheringay-Phipps, the desk clerk. They had come, they said, to present him with a slight testimonial of their esteem. Whereupon, after a few graceful words from Mr Potter, who seemed to have constituted himself master of the ceremonies, Cyril Fotheringay-Phipps had pressed into Mr Anderson's hand a large, slimy, wriggling frog.

They had then withdrawn, laughing heartily, like a couple of intoxicated ambassadors who have delivered their credentials to a reigning monarch and are off to get a few more quick ones before the bars close.

It is a very lenient employer of labour who can view with equanimity conduct of this description in a minor member of his staff. Cyril Fotheringay-Phipps was an excellent desk clerk, polite and painstaking and with a good desk-side manner, but a blameless record over the space of two years was not enough to save him from the lightning of Mr Anderson's wrath after goings-on like last night's goings-on. Legal red tape prevented Mr Anderson doing what he would have liked to do – viz. skin Cyril Fotheringay-Phipps with a rusty knife and dip him in boiling oil, but within his limitations he proposed to deal faithfully with him.

Their relationship of hotel proprietor and guest made it impossible for him to do the same in the case of Mervyn Potter, but he could give him a nasty look, and he did so. It was a look that seemed to bring into the office an Edgar Allan Poe-like atmosphere of wailing winds and family curses.

'Good morning,' he said stiffly.

'Good morning, good morning, good morning, good morning,' said Mervyn Potter, taking a chair and one of Mr Anderson's cigarettes and placing in his buttonhole a rose from the vase on Mr Anderson's desk. If there was a sunnier man than this refugee from Hollywood within a radius of fifty miles of the Lakeside Inn, it would have required a long search to find him. 'What a beautiful world it is, is it not? One of the nicest I ever came across. But you are wondering why I am here, no doubt, though delighted, of course, to see me. Well, when we were chatting on the telephone just now – and what a wonderful invention that is, the telephone. Good brains there, I always say when they bring up the subject of Alexander Graham Bell – I suddenly remembered that there was something I wanted to tell you. Not that it was a beautiful world. Something else. Some little secret that I wanted to share with you. So up I came, going hoppity-hoppity-hop.'

A disturbing thought struck Mr Anderson.

'You haven't been sitting at the desk, dressed like that?'

'I have indeed,' said the human sunbeam, blowing a jovial smoke-ring, 'and I was a sensational success. It was pretty to see my public's enthusiasm. I got writer's cramp, signing autographs. This costume is part and parcel of my story. Anderson, my poor old deadbeat, you have had a bereavement. I burned my bungalow down last night.'

The stony expression on Mr Anderson's face became intensified. He might have been something Gutzon Borglum had carved on the side of a mountain. As so often when in Mervyn Potter's society, he was trying to think who it was that he reminded himself of. Then he got it. Job. Job after he had lost his camels and acquired all those boils. Not that Job's sorrows could be compared with those of a man forced to associate with Mervyn Potter.

'So I am informed,' he said curtly.

'Ah, they don't keep things from you? They come running to the boss with their little troubles, do they? Capital, capital. I like this spirit of confidence and frankness.'

'You were smoking in bed, no doubt?'

'That would seem to be a fair inference from the known facts,' assented Mervyn Potter, adjusting the rose in his buttonhole and taking another of Mr Anderson's cigarettes. 'I was also, if I am not gravely mistaken, somewhat pie-eyed. I got engaged to be married yesterday, and you know how it is when the heart is young and the laughing love god doing his stuff. You dance. You sing. You get the party spirit. You reach out for the blushful Hippocrene and celebrate till your eyes bubble. Ah, love, love!' said Mervyn Potter. 'Is there anything like it, J. G. Anderson? But I mustn't take up your time with a lover's rhapsodies. You are all agog to hear about the sinister affair of the burning bungalow. Stripping the thing to its bare essentials and omitting all tedious preliminaries, I awoke from a refreshing sleep to find a hell of a conflagration in progress and myself being hauled out of it by that admirable young man, Cyril Phipps.'

'That what?' said Mr Anderson.

'He had apparently observed the doings from his bedroom window and thought it wise to step across and lend a hand. It was a close call. Now that I have had leisure to reconstruct the scene, I remember waking up and feeling a sort of genial glow and seeing flames leaping hither and thither about the bedchamber, but it didn't occur to me that there was anything I could do about it, and I had just curled up and dozed off again, when in rushed this visiting fireman and extracted me from the sheets like a cork out of a bottle. I was rather annoyed at the time, I recollect, because, unlike the heroine of "I'm to be Queen of the May, Mother", a poem which is no doubt constantly on your lips, I object to being called early. But I can see now that it was most fortunate.'

'Fortunate?' said Mr Anderson.

'Another minute or two, and you would have lost me.'

'Yes,' said Mr Anderson.

Mervyn Potter took another cigarette.

'Although I say it myself,' he proceeded, 'I think I showed up pretty well under these testing conditions. Many men in such a situation, finding themselves in the process of being toasted like a Welsh rarebit, would have lost their heads, but I kept my presence of mind and saved a couple of bottles of whisky. My wardrobe perished in the holocaust, of course. When you're being given the sleeve across the windpipe by Acts of God, you don't waste time fumbling around for socks and trousers. I stood not upon the order of my going, but got out in my pink pyjamas. That is why you see me now in what may appear to you fancy dress. I broke into your Summer theatre and borrowed this costume from one of the dressing-rooms. After which we repaired to Phipps's boudoir and started in on the wassail bowl. There are moments when one needs a drink. Are there moments, indeed, when one doesn't? Well, there you are, Toots,' said Mervyn Potter, rising. 'That's all I came to tell you.'

An animal snarl escaped Mr Anderson. He had remained silent while his visitor was speaking, because the other was a difficult man to interrupt. Seeing an opportunity now of getting a word in edgeways, he seized it.

'Indeed? I thought you might possibly have come to explain your behaviour of last night.'

Mervyn Potter wrinkled his forehead. It was plain that he was at a loss.

'Last night? Behaviour?'

'You have forgotten the incident?' said Mr Anderson, gnashing his teeth slightly. 'To refresh your memory, at three o'clock this morning, accompanied by my desk clerk, you invaded my bedroom and gave me a frog.'

Mervyn Potter's face cleared.

'Of course, yes. It all comes back to me. My dear fellow, we want no thanks. Keep that frog, J. G. Anderson, and make of it a constant companion. I thought Phipps was looking very well, didn't you?'

'I beg your pardon?'

'Last night. Very rosy, he seemed to me. The pure Maine air and your fatherly care have done wonders for him. When I met him in London two years ago, he seemed to me a little peaked. I was over there making a picture and the Drones Club gave me a dinner at which he was in the chair, and of course we fraternized. We got on together like a couple of Warner Brothers. Charming chap. His name's really Fotheringay-Phipps. Did you know? One of those hyphenated things. How did you and he happen to come together, by the way? It's a long long trail from London to Skeewassett, Maine.'

Mr Anderson was feeling far from in the mood to sit chatting with Mervyn Potter about Cyril Fotheringay-Phipps, one of the most nauseous topics it would have been possible to select, and this lent an additional coldness to his manner.

'As you appear interested and seem to have plenty of time on your hands for casual conversation, which I may mention is not the case with me, and . . . er . . .'

'Start again,' advised Mervyn Potter.

Mr Anderson counted ten slowly. His doctor, anxious about his blood pressure, had recommended this stratagem in times of stress. The great thing on these occasions when some pest has cornered you and is making you hot under the collar and all steamed up, his doctor had said, is to be calm . . . calm. Otherwise, he had gone on to explain, you come unstuck at the seams, get apoplexy, and before you can say 'What ho' spin round in a circle and hand in your dinner pail. These medical men express themselves oddly.

'Two years ago,' he said, speaking carefully so that his remarks would be clear and would not have to be repeated, 'I made the acquaintance of Phipps's uncle, Lord Binghampton. Lord Binghampton,' said Mr Anderson, still spacing his words carefully, 'breeds Siamese cats. The annual convention of the American Siamese Cat Breeders Association was taking place in Bessemer that year. Lord Binghampton, being in New York, visiting his father-in-law, decided to attend the convention. He stayed at my hotel.'

'All the other hotels full, eh?' said Mervyn Potter, seeing a possible explanation of this eccentric behaviour.

Mr Anderson counted ten once more, rather more slowly than the first time.

'We became acquainted. He told me that he had a nephew in England for whom he was trying to find occupation, and persuaded me to engage him as a desk clerk,' said Mr Anderson, his face darkening as he thought of the rash act into which he had allowed himself to be cajoled by that silver-tongued Briton. It had resulted, as so many rash acts result, from a good dinner which had left him mellow and co-operative, and he was wondering now how he could ever have become as mellow and co-operative as that, even after a banquet of Lucullus.

Mervyn Potter nodded.

'I see. So that's how it came about. I was surprised to find him here.'

'You won't find him here much longer.' Mr Anderson took up the telephone. 'Give me the desk . . . Phipps? This is Mr Anderson. Come to my office immediately.'

Mervyn Potter shook his head disapprovingly.

'What do you want Phipps for? He can add nothing to my story. Besides, he needs complete repose this morning. He has a headache.'

'I'll make it worse,' said Mr Anderson, grimly replacing the receiver.

For the first time, the sombreness of his companion's demeanour seemed to impress itself on the motion picture star.

'From a certain guarded something in your manner, I gather that Phipps has incurred your displeasure.'

'He has.'

'You feel he was a bit informal last night?'

'I do.'

'You are thinking of firing him?'

'I am.'

Mervyn Potter laughed amusedly.

'There is no terror, J. G. Anderson, in your threats, for Phipps is armed so strong in honesty that they pass by him like the idle wind, which he respects not. Fire him, forsooth! Why, he's probably on his way up here now to spit in your eye and hand in his resignation. He's come into money.'

'What!'

'Some sort of deceased grandfather, if I got the story right. A millionaire, I believe. So you can readily understand why he was feeling a bit above himself last night. He had had the news in the afternoon. And as I had plighted my troth that same afternoon to a girl whom it would be conservative to call a pippin, you can understand why I was feeling a bit above myself. I hope I am not making this too abstruse for you? You have the picture clear? Phipps, on the one hand, in excellent fettle because of his sudden wealth, I, on the other, in excellent fettle because love had found the way. Both in excellent fettle.'

If the bird to which we alluded earlier had happened to seize this moment to perch on Mr Anderson's window-sill and look in, it would have observed a remarkable change for the better taking place in the hotel proprietor's aspect, starting on the cue 'come into money'. His resemblance to an Epstein statue had vanished, leaving him a softer, kindlier J. G. Anderson.

'Well, I'll be darned,' he said, and his voice was virtually a coo, as if he had been a cushat dove in conference with another cushat dove. 'Come into money, has he? Much?'

'Wealth beyond the dreams of avarice, I gathered. That's why he let you have that frog. "See, Potter," said Phipps, ducking under a bush and coming up with the batrachian, if batrachian is the word I want. "A fine frog. Come in useful, this will." "You are going to keep it?" I said. "Of course I am going to keep it," he replied, adding that he proposed to teach it a few simple tricks and get it dates on television. Well, I talked him out of that. "What do you need with performing frogs, Phipps?" I said. "You are rich. Be broad, be generous. Share the wealth. Many a poor man would be glad of this frog. Give of your plenty, Phipps," I said. And after a certain amount of argument he saw my point and, your name happening to come up, he consented to hand it over to you. He said you were a priceless old stinker who in a less tolerant community would years ago have been shot at sunrise, but that your need was greater than his. I thought it showed a nice spirit in the lad. And now I really must be tearing myself away. I have to go to Skeewassett to replenish my wardrobe. Did I mention,' said Mervyn Potter, rising from the desk on which he had been sitting, 'that this was a beautiful world? I did? Then I have nothing more to add. A very hearty good morning to you, J. G. Anderson.'

2

FOR some moments after his visitor had left him, Mr Anderson sat musing. And though he was musing on Cyril Fotheringay-Phipps, he experienced none of that shrinking horror which had distressed him when musing on Cyril Fotheringay-Phipps before, causing him to feel, as he examined Cyril Fotheringay-Phipps's soul, as if he were peering into some black abyss with hissing snakes at the bottom of it. The thought had floated into his mind like drifting thistledown that, given a little service and co-operation, here was his chance of severing his connection with the Hotel Washington and the town of Bessemer, Ohio.

Towns like Bessemer, Ohio, are all right, if you like towns like Bessemer, Ohio, but they have this defect, that in the winter months they tend to get a bit chilly, and Mr Anderson, as the years went by and his blood grew thinner, had come more and more to feel how agreeable a move to a warmer climate would be. If he could get the Washington off his hands, he could buy some nice little hotel in Florida for the winter . . . what pleasanter life could a man who suffered from chilblains have? And who more suitable to take the Washington off his hands than an ambitious young desk clerk who had just inherited a vast fortune? For the first time that morning Mr Anderson found himself seeing eye to eye with Mervyn Potter and agreeing with him that this was a beautiful world. Mervyn Potter, in his opinion, had in no way exaggerated its charms.

He had fallen into a roseate daydream and was within an ace of humming a gay tune when, as had happened previously, his reverie was broken by a knock on the door, but this time a meek, deprecating knock like the apologetic scratching noise which a dog makes when returning to the old home after having been out all night hunting. Cyril Fotheringay-Phipps sidled in, giving at the knees a little as he always did when entering the presence of the big chief. Wealth beyond the dreams of avarice might have come to Cyril Phipps, but J. G. Anderson still scared the daylights out of him.

Cyril Phipps was tall and willowy, a young Englishman of the type so common in the Drones Club, Dover Street, London, an institution of which, though it was now two years since he had enrolled himself under Mr Anderson's banner, he remained a member in good standing.

His disposition was intensely amiable, his hair the colour of creamery butter and his face one of those open, engaging faces which arouse the maternal instinct in women but, for these things cut both ways, incline male employers whose livers sometimes trouble them of a morning to be brusque and irascible. On days when he was not feeling quite himself, J. G. Anderson found the sight of that mild, deferential face infuriating and was apt to touch on the fact in his conversation.

On his good mornings he was able to console himself with the reflection that this desk clerk of his, though handicapped, in his opinion, by an I.Q. somewhat lower than that of a backward clam – a clam, let us say, which had been dropped on its head when a baby – was at any rate ornamental.

This Cyril Phipps unquestionably was, and as for the slur on his intelligence, he would have been the first to agree that he had never been one of those brainy birds whose heads bulge out at the back. Some birds bulged and some birds didn't, you had to face it, he would have said, and he was one of the birds who didn't. At Eton everyone had called him Barmy. At Oxford everyone had called him Barmy. And even in the Drones Club, a place where the level of intellect is not high, it was as Barmy that he was habitually addressed. And when you looked at him, you felt how right and inevitable this was. The *mot juste*, you said to yourself.

It was not easy for Mr Anderson to smile sunnily, but he forced his unaccustomed lips into something as nearly resembling a sunny smile as he could manage. It started to slide away as he recalled that this was the young man who had alluded to him as a priceless old stinker, but he grabbed it and put it back again. He was resolved to scatter sweetness and light, if it choked him.

'Come in, Phipps, come in,' he cried effusively. 'I hear you have a headache this morning. Too bad, too bad. You must take the day off. Sit down, Phipps, sit down. I want to have a little talk with you, my dear fellow.'

Barmy sat down. It is doubtful if his legs would have supported him much longer. This effervescent cordiality, so different from what he had been expecting, had unmanned him. Thinking shudderingly of last night's dark doings, he had anticipated from the man up top something rather outstanding in the way of pique at their next meeting. He had not actually been present at the testing of the atom bomb at Bikini, but he had read about it, and something along these lines was what he had been envisaging in his mind's eye.

For consider the facts. After two years of unremitting respectfulness, two years of 'Yes, Mr Anderson', 'Right ho, Mr Anderson', 'Absolutely, Mr Anderson' and 'Oh, rather, Mr Anderson', he had so lapsed from his high standard of obsequious correctness as not only to break in on the other's sacred slumbers but actually to load him up with frogs, a reptile of which he had no reason to suppose that his overlord was fond. 'How art thou fallen from heaven, O Lucifer, son of the morning?' he had pictured Mr Anderson saying. Among other things.

And now this breath-taking geniality. It was enough to remove the stuffing from a stronger man than Cyril Phipps.

'Cigarette, my boy?' said Mr Anderson after a brief interval of silence, during which he was regretting that the latter's extraordinary wealth made it impossible for him to hurl at Barmy's head the silver presentation inkpot on his desk, to teach him not to let his lower jaw droop like that.

'Oh, thanks, right ho, thanks,' said Barmy, accepting the peace pipe. His was one of those simple natures which respond readily to kindness, and he was beginning to feel at his ease again. He stopped fiddling with his Drones Club tie, his habit when perturbed, and prepared to be chatty. He saw now that he had been mistaken in supposing that his employer had sent for him in order to disembowel him with his bare hands. The way the interview was shaping, it looked more as though Mr Anderson, feeling a little lonely, as we all do at times, and longing for somebody to pep him up, had said to himself, after running through the roster of his acquaintances, 'Phipps! That's the chap! Always merry and bright, always a fountain of entertaining small talk, I'll have Phipps up and get a laugh or two. Say what you will, there's nobody like good old Phipps.'

'A drink?' said Mr Anderson, still coming through strongly with the sweetness and light.

Barmy shuddered a little.

'No, thanks frightfully,' he said. A young man with a weakish head cannot revel in the grand Hollywood manner with someone like Mervyn Potter without feeling the effects next day, and he would have preferred not to have the word 'drink' mentioned in his presence. True, whoever it was who had been driving white-hot spikes into his skull had momentarily desisted from his activities, but he had still a long way to go before he could think of alcoholic refreshment without wincing.

'Then let's get down to it,' said Mr Anderson, who did not believe in beating about bushes. 'Potter tells me you've come into money.'

'Yes, sir.'

'A great deal of money.'

'Yes, sir. My grandfather on the mother's side. He ceased to tick over last Wednesday.'

'Too bad.'

'Yes, sir.'

'Still, all flesh is grass.'

'Yes, sir.'

'We're here today and gone tomorrow, as the fellow said. Was your grandfather American?'

'Yes, sir. Oh, rather. Specifically American. His name was P. Middlemass Poskitt, and after – or while – making the dickens of a packet selling cut-out paper patterns, though why there should be any money in that is more than I can tell you, he took time off to have issue – two daughters, Emerald and Ruby. Emerald married my Uncle Theodore, a thing I wouldn't have done myself on a bet, he being a sort of human snapping turtle, well known throughout England as the Curse of the Eastern Counties.'

'That would be the Lord Binghampton I know?'

'That's right. I'd forgotten he was a pal of yours. Charming chap, I expect, when relaxing with the boys. I never saw that side of him. To me, from early childhood, he was always like one of those Human Fiends you get in the mystery stories. He could have stepped straight into an Edgar Wallace novel, and no questions asked.'

'Maybe his bark was worse than his bite.'

'Very possibly, though I cannot make any authoritative pronouncement, the old relative never having actually bitten me. I don't say he hasn't come close to it on occasion, but so far I have always escaped unscathed. But I was telling you something, wasn't I?'

'You were saying that your grandfather had two daughters.'

'Ah, yes. Well, the other one, Ruby, married my father and had issue one son. In a nutshell, me. You know, it's a rummy thing,' said Barmy, who had recovered all his native chattiness and was looking on J. G. Anderson by this time as quite an old friend, 'I had never for a moment expected to click. I hadn't so much as set eyes on this grandfather since I was a kid of fourteen in knickerbockers and pimples, and he gave no sign of being aware of my existence. I doubt if a bookie would have chalked me up on the slate as anything better than a thirty-to-one shot. It just shows you, doesn't it? Makes you think a bit, what?'

Mr Anderson was wishing that his young guest would stop talking and give him an opportunity of getting down to business, but these big-moneyed men have to be humoured, so he agreed that it made you think a bit.

'And I'll tell you another rummy thing,' said Barmy, now the life and soul of the party. 'Do you believe in what-d'you-call-its?'

'Eh?'

'Fortune-tellers.'

'Oh, fortune-tellers? No, I do not.'

'Then you're a chump of the first water, my dear old hotel proprietor, if you'll excuse me saying so. They're amazing birds. Just before I left England, I got lugged into attending a charity bazaar down Wimbledon way, and there was a fortune-teller there, operating in a tent, and as my shoes were a bit tight and the only prospect of taking the weight off my feet seemed to be to go and get five bobs' worth of this Gypsy Sybil, as she called herself, I filtered into the tent, and there she was, ensconced at a table with a crystal ball in front of her. I sank into the customers' chair, glad to rest the old dogs, and she scooped in my five bob, spat on her hands and snapped into action. Are you listening to any of this?'

Mr Anderson said he was all ears, which, as a matter of fact, was very nearly true.

'Well, I won't be long. I'm coming to the nub. This Gypsy Sybil, having peered into the crystal ball, told me I had a rare spiritual nature and great personal charm, though people meeting me for the first time were apt not to appreciate me to the full because I had such deep reserves and hidden depths. She then touched on the future, and this is where I got my full five bobs' worth. She said I was about to take a long journey and was going to meet a fair girl and have a spot of trouble from a dark man and – mark this – I was going to get pots of money. Well, I've taken the long journey and I've got the pots of money, so now what ho for the fair girl, what?'

Mr Anderson, with a strong effort of the will, forced himself to say, 'Exactly.'

'I'm not worrying so much about the dark man, though I suppose dark men can make themselves pretty unpleasant if you stir them up, but I do want to meet that fair girl. Nothing was actually stated in set terms, but the Gypsy Sybil rather hinted that she would be all over me. Fling herself into my arms and say "My mate!", and all that sort of thing. Well, nothing could fit in better with my plans, for if there's one thing one wants, it's fair girls flinging themselves into your arms and saying "My mate!". Or don't you think so?'

Mr Anderson, who would have called the police if a fair girl had made a single step in his direction, said he certainly did, and, taking advantage of the fact that his young friend had fallen into a reverie and was gazing into space in a starry-eyed manner, changed the subject and turned the conversation to business.

'Tell me,' he said. 'What are you planning to do with all this money of yours?'

Barmy came to himself with a start. He gently removed the fair girl, who had been sitting on his lap, curling his hair with her fingers.

'Eh? My money? Oh, you mean my money. What am I going to do with it? Well, really, dash it, I don't quite know.'

'I do,' said Mr Anderson jovially. 'You're going to buy the Washington.

'The Washington?' he said. His mind was not at its nimblest this morning.

'That's right.'

'The Washington Hotel?'

For an instant it seemed as though Mr Anderson were about to forget sweetness and light and say that he had not been alluding to the Washington Monument, you mutton-headed half-wit, and go on to speak forcefully of dumb bricks with about as much quickness in the uptake as a frog. And talking of frogs . . .

The weakness passed. He reassembled the sunny smile, fastening it painfully on his face once more as if with pins.

'The Washington Hotel. You've been working there long enough to know it's a gold mine. Most people would say I was a fool to let it go, but here's how it is. I want to spend my winters down South, and I'm planning to buy a hotel in Florida. Palm Beach or Miami or wherever it may be. Before I can do that, I've got to get rid of the Washington, and there's no one I'd rather have it than you. Young fellow I've trained myself. Now naturally,' said Mr Anderson, observing that the party of the second part was still looking like a ventriloquist's dummy and realizing that something in the nature of an interval would have to elapse before his mind, using that word loosely, would be able to absorb the salient points of the scheme, 'I don't expect you to decide a thing like this offhand. Go away and think it over, and then come back and we'll have another talk.'

3

AS Barmy left the presence and made for the open air, his mind was in a whirl and there was a fever in his blood. Mr Anderson's proposition had enlarged his horizon and opened up new vistas before him. For the first time since he had received the lawyer's letter informing him of his novel affluence, he was feeling the surge of power which great riches bring with them.

Until now, though his headache had been too painful to allow him to give much thought to it, he had supposed that all you could do with any money that came your way was to bung it into safe income-bearing securities and return to position one, continuing as before to sit behind a desk and give patrons their keys and letters. He had long realized that he was not a man of exceptional gifts, being rather one of the multitude who are dashed lucky to land a job of any kind and priceless asses if they do not stick to that job like glue. Fate had made him a desk clerk, and a desk clerk he must continue to be.

But this, Mr Anderson had made him see, was a tame policy, unworthy of a man of enterprise. By making that amazing proposal, J. G. Anderson had removed the scales from his eyes, and with this clearer vision had come ambition and the desire to escape from the humdrum round and live the larger life, like Mervyn Potter. Barmy had not seen very much of Mervyn Potter since that first meeting in London, but he had seen enough to be convinced that when it came to leading the larger life, he had few equals.

It was as he came out on to the gravel sweep outside the main entrance to the hotel that he heard his name called and, looking up, saw Mervyn Potter. The motion picture star was seated at the wheel of his car, distributing a few autographs to members of his public.

'Hello, there,' he said, as Barmy came up. 'How's the head?'

'Eh? Oh, much better, thanks. Agony considerably abated.'

'I am rejoiced to hear it. But the mere absence of a headache is not enough to account for the rapt expression that was on your face as you emerged from the hotel. You looked like the Soul's Awakening. Why were you going around with rapt expressions on your face, Phipps, old friend?'

'I was doing a spot of thinking.'

'About what?'

Barmy was only too happy to confide in this knowledgeable man. The one thing he had been subconsciously longing for was a sympathetic adviser in whose judgment he could trust. He was not aware that America was full of broken men who had asked Mervyn Potter for advice and taken it. He poured forth the story of J. G. Anderson's proposal, and Mervyn Potter simply sneered at the idea of buying the Hotel Washington of Bessemer, Ohio.

'Buy his hotel?' said Mervyn Potter.

'That's what he suggested.'

'You don't want to buy any ruddy hotels.'

'Don't I?'

'Certainly not. It would be madness. Just chucking your money away. Men who own hotels always wind up in the bread line with holes in their socks. It's the overheads that does them in. The most bottomless purse cannot stand the constant drain of having to buy fresh supplies of soap and new towels, to replace those taken away by guests in their suitcases. You would be astounded, Phipps, if I told you how much soap and how many towels are pinched annually from hotels. I myself have pinched soap and towels from practically every hotel from the rockbound coast of Massachusetts to the alligator-haunted Everglades of Florida, and I am not one of the really big operators. No, no, we must think of something better than a hotel. I don't want to be strolling through the Bowery some night and see a ragged form asleep in the gutter and recognize it with a visible start as that of my old friend Phipps. I'll tell you what I'd do, if I were as rich as you.'

This surprised Barmy.

'Aren't you?'

'Of course I'm not. We Hollywood hams are not rich men, Phipps. We think we are for a few happy moments when we are counting the contents of the envelope on pay day, and then we feel a tap on our shoulder; there, standing beside us waiting to twist our arm, is a gentleman with whiskers who takes it all off us, skinning us to the bone.'

'Taxes, you mean?'

Mervyn Potter winced.

'Don't mention that word, Phipps. Without wishing to wound, you have touched an exposed nerve. Yes, taxes, if you must have it.'

'I suppose they're pretty big.'

'Supercolossal. And then there are all the incidental expenses of life in the golden West. Polo ponies, yachts, swimming pools, wives . . . it all mounts up. I have been forced to abandon Hollywood for the time being in order to make my economies. In New York, with its comparative absence of temptations to extravagance, I may be able to put by a little nest egg. I am appearing shortly in a play on Broadway.'

'Yes, somebody told me that. It's bound to be a success.'

'Naturally.'

'I mean to say, you have a terrific following, haven't you?'

'Enormous. And practically all women. The ladies love me, Phipps, and who are we to blame them, poor saps?'

'I suppose that's what counts in the theatre?'

'It's the only thing that counts. Get the women, and it's in the bag. There won't be an empty seat in the house or a dry eye or any of the usual things. Which brings me back to what I was about to say just now. It's obvious what you must do with your wealth. You must put it into this play of mine. I like you, Phipps, and I want to see you doubling – nay, trebling – your vast fortune, so that in the years to come, when my hair is grey and the profile marred by a couple of extra chins, I shall be able to touch you for the means of livelihood. Lehmac Productions, Incorporated, are running the venture, if you can call such a cast-iron certainty a venture, and I am sure Lehman would be delighted to sell you a slice. Go to New York and see him. You'll like being a manager. Nothing to it but sit back and watch the other fellows work and draw your handsome profits. The ideal life, if you ask me. So trot along and tell Anderson the deal is off, because you have decided to invest your millions in the drama. And now,' said Mervyn Potter, 'I must leave you. I am going to Skeewassett to purchase as much of a gent's nobby outfit as I can find there. Good-bye, Phipps. We shall meet at Philippi. My fiancée and I are flying to New York after lunch, for rehearsals have already begun, and my place is by their side. By the time I see you again, I shall expect to find you a full-blown manager. I shall have to touch my hat to you and call you Sir.'

And having signed a few more autographs for a few more members of his public who had happened to wander by, Mervyn Potter drove off, waving a cheery hand.

For some moments after he had disappeared, Barmy stood motionless on the gravel, weighing pros and cons. Like Mr Anderson, Mervyn Potter had enlarged his horizon and opened up new vistas, and he had unquestionably been conscious during the motion picture star's harangue of a quick upsurge of the spirit of adventure. But gradually this began to ebb.

After all, he reasoned, the Washington was his home. It was a safe haven, and would he not be rash in the last degree to leave it for uncharted seas? He decided that he would. As he made his way to Mr Anderson's office, he was once more feeling strongly in favour of closing with his employer's offer. Mervyn Potter's gloomy estimate of the hotel business had shaken him for a while, but now Reason was returning to its throne.

Mervyn Potter, it seemed to him, had got his facts twisted. Barmy had been working for J. G. Anderson long enough to know that he was an extremely prosperous old gentleman. Even allowing for losses on soap and towels, it was obvious to one who had held the post as desk clerk in his caravanserai for two years that J. G. Anderson found the pickings good. He ate expensively, dressed expensively, bought expensive automobiles and smoked dollar cigars. There was no room for question that the man was on velvet and that anyone who succeeded him as owner of the Hotel Washington would be on velvet, too.

Mr Anderson was smoking a dollar cigar as Barmy entered the office. He looked up, beaming with all the old chumminess.

'Ah, Phipps. Back again?'

'Yes, sir.'

'Feeling better?'

'Yes, sir.'

'Good. Well, you've caught me just in time, my boy. I have to go to Skeewassett to see my lawyer. But I'll be able to give you a few figures before I start. These are for the year ending December thirty-first last,' said Mr Anderson, and began to spout them like a geyser.

To Barmy they conveyed precisely nothing, but from the way his employer rolled them round his tongue as if they were vintage port he divined that they must be pretty hot, and his last doubts vanished. When Mr Anderson, pausing and lowering the paper from which he was reading, said 'Well?' it was without hesitation that he replied 'Oh, rather. Absolutely.'

'Pretty good?' said Mr Anderson.

'Dashed good,' said Barmy.

'You want to buy the Washington?'

'Oh, definitely.'

'Then here's my proposition. You can have it for a hundred thousand.'

There came over Barmy that sensation of having been suddenly slapped in the face with a wet towel which is so unpleasant. He also felt as if he had been kicked in the stomach by a more than usually sinewy army mule. He gasped, gurgled, tottered and stood fingering his Drones Club tie.

'A hundred thousand?'

'A hundred thousand.'

'But I say, dash it, I haven't got a hundred thousand.'

'How much have you got?'

'Twenty-two thousand, eighteen cents.'

Mr Anderson quivered in every limb. He ceased to beam. The love feast was over. The look which he was now directing at his desk clerk was one of those hard, reproachful looks which hotel proprietors anxious to unload a portion of their holdings direct at desk clerks who have led them on, played the fool with them, wasted their time and raised their hopes only to dash them to the ground. Not even when accepting that frog at his hands at three o'clock in the morning had J. G. Anderson felt so keen a distaste for his young subordinate.

'Twenty-two thousand?' he said hoarsely.

'And eighteen cents. You see,' explained Barmy, 'my Uncle Theodore of course copped the jackpot. Most of the stuff in the old oak chest went to him. After all, he was the old boy's son-in-law and had always clustered round him pretty assiduously, paying annual visits to New York to slap him on the back and say "What ho", whereas I—'

Mr Anderson had been counting slowly.

'Ten!' he said, having arrived at that figure. Then, speaking with a curious mildness, 'Phipps,' he said.

'Hullo?'

'You busy?'

'Oh no, rather not.'

'Then I wish you would do something for me.'

With a quick gesture, Mr Anderson directed Barmy's attention to the open window. It afforded an excellent view of Lake Skeewassett.

'It won't take you long. You see that lake?'

Barmy said he saw that lake.

'Well, I want you to get a boat and go out on that lake. Row out about two hundred yards from the shore. The water is deep there?'

'Oh, rather. Very deep.'

'Good. Then row out about two hundred yards from the shore, and when you're there tie something heavy around your damned neck and jump in and drown yourself. Good morning,' said Mr Anderson, and left the room. He was already late for his appointment with his lawyer.

Barmy drew himself up. A mild young man normally, there had been something in Mr Anderson's words – his tone, possibly – which had offended him. When the other suddenly reappeared in the doorway, his eyes did not actually flash, for they were the sort of eyes which do not flash readily, but his manner was cold.

'Something I forgot to say,' said Mr Anderson. 'You're fired. If I see you here again, I'll kill you, if I have to do it with a corkscrew.'

Barmy laughed raspingly. A strange light had come into his eyes. His mind was made up. He had decided to follow Mervyn Potter's admirable advice and do the drama a bit of good. He wondered how he could ever have been attracted by the silly idea of becoming a hotel proprietor when this other glittering path lay open before him.

'I am, am I?' he said. 'Fired, eh? Well, it may interest you to learn, you blighted old object, that if you hadn't buzzed off like a scalded cat, I was just about to tender my resignation as of even date. If you want to know what I'm going to do—'

'I don't.'

'I'm going to be a manager.'

'Hotel manager?'

'Theatrical manager. I'm going into show business.'

'God help it!' said Mr Anderson, and disappeared again, this time permanently.

4

IT was on a Monday that this painful scene had taken place, and Barmy, feeling correctly that there was nothing to keep him, left Skeewassett by the evening train, arriving in New York on the Tuesday morning in time for a lateish breakfast at the hotel off Madison Avenue which had been his first home when he had come to America two years ago.

The journey, like all American train journeys, had been bumpy, leaving him limp and jaded, and it was not until he had slept through the afternoon and taken a refreshing shower that he felt equal to sauntering out and seeing the sights.

When he did so, one of the first sights he saw was Mervyn Potter. The motion picture star was standing at the corner of Madison Avenue and 65th Street giving his autograph to a small girl in pigtails.

'Ah, Phipps,' he said cordially, as Barmy approached. 'You do pop up, don't you? I believe I mentioned to you in the course of a recent conversation that this was a beautiful world. What makes it so beautiful is that there is never any shortage of Phippses. Wherever you go – north, south, east or west – there you find Cyril Fotheringay-Phipps. I will be with you in a moment.'

He finished inscribing his name in the grubby album, and the small child toddled away into the unknown. Mervyn Potter passed a weary hand over his forehead.

'One's public, Phipps, one's public!' he sighed. 'A great strain, this continual coping with the incessant homage of the fans. Not that I mind my own fans so much. The human rats into whose malted milk shakes I feel an urge to slip a shot of some little-known Asiatic poison are the ones who ask me for my autograph under the mistaken impression that I am Gregory Peck. I believe genuine Gregory Pecks sell for forty cents on the black market, while I fetch only a quarter, and I resent the way the young reptiles gulp with ill-concealed chagrin when they see what they've got. But let us change a distasteful subject. So here you are in New York. Ah, New York, New York! The centre of the universe. I used to be the brightest jewel in its crown before I went to Hollywood, and I hope to resume that position when this play is running in a blaze of glory.'

'I suppose you've been rehearsing?'

'All day. Another great strain. Rehearsals are dull work.'

'Pretty ghastly, I imagine.'

'Tedious to a degree. One has to be constantly on the alert to find ways of alleviating the monotony. I think, however, that I begin to see daylight. There was a fat gentleman there today who slept soundly all through my big scenes. Tomorrow, if he is there again and repeats his act, I shall give him a hot foot.'

'What's that?'

Mervyn Potter was amazed.

'You mean you have been in America two years and don't know what a hot foot is? Why, over here children learn to give the hot foot in kindergarten. It is the first thing they are taught. You take a simple match, you look about you till you see some friend or acquaintance whose attention has been diverted elsewhere, you insert the match between the sock and the side of the shoe, light it and let Nature take its course. As simple as that. We should have tried it on J. G. Anderson. How did you leave dear old J. G., by the way? Did he hit the ceiling when you told him you were not going to buy his termite-ridden hotel?'

'He did seem a bit stirred.'

'I'll bet he was as mad as a wet hen. And you know how mad hens are, when wet. Have you got in touch with Lehman yet?'

'I thought of ringing him up tomorrow.'

'And tonight? What are your plans for tonight?'

'I don't think I have any.'

'Excellent. Perhaps you would come and have a bite of dinner with me?'

'I'd love it.'

'My fiancée is going to a dance or some such rout or revel out at King's Point, Long Island, where she resides, and your jolly society is just what I need to cheer me up. We'll go to some quiet restaurant. Look me up around eight at the Renfrew on East Sixty-Sixth Street, where I have taken a modest apartment. Don't dress. Oh, Phipps?'

'Hullo?'

'Have you had my autograph? No. It is a thing no young man starting life ought to be without. Here you are. Wear it next your heart or sell it for a quarter, whichever course appeals to you. Au revoir, then, Phipps. At the Renfrew as the clocks are striking eight,' said Mervyn Potter. 'Give three quick rings and whistle the first few bars of "The Star-Spangled Banner".'

He passed on with a benevolent nod, and Barmy resumed his walk, puffing happily at the cigar which he had bought at the hotel counter and enjoying the coolness which had crept into the air with the approach of evening. He looked forward with bright anticipation to tomorrow's interview with Mr Lehman of Lehmac Productions.

He was not quite sure at what hour theatrical managers liked to be called up and asked for an appointment, and wished that he had consulted Mervyn Potter on this point, but, allowing Mr Lehman a reasonable time for lunch, he supposed that somewhere in the neighbourhood of two-thirty would be about it.

He also looked forward to tonight's dinner with Mervyn Potter, always such excellent company. If a passing thought of dangers of hobnobbing with that eccentric character flitted into his mind, he dismissed it. Even Mervyn Potter, he reflected, could scarcely introduce any novel variations into a quiet restaurant dinner. He had yet to realize that there was no social function into which the other could not introduce novel variations.

It was at this point in his saunter, just as he was thinking what a capital fellow Mervyn Potter was and what a capital fellow Mr Lehman would doubtless prove to be, that he beheld something which brought him up with a round turn, the cigar frozen on his lips, his impressionable soul seething like a cistern struck by a thunderbolt.

'Oof!' he said, tottering.

What his eye had rested on was the back view of a girl in some sort of beige upholstery, who was standing looking into a shop window, and it was a back view which seemed to speak to his very depths. Back views, of course, are not everything, and he was aware that the prudent man reserves judgment until that crucial point in the proceedings when the subject turns round, nevertheless he stood stunned and goggling. He had that feeling, which comes to all of us at times, that a high spot in his life had been reached and that he was about to undergo some great spiritual experience.

With a vague thought that at a sacred moment like this a man with any claim to the finer feelings ought not to be puffing a great, fat, smelly cigar, he hurled the remains of his from him with a passionate sweep of the hand, and having done so, stood petrified.

'Oh, my sainted aunt!' he ejaculated.

The girl, absorbed, did not hear the observation. She had come all the way from Broadway to gaze at this shop window, and she was not to be distracted by the mere mention of somebody's aunt, sainted or otherwise. She continued to press her nose against the glass.

Eileen ('Dinty') Moore was one of those girls of the fifty-to-sixty-dollars-a-week class who do most of their big shopping through windows. On fine evenings, when her day's work was done, it was her practice to walk across town and indulge in an emotional orgy among the Madison Avenue shops. The emporium in front of which she was standing now was that of Noreen O'Hara, who sells hats. And she was staring wistfully at a superb specimen which looked like a fruit salad, wishing that she could afford a spectacular number like that in place of her own modest lid, when a finger touched her arm, a voice said,

'I say' and, turning, she saw that what had come into her life was a willowy young man with hair the colour of creamery butter and an open, engaging face.

'I say,' he said.

'Yes?' said Dinty.

She spoke with a certain cold austerity, and a hard glaze had formed itself over her attractive eyes. She disliked wolves, and though this young man did not look like one, she had been earning her living in New York long enough to know that many wolves, and not the least predatory of them, go about in sheep's clothing, deceiving the eye with open, engaging faces.

Her voice, accordingly, was chilly and packed with menace, and the chill and the menace would have been more noticeable than they were, but for the fact that Barmy's open, engaging face had aroused the maternal instinct in her. It has been mentioned that this was frequently the effect it had on women. Even while eyeing him with the same hard intentness with which Jack Dempsey used to regard his opponents in the ring, she was conscious of a strong impulse to stroke his head.

Had she done so, it would have been all right with Barmy. Seeing her steadily and seeing her whole, he felt no slackening-off of the turmoil in the depths of his being. It had, indeed, risen to a new high. For, sensational though the back view had been, the front view topped it. In spades. A single rapid glance had been enough to tell Barmy that of all the girls he had ever set eyes on this was the Girl Supreme. He had never fallen in love at first sight with such wholeheartedness before, not even on the occasion, three years ago, when he had come into the grocer's shop at Bridmouth-on-Sea with Catsmeat Potter-Pirbright and seen Angelica Briscoe of the Vicarage, Maiden Eggesford, buying five ounces of streaky bacon.

The warmth of his emotion would have surprised many of Dinty's circle, her employer for one. If you had asked him for a word portrait of his secretary, he would have told you that there was nothing very special about her. Just an ordinary kid, he would have said, fairly pretty, blue eyes, fair hair, much the same as all the other kids you saw around, nothing much about her one way or the other. But to Barmy she seemed like some ethereal spirit possessed of everything that it takes. Gazing at her, he marvelled that there could ever have been a time when he had supposed Angelica Briscoe, of the Vicarage, Maiden Eggesford, to be what the doctor had ordered. This girl, it seemed to him, began where Angelica Briscoe left off. He took off his hat to the Gypsy Sybil. This, he felt, was a fair girl to end all fair girls.

If there was any possible criticism that he could have made of her façade, it would have been that he could have done with a shade less stoniness in the eyes. But even though stony, they dazzled him.

He was fascinated by the way her nose turned up at the tip, and if ever a mouth like hers had been issued to any other girl, the fact had not been drawn to his attention.

It was a mouth, indeed, capable of smiling delightfully and with a friendly warmth, but at the moment the lips were set in a hard, straight line, and they scarcely parted as she put her question once more.

'Yes?' said Dinty. 'And what can I do for you, brother? Do you want to sell me the Brooklyn Bridge?'

Barmy saw that there had been a misapprehension. He did not own the Brooklyn Bridge. He mentioned this.

'No?' said Dinty. 'What do you own . . . besides a lot of nerve?'

A sudden uncomfortable thought struck Barmy. He was not exceptionally intuitive, but he could reason and deduce.

'I say, you aren't shirty because I spoke to you?'

'A little displeased.'

'Oh, my aunt, I'm frightfully sorry. I wouldn't have done it, but a rather serious situation has arisen and I thought I ought to clarify it.'

'Start clarifying.'

Barmy marshalled his thoughts, as well as his emotion would let him.

'Well, it's this way – I'm staying at a hotel round the corner—'

'Nice place?'

'Oh, rather.'

'Comfortable there?'

'Oh, rather.'

'Good. It makes me very happy to know that. Yes? You were saying?'

'Well, I was coming out for a stroll, and I bought a cigar at the hotel counter—'

'Good cigar?'

'Oh, very.'

'Fine. Proceed. When do we get the big situation?'

'I'm just coming to it. You see, I was smoking this cigar, and I chucked it away with a careless gesture—'

'Like the fellow who shot an arrow into the air. Did you ever meet him? It fell to earth, he knew not where.'

'It did, eh? Yes, one can see how that might be so. But between that arrow and my cigar there is a substantial difference, because my cigar didn't fall to earth, not by a jugful. It fell on your hat.'

He had arrested her attention. His story had gripped her.

'My hat!'

'That's right. And I have a growing suspicion that it's on fire.'

'You mean that at any moment I may be going up in flames?'

'I wouldn't be surprised.'

'Why couldn't you have told me that at once?'

'I was sort of leading up to it.'

'You needn't have tried to break it gently. Girls like to know these things. Have a look,' said Dinty, bending down.

Barmy removed the cigar, flung it aside, hit a passing pedestrian, said 'Oh, sorry' and issued his bulletin.

'Well, you seem to have stopped smouldering—'

'That's good.'

'—but I'm afraid the old lid isn't what it used to be. Pretty much of a devastated area, I fear.' His eye fell on Noreen O'Hara's shop window, and inspiration came to him. 'I say, you must let me buy you another.'

'Oh, no, that's all right. Don't bother.'

'What do you mean, don't bother? I can't go about the place ruining people's hats and not replacing them. I'll buy you a dozen, if you like.'

'Who are you? The Great Gatsby?'

'Gatsby? No. My name's—'

'I mean, are you a millionaire?'

'Well, I've got quite a bit of the stuff. My grandfather on the mother's side conked out recently, respected by all, and left me a considerable packet.'

'I see. Well, in that case, all right, and thanks a lot. But a cheap one.'

'Cheap be blowed,' said Barmy. 'The best the place can supply.'

He escorted her masterfully into Noreen O'Hara's.

Noreen O'Hara proved a willing and sympathetic collaborator. Barmy's statement that the lady required a hat brought her up on her toes in an instant, and when he added that in the matter of price the sky might be regarded as the limit, it seemed to arouse all that was best in her. She bustled about, exhibiting specimen after specimen, but it was the one that looked like a fruit salad that received Dinty's vote. She came out with it poised on her head, and Barmy quivered to the soles of his suede shoes as he gazed at it. He had not supposed that it would have been possible to enhance her radiant beauty, but the fruit salad did it by as much as twenty per cent.

'Well, thank you again ever so much,' she said. 'If you knew how I hated that old hat of mine, and I thought I would have to make it last for ever. Gosh, I feel like the girl who got a fur coat by standing outside Bergdorf Goodman's and saying "Brrrrh!" Not my own, but I'm glad it went so well,' said Dinty, observing that her companion was chuckling with some heartiness.

Barmy explained the cause of his mirth.

'I was just laughing because of a rather odd coincidence. It suddenly occurred to me that this is the second time in two days that I've got mixed up in a fire.'

'That tickled you?'

'It did a bit.'

'You must be as easily amused as a studio audience. What happened the other time?'

'I rescued a chap from a burning bungalow. Snatched him from the flames, as you might say.'

'And now you've snatched me from the flames. You want to watch yourself. You're getting into a rut. Well, I'll have to be moving along.'

'Oh, I say, must you?'

'I've got a date miles away uptown.'

'Oh, dash it. All right, I'll hail you a cab.'

'You millionaires! I don't take cabs. I take buses.'

She leaped lightly into the one which had just pulled up at the kerb and, as it moved away, Barmy stood gaping after it, his lower jaw drooping in the manner which had so often aroused the fiend that slept in J. G. Anderson. It had just occurred to him that, having met his fair girl, precisely as predicted by the Gypsy Sybil, he had omitted to inform himself of her name, address and telephone number. And now she was gone, gone like the wind, and he would never see her again. They were ships that pass in the night, he was thinking. Just a couple of ruddy ships that pass in the bally night.

Madison Avenue swam before his eyes. He had never seen a more flickering thoroughfare.

5

IT was a sombre, Byronic Barmy, a Barmy with a heart bowed down with weight of woe and a soul with blisters on it, who at eight o'clock that night presented himself at the door of Mervyn Potter's apartment. The more he brooded on the afternoon's happenings, the more he found himself resenting Fate's distorted sense of humour. By dangling the only girl in the world before his eyes and then snatching her away just when it seemed possible that business might result, Fate, he considered, had played a low practical joke on him. He could appreciate now how that swan on the lake of Binghampton Hall must have felt, that time when, a boy of twelve, incapable of understanding the other fellow's point of view, he had offered it a piece of Bath bun tied to a string, dexterously jerking it out of reach every time the bird snapped at it. It had made the swan as sick as mud, he recalled, and he had laughed consumedly, but, himself the victim of a similar pleasantry, though of course on the spiritual plane, he blushed to think that he could have been guilty of such sharp practice.

'Ah, well,' he said to himself, or words to that effect, and pressed the Potter doorbell. Footsteps sounded, the door opened, and he was immediately pinned by the right trouser leg by a large saffron-coloured dog which had come oozing silently over the threshold.

'Ouch!' he cried, a good deal stirred and momentarily forgetting his frustrated love life.

Mervyn Potter, who followed in the animal's wake, greeted him cordially. He had a glass full of amber liquid in his hand, and inhaled a draught from this.

'Hello there,' he said. 'Fotheringay-Phipps, is it not?'

'That's right.'

'The Fotheringay-Phipps there has been so much talk about? *The* Fotheringay-Phipps? Well, well, well,' said Mervyn Potter, 'this is the proudest day of my life. Come on in and have a drink.'

'I'd love to,' said Barmy, 'only there seems to be a dog of sorts attached to my leg.'

Mervyn Potter narrowed his gaze.

'You're perfectly right. My Tanganyika lion dog, Tulip. You're a very quick observer, Phipps. Many fellows wouldn't have noticed that.'

Barmy, as he followed his host into the sitting-room, began to find a certain uneasiness mingling with his spiritual anguish. It was plain to him that the other, fatigued no doubt after a long day's rehearsal, had yielded to the dictates of his lower self and for some considerable time must have been mopping up the stuff like a vacuum cleaner. If not actually ossified, he was indubitably plastered, and Barmy could only hope that he would not eventually reach the truculent stage. A bimbo as large and muscular as Mervyn Potter was not at all the sort of bimbo you wanted to have getting truculent around you.

At present he was all amiability. He pressed refreshment on Barmy, absorbed a considerable quantity himself and spoke interestingly of life in Hollywood, telling many a diverting anecdote about fellow stars of his and studio executives he had met.

'You ever been cornered by a wounded studio executive, Phipps? No? It's an experience every young man ought to have. Broadens the mind and helps to form the character. How well I remember the day when I was wandering through the jungle on the Metro-Goldwyn lot and Louis B. Mayer suddenly sprang out at me from the undergrowth. He had somehow managed to escape from the office where they kept him, and I could see from his glaring eyes and slavering jaws that he had already tasted blood. Fortunately I had my elephant gun and my trusty native bearer with me . . .' Mervyn Potter's attention seemed to wander. 'Well, good night all,' he said, and fell asleep.

Barmy ventured to touch him on the arm.

'I say!'

Mervyn Potter opened his eyes.

'I have the skin hanging on my wall at Beverly Hills,' he said, concluding his narrative.

'I say!'

'Yes, Phipps?'

'It's getting pretty late. Don't you think we might go and have dinner?'

Mervyn Potter stared. 'Have *dinner*? You don't want any dinner.'

'Yes, I do.'

'No, you don't. Sit down!' bellowed Mervyn Potter in a voice of thunder.

Barmy sat down. It was clear that his host had now reached that truculent stage which he had hoped might have been avoided, and he found himself wishing that he had got mixed up with one of the rather smaller motion picture stars.

'Dinner!' said Mervyn Potter, and adding the word 'Faugh!', closed his eyes and fell once more into a refreshing sleep.

From the way he had said 'Dinner! Faugh!', Barmy could see that Mervyn Potter did not think much of the meal, but he could not share the other's contemptuous detachment. He had eaten nothing since his lateish breakfast, and with every moment that passed was becoming more conscious of the need for nourishment. His stomach had begun to make low, querulous noises, and it seemed to him that it would be an excellent idea to take advantage of his companion's slumber to creep out and fortify himself. If a chap asks you to dinner, he reasoned, you naturally stick around till he gives the signal for putting on the nosebag, but once it has become obvious that mine host has no intention of giving such a signal and that, as far as he is concerned, no calories may be expected, you can consider yourself at liberty to slide out and forage on your own. Emily Post, he was sure, would endorse this view.

He rose, accordingly, poising himself for flight, and instantaneously the room became filled with a curious gargling sound, as if some giant were using mouth-wash in the vicinity. Between himself and the door the dog Tulip was standing with a wealth of meaning in his eyes. The most amateur physiognomist would have discerned that there stood a dog prompt on all occasions to deal with funny business. And that Barmy's desire to leave the premises fell in his opinion into this category was only too sickeningly evident.

Barmy attempted to find a formula.

'Nice doggie,' he said. 'Won't oo let me pass?'

The animal gave a quick impressionist imitation of a mad bloodhound with a fishbone in its throat.

'Oh, all right,' said Barmy, a little stiffly. 'I merely asked.'

The hour now was about eight-forty-five. At a quarter-past eleven Mervyn Potter sat up and stretched himself. He seemed fresh and rested.

'Nothing like a bit of sleep,' he said, reaching for the decanter and taking an aperitif. 'Knits up the ravelled sleeve of care, I often say. And how's my old Phippsy?'

'I'm all right,' said Barmy, though it was a loose interpretation of the facts.

'You managed to amuse yourself while I was having my nap? I was sure you would. No doubt you and Tulip exchanged views on this and that? A fine dog, is he not?'

'Oh, rather. Very fine. But is he safe?'

'Perfectly, I should imagine. Nobody would be ass enough to try to attack Tulip. His strength is as the strength of ten, because his heart is pure. Well, Phipps, the night is drawing on. Shall we go out and see what the town has to offer? They tell me the cabaret at the Piazza is worth a visit.'

'That would be fine.'

'Then let's go. Come on, Tulip.'

'But you can't take a dog to the Piazza.'

A dangerous look came into Mervyn Potter's face. His eyes narrowed, as if he had been the hero of a Western film confronted with cattle rustlers. Nothing annoys the man of haughty spirit more than having people dictating to him.

'Who says I can't take a dog to the Piazza? Did you?' he said, eyeing Barmy keenly.

'No, no.'

'I could have sworn I heard somebody say it,' said Mervyn Potter, puzzled. 'Some trick of the acoustics, no doubt. Come along, Phipps. Fall in, Tulip. Next stop, the Piazza.'

Revellers in considerable numbers had assembled to watch the cabaret at the Piazza Hotel, and the Champagne Room, where it broke loose twice nightly, was congested, but by force of personality Mervyn Potter succeeded in securing a table at the edge of the dancing floor. The dog Tulip, after a certain amount of rather acrimonious argument, had been accommodated with a shakedown in the cloak-room. The waiter brought the menu, and Barmy's stomach caught Barmy's eye in a congratulatory sort of way, like a stomach seeing the approach of the happy ending.

Mervyn Potter waved the man aside.

'Nothing to eat,' he said. 'Just a bottle of champagne.'

Barmy felt his stomach spring to its feet with raised eyebrows.

'I say!' he bleated. 'I could do with a few kidneys or a couple of steaks or something.'

'No, you couldn't. Kidneys? Steaks? After that enormous dinner? You mustn't make a god of your stomach, Phipps,' said Mervyn Potter rebukingly. 'Put it down out of my friend's reach,' he added, as the waiter arrived with the champagne. 'A nice chap,' he explained, taking the man into his confidence with the genial charm which was so characteristic of him, 'but one of those fellows who never know when to stop. He's been swilling it down since breakfast. One glass, Phipps, just to be sociable, but no more.'

'But, I say—'

That dangerous look came into Mervyn Potter's face again.

'Not going to start an argument, are you, Phipps?'

'No, no.'

'Good,' said Mervyn Potter, and dozed off.

It seemed to Barmy that the time had come to call it a day. He could see no pleasure or profit resulting from the continued society of this plastered idol of the silver screen. There came upon him an urge to get away from it all.

He drew back a leg preparatory to rising, and an unseen something gripped it in strong teeth. Reckless of the possibility that the other might wake up cross, he shook his host by the arm.

'Yes?' said Mervyn Potter, stirring in his sleep. 'Oh, hullo, Phipps.

I was hoping I'd run into you. Is that Fotheringay sitting at your side? How are you, Fotheringay? Listen, you two, I've just remembered something that may be useful to you. When a studio executive charges you, look to the left but leap to the right. This baffles the simple creature.'

Barmy thanked him, and said that he would make a note of it.

'Changing the subject for a moment,' he said, 'that dog of yours is under the table. He's got me by the leg.'

Mervyn Potter raised the cloth and verified the statement.

'You're perfectly correct, Phipps. So he has. Hi ya, Tulip.'

He resumed his slumbers.

It was some faint relief to Barmy that the cabaret now began. He had been feeling the need of something to take him out of himself. Watching it, he was able to a certain extent to ignore the peevish complaints his stomach persisted in making. Mervyn Potter continued to sleep.

But not for long. In every cabaret entertainment there is included a concerted number in the course of which the personnel of the ensemble start throwing things at the customers, and those responsible for the arrangement of the programme at the Piazza had not omitted this item. A few minutes later a cottonwool snowball, an indispensable adjunct to the concerted number 'Winter Time', struck Mervyn Potter on one of his closed eyes. As he opened it, another struck him on the tip of the nose. When chorus girls see a client asleep at a ringside table, they do not waste their ammunition on more wakeful patrons.

The song 'We don't want to fight, but by Jingo if we do!' might have been written by its author specially with someone like Mervyn Potter in mind. Mervyn Potter was a man who, if you left him alone, would leave you alone. He was all for peace in our time. But anybody who supposed him lacking in pride and spirit was vastly mistaken.

'This can't go on,' he said quietly, and those who knew Mervyn Potter best could have told you that he was never more to be feared than when he spoke in that grim undertone.

He raised the tablecloth. A saffron head peered out inquiringly. Mervyn Potter waved a hand in the direction of the personnel of the ensemble, who were now doing something mysterious with snow-shoes.

'Sic 'em, Tulip,' he said.

6

BARMY rose from the gutter outside the Piazza Hotel and dizzily adjusted his tie. He could not recall exactly how he had got there, but he remembered the order in which their little party had struck the pavement. First himself, then Mervyn Potter, and finally Tulip, who had sailed through the air and hit him between the shoulder-blades. Looking about him now, he saw his two companions respectively dusting trousers and barking at the management. Neither seemed in any way disconcerted by what had occurred. Mervyn Potter in particular appeared to be in radiant spirits. That slight irritability which had occasionally been noticeable in his manner of late had entirely gone.

'And what now, Phipps?' he said cheerily.

'Bed?' suggested Barmy.

Mervyn Potter seemed astounded.

'Bed? At this time? The shank of the evening? No, Phipps, I think we can do better than that. The neighbourhood in which we are is so congested with cabarets that the pleasure-seeker has an almost illimitable choice. Shall we say the Diamond Horseshoe?'

'I don't think so, thanks.'

'Or the Latin Quarter?'

'Not for me, really.'

'Or Leon and Eddie's? Or the Copacabana? You have only to speak the word, Phipps. Whither thou goest I will go.'

Barmy said that on the whole he would prefer to attend no more cabaret performances, and Mervyn Potter accepted his decision with charming good temper.

'Then I'll tell you what we'll do. Taxi-cab driver,' said Mervyn Potter, addressing the driver of a passing taxi-cab, 'take us to King's Point, Long Island, and don't spare the horses. We will go and have a crack with my fiancée, Phipps.'

'But, I say!'

Mervyn Potter's geniality waned. That quiet, dangerous note came into his voice.

'Have you some objection to meeting my fiancée?'

'No, no, but—'

'You have nothing against my fiancée, have you, Phipps?'

'No, no, rather not.'

'So I should hope,' said Mervyn Potter. 'A charming girl, if ever there was one. She is a Miss Hermione Brimble, daughter of the well-known financial magnate, C. Hamilton Brimble, and by a curious coincidence of Mrs C. Hamilton Brimble as well. You probably saw her flitting about the hotel at Skeewassett. Tallish girl with a complexion the colour of marble in starlight and eyes that glittered like emeralds when the sunlight fell on them. They are green,' explained Mervyn Potter. 'You'll like her enormously, and I feel sure that meeting you will set the seal on her happiness.'

'But, dash it all, she won't want to see me in the middle of the night.'

'You underestimate your attractiveness, Phipps. No matter what the hour, you still cast that spell of yours. If I have heard it said once, I have heard it said a hundred times, by people whose judgment I respect, that it never matters how late Cyril Fotheringay-Phipps blows in, because in the final analysis he is always Cyril Fotheringay-Phipps. Drive on, driver. When we get to King's Point, I will direct you with word and gesture.'

To reach King's Point, Long Island, one has to cross the Triborough Bridge, carry on to Great Neck and turn up the Middle Neck Road. It is a long journey and one that might have proved tedious had not Mervyn Potter enlivened it with snatches of song in a pleasant light baritone. When they arrived, it seemed to annoy him that the house should be in darkness. A stickler for etiquette, he pointed out that there ought to have been a light shining in the window to guide the wanderer home.

'A lamp. Or at least a candle. However,' he said, becoming his old cheerful self again, 'I suppose we must skip the red tape. That, I rather think,' he went on, 'is my fiancée's room and, as I see it, three courses are open to us. We can stand here and yell. Or we can throw gravel. Or you could shin up the waterpipe. Yes, that is the best plan. Up you go, Phipps. Knock twice and mention my name.'

A healing thought came to Barmy.

'But your fiancée isn't there.'

'How can you tell that till you've knocked?'

'You told me she was going to a dance tonight.'

'So I did. Bless my soul, so I did. Well, in that case, just shin up and break the window.'

'That little more,' says the poet, 'and how much it is.' If Mervyn Potter had been a shade smaller, a trifle less intoxicated, the teeniest bit less apt to take offence when thwarted, Barmy might have declined the suggestion. As it was, he felt it prudent to fall in with his companion's wishes. He was dully aware, as he started to mount the pipe, of the latter leaning against the side of the house reciting

'Excelsior' in a sonorous voice. His arrival at the sill synchronized with the verse about the maiden throwing out her kindly invitation to the young Alpine climber to stay and rest his weary head against this breast.

It was as he broke the window that from another window a little further along the house the head and shoulders of a man in a dressing-gown suddenly protruded. An electric torch shone upon Barmy, and then the man in the dressing-gown, raising a revolver, proceeded to discharge it in his direction. Bulstrode, Mrs C. Hamilton Brimble's English butler, had heard noises in the night and, when English butlers hear noises in the night, they act.

The shots whistled harmlessly past Barmy's ears, but the hint behind them was so unmistakable that he lost no time in taking it. Mervyn Potter's startled 'Hoy!', the dog Tulip's annoyed bark and his own downward swoop were simultaneous.

When he reached the ground, Mervyn Potter had vanished into the night. But Tulip was still there. He was gargling in an offended undertone and stropping his front paws on the turf.

The mentality of dogs is odd. One might have supposed that a moment's reflection would have told Tulip that even the most unbalanced man does not climb waterpipes in order to fire revolvers at himself. Nevertheless, he was firmly convinced that it was Barmy who had been responsible for the fusillade. Looking back over the evening, it seemed to him that from start to finish Barmy had been the disrupting influence, and he was resolved to settle accounts with him once and for all. He hated horseplay. He gave his paws a final strop and advanced.

It was his quickness off the mark that saved Barmy. The merest pause for reflection, and he would have been undone. 'Oh,' he said to himself, 'for the wings of a dove', and the next moment he was in the upper branches of a large cedar at the edge of the lawn. From this eminence he was able to obtain an excellent view of the subsequent proceedings.

Mervyn Potter would have had no reason now to complain of the absence of lights in the windows. The house was as brilliantly lit up as he himself. And presently figures began to emerge and search the grounds – reluctantly, it seemed to Barmy, but going through the distasteful task under the spell of the magnetism of Bulstrode, the butler, who directed the operations in his dressing-gown. Barmy had never seen a butler in a dressing-gown before, and he would willingly, impressive though it was, have forgone the experience now.

It took some little time to convince the master of the revels that a blank had been drawn, but eventually the search-party returned to the house and the lights began to go out again. The front door closed. The house was in darkness. And Barmy was just about to yield to that old familiar urge, so often felt by those who spent the evening with Mervyn Potter, to get away from it all, when the scent of a cigarette came to his nostrils and he saw that Bulstrode was standing under the tree enjoying a soothing smoke.

The sight kept him roosting on his branch, and about a quarter of an hour later there was the sound of a vehicle stopping at the gate and Mrs C. Hamilton Brimble and her daughter Hermione came walking down the drive. He deduced that the short, stout lady was Mrs Brimble and the taller, more slender girl her daughter from the fact that the former said 'Hermione, there is somebody under that tree', to which the latter replied 'It's Bulstrode, mother. Golly! Pipe the dressing-gown!'

It was plain that the spectacle of her butler roaming the grounds in the small hours in a dressing-gown had stirred Mrs Brimble. Until this moment Bulstrode had been to her a suave, tail-coated figure, the keynote of whose costume was a sober grey and black. She had not known that he possessed a dressing-gown among his effects, let alone one of Chinese silk with yellow dragons embroidered on it. Her air as she advanced was that of a woman who, if her upbringing had been less careful and her social position less high, would have said 'Gee whiz!'

'Bulstrode,' she cried, 'what are you doing out here at this time of night?'

The butler preserved the calm of one who knows that his story is good and worth sticking to

'Good evening, madam, I have been pursuing burglars.'

'Burglars?'

'Yes, madam. They were two in number. I heard noises and proceeded to institute an investigation, and I observed a nocturnal marauder climbing the waterpipe.'

'Good gracious, Bulstrode!'

'Yes, madam.'

'Who was he?'

'He did not give me his card, madam. But I recognized his accomplice, who remained at the foot of the waterpipe, reciting "Excelsior".'

'Doing *what*?'

'Reciting "Excelsior", madam, a poem by the late Henry Wadsworth Longfellow. Possibly the work is familiar to you? The shades of night were falling fast, madam, as through an Alpine village passed a youth who bore "mid snow and ice, madam, a banner with—"'

Mrs Brimble stopped him. It was not that she was not fond of poetry or thought that the butler did not render it well, but she wished to stick to the agenda.

'You say you recognized him?'

'Yes, madam. It was the individual describing himself as Mervyn Potter.'

'Mervyn Potter? But he dined here last night.'

'Casing the joint, no doubt, madam.'

The girl Hermione uttered a passionate cry.

'Bulstrode, you're cuckoo. Mervyn is not a burglar.'

'I disagree with you, miss.'

'He is a very celebrated motion picture star.'

'That is possibly his story, miss. I can only asseverate that I caught him in the act of encouraging a young man of obviously criminal aspect to climb the waterpipe and effect an entry through a window, miss.'

Mrs Brimble intervened. Possibly, she felt that feelings were running high and that in another moment she would have an ugly brawl on her hands. If she had been a policeman, she would have said 'Break it up there, break it up'. As it was, she told Bulstrode to go to bed, and the butler with a courteous 'Good night' withdrew.

From the sound, like the expiring hiss of a syphon of soda water, which broke the silence after he had disappeared, Barmy divined correctly that his hostess had expelled a deep breath.

'So!' she said, and the ear could detect a certain generous warmth in her voice. 'So this is your Mervyn? I told you, the moment I laid eyes on him—'

'I'm sure he must have some explanation, mother.'

'Then let him give it,' said Mrs Brimble, and with a wave of her hand indicated a lissom figure which was emerging from the shadows across the lawn.

'Mervyn!' cried Hermione Brimble.

Mervyn Potter seemed glad to see her. There was a lover's genuine enthusiasm in his voice as he bellowed, 'Hello, there, babe!'

'What are you doing here?' demanded Miss Brimble.

'Just sauntering around. As a matter of fact, I'm looking for a chap named Phipps, whom I appear to have mislaid somewhere. You may possibly know him as Fotheringay. He sometimes goes under that alias. We were thrown out of the Piazza together an hour or so ago, and while we were relaxing in the gutter, he said to me, "Potter, I would dearly love to meet your fiancée". To which I replied, "Nothing simpler, my dear Phipps. We will hire this passing taxi-cab and tool out and see her now".'

'Mervyn, you're blotto!'

A bitter hiccough escaped Mervyn Potter.

'And who wouldn't be after an evening with Fotheringay-Phipps?' he demanded. 'There's a wild Indian for you. He turned up at my apartment and intimidated me from the start. He's one of those fellows who get very ugly when sozzled, and I could see from his manner as he muscled in that he was fried to the gills. He had a gun with him.

He's been blazing away with it all the evening. Slain his thousands, if you ask me. I was all in favour of a quiet home evening, a modest dinner and a couple of good books afterwards, but he would have none of it. "I'm a timber wolf from the great frozen north-west," he said, "and tonight's my night to howl", and he takes me off to the Piazza. What could I do? I was helpless. He had that gun. And when we get to the Piazza and take our seats, he jumps up and shouts "Watch out, everybody! I'm going to start. I'm going to begin. Pick up your dead, chaps, pick up your dead. A souvenir goes with every corpse." So they threw us out, and we landed on our ears on the sidewalk. You may take it from me that Fotheringay-Phipps is the sort of man who could get self and friend thrown out of a saloon on the Marseilles waterfront. I shall see him very sparingly after the honeymoon, I can tell you.'

'There may not be a honeymoon,' said Hermione Brimble grimly. 'Mother, will you go in. I wish to speak to Mervyn.'

She led her betrothed across the lawn, and Barmy was alone in the silent night. Relieved of the society of Mrs C. Hamilton Brimble and her daughter Hermione, he could have descended from his perch, had he wished, but he did not wish. He could not bring himself to face whatever further shocks this house of terror might be saving up for him, and he was still clinging to his bough like a preoccupied opossum when he observed a little group returning. It consisted of Mervyn Potter, looking subdued, the dog Tulip, attached to Mervyn Potter by a leash, and Hermione Brimble, who was walking with her chin in the air. She entered the house coldly and proudly, and the front door closed behind her. No lovers' kisses had been exchanged.

Barmy climbed down – cautiously, for in a place like this you never knew what horrors might not be lurking in the shadows. The dog Tulip's passionate bound in his direction, mercifully brought up short by the leash, apprised Mervyn Potter of his presence.

'Ah, Phipps,' he said dully. 'I've been looking for you everywhere. Where did you spring from?'

'I was up that tree.'

'You are fond of climbing trees?'

'No, I'm not fond of climbing trees. That bally man-eating dog of yours was chivvying me.'

'Just playing, no doubt.'

'Was he? I didn't stop to ask. I simply made the leap for life.'

Mervyn Potter reflected.

'You were up that tree, you say? Then you may have caught snatches of the recent conversation?'

'I did.'

'But you missed the best, for by that time you were out of earshot. You aren't married, are you, Phipps?'

'No.'

'Then you are probably unaware of the lengths to which an angry woman can go when putting her loved one where he belongs. I can remember nothing like it since the day when I stole a scene from a female star who was a native of Mexico. Where girls get these expressions from, I can't think, I suppose they learn them at their finishing schools.'

'Has she given you the raspberry?'

'If by that you mean is the engagement off, the answer is no. We are still affianced. But at what a cost! At what a cost, Phipps! The boss has issued an ultimatum. From now on spirituous liquor is not to pass my lips. One move on my part toward the sauce, and those wedding bells will not ring out. Dating from tonight, I am on the wagon.'

Mervyn Potter fell into a sombre silence, his thoughts on the grey future.

'I wonder, Phipps,' he said, 'if you have the slightest conception what it means to be on the wagon. I shall go through the world a haunted man. There will be joy and mirth in that world, but not in the heart of Mervyn Potter. Everywhere around me I shall hear the happy laughter of children as they dig into their Scotch highballs, but I shall not be able to join them. I shall feel like a thirsty leper. Still, if it must be, it must be. Come, east, west, home's best. Let us be getting back to New York.'

'Stopping on the way for a sandwich or something?'

Mervyn Potter raised his eyebrows.

'It's incredible. Don't you ever stop eating, Phipps? Digging your grave with your teeth, that's what you are doing. Oh, well, tapeworms will be tapeworms,' said Mervyn Potter philosophically.

He led the way to where the taxi-cab awaited them.

7

THE headquarters of Lehmac Productions, Inc., were situated in one of those grimy buildings that sprinkle Broadway in the Forties, the kind of building whose lifts are invariably a trifle too small and are filled with blonde girls who look exactly alike and dark-chinned men similarly cut to a pattern. One and all are in show business, or on the fringe of it, and as the lifts go up and down you hear snatches of conversation about Summer stock and camera angles and being sent for by Lindsay and Crouse.

They are mainly given up, these buildings, to the offices of those interested in Vaudeville, the films and Television. Joe Lehman had been a prominent Vaudeville agent, and it was a mark of his Vaudeville training that on becoming a producer in what is known as the legitimate he had pitched his tent in one of them. Established legitimate producers are generally to be found on top of somebody's theatre, or else hidden away in decayed brownstone fronts in 55th Street.

The premises of Lehmac Productions consisted of an outer hall where a pimpled office boy sat throughout the day chewing gum, a cubbyhole affording just room for a secretary and a typewriter, and an inner sanctum where Mr Lehman held conferences with his partner, Jack McClure.

At two-thirty on the afternoon following Barmy's visit to King's Point, Long Island, he was conferring there not with Jack McClure, who was up at the Morris Rooms watching a rehearsal, but with his wife, Fanny Lehman, formerly Fanita, the World's Greatest Juggler.

It was a dingy and dishevelled apartment, very different from the rich interiors in which men like the Messrs Lee Shubert and John Golden conduct their affairs. A sensitive decorator, suddenly introduced into it, would have winced and cried aloud. Joe Lehman's Vaudeville days lay in the quite recent past, and a pile of miscellaneous junk from his old office occupied a large part of one of the walls. There were great bundles of newspapers, most of them copies of the Christmas issue of *Variety*, containing Mr Lehman's advertised seasonal greetings to all artists everywhere. There were a few mouldy box files, part of a stray, bespangled costume, and even a ballet dancer's slipper. Except for a huge and obviously new desk, slightly filmed with dust, the pile was the most prominent object in the room.

The rest of the furniture was also new – a swivel chair at the desk, a visitor's chair in front of it and a smaller one at one side. A water-cooler completed the list of goods and chattels, but Mr Lehman, moving into his new quarters, had brought with him some sixty or seventy photographs of artists who at various times had availed themselves of his professional services. These decorated the walls in interesting disarray. They were all inscribed 'With love to Joe', 'To Joe from La Belle Marguery', 'To the Greatest Agent in the World' and so on – inscriptions bespeaking a business affiliation rather than a personal bond.

Mr Lehman was seated in the swivel chair, his feet on the desk, between his lips the stump of a cigar which he chewed rhythmically. His wife, a woman in the late thirties with an enormous poise and an easy assurance acquired by years of touring the South Bends and Wichitas, preferred to pace the floor.

'Well, sir,' she was saying, 'I just been taking a peep at that trick troupe of yours.'

'Yah?' said Mr Lehman guardedly.

'Yessir, I seen a rehearsal, and I know now what they mean when they talk about the fate that is worse than death.'

'Is that so?' said Mr Lehman with a snarl. 'Well, you keep out of them rehearsals, you hear me?'

Mr Lehman was a large, bulky, forceful man, inclined to breathe hard in moments of professional strain. Except for a coloured shirt, his clothes were not actually loud, and yet he had the knack of making them seem so. He wore a derby hat. He always wore it. It was part of him. The most imaginative could hardly picture him bareheaded.

Fanny was not the woman to be intimidated by snarls. She continued equably.

'Yessir, you got a show there that's going to make history, do you know it? They're going to date things from the time you open this one.'

Mr Lehman stirred uneasily in the swivel chair. His hand, moving up to scratch his head, encountered the derby hat, and he seemed to draw strength from it.

'So what's it got to do with you?' he demanded warmly. 'It ain't your money, is it?'

'It would have been, if I'd of been sap enough to let you talk me into it. But I wasn't.'

'All right, you wasn't. And when you wouldn't see your duty as a wife, I stepped straight down the street to Lester Burdett, and he come in for twenty grand. Quick. Just like that. He's giving me his cheque today.'

'Sooner him than me,' said Fanny. 'I like to keep my dough.'

Joe Lehman regarded her sourly. Fanny's dough was a sore subject. There ought to be some law against a wife's having a lot of money in her own name, he felt, echoing the sentiments of a thousand Broadway husbands.

'You'd have thought that after all I done for you, you'd of had some gratitude,' he said morosely. 'You wouldn't have had a sou if I hadn't dug you out of that Texas honky-tonk you were messing around in and put you in regular Vaudeville. Fanita, the World's Greatest Juggler!' said Mr Lehman with a wealth of satire. 'If it wasn't for me, you'd be keeping four clubs in the air right now for some ten-for-a-nickel management nobody ever heard of.'

Fanny bridled. Her professional pride had been touched.

'Don't you go four-clubbing me. I done six clubs for the wow at the finish, and done it for years.'

'Yeah, and there ain't a stage between here and California ain't got dents in it from them clubs of yours. They wouldn't let nobody sit in the first five rows. Fanita!'

'Yes, Fanita. And I'm as good today as I ever was.'

'Just about,' said Mr Lehman.

Fanny waved a nonchalant hand.

'All right, all right. I was a rotten juggler and you were a great agent. But I'm the one that's got the house and lot in Freeport, not to mention a hunk in the bank that come due this morning on a bond or sump'n. Listen, Joey,' said Fanny, softening as she always did after getting a domestic quarrel out of her system. 'This ain't your game. Why don't you go back to agenting, where you know the ropes?'

'Because I don't want to, see?'

Fanny sighed. A casual observer might have thought it could not have been done, but she loved this man – fat head, cigar, derby hat and all.

'Okay,' she said resignedly. 'Have it your own way. Go on and produce the show and let's watch it make history, like I said.'

'It'll make history all right, though not the way you mean. How can it help being a smash with Mervyn Potter starring? Every woman in America is going to come and see him.'

'Unless he burns down the theatre on the opening night, and I wouldn't put it past him. If I was a producer, I'd rather manage a wagon-load of monkeys than that crazy lunatic. And personally I doubt if the customers will pay to see even Mervyn Potter, once it gets around what sort of a leading woman you've got.'

'Whittaker's going to be fine.'

'Is that her name? Who is she, if any?'

'She's Jack McClure's—'

'Mother?'

'Sister-in-law. She's his wife's sister. So kindly don't go getting off any of your cracks about her in front of Jack.'

Fanny nodded sagely.

'So that's why she's in the show.'

'No, it ain't. She's all right.'

'If you like stout Dames of the Colonial Revolution. I caught that bit at the rehearsal where she's climbing up apple trees in the ancestral orchard. The stuff to make them trees out of is reinforced concrete,' said Fanny, and feeling it doubtful whether she could improve on this as a last word, bestowed a kindly smile on her husband and left the room.

A few minutes later there entered a girl at the sight of whom Barmy, had he been present, would have tottered on his base and experienced a difficulty in keeping his eyes in the parent sockets. She had fair hair, and was wearing a hat that looked like a fruit salad. Her blue eyes, as they rested on Mr Lehman, twinkled with suppressed amusement. Eileen ('Dinty') Moore, Mr Lehman's secretary, found her employer a constant source of entertainment.

Mr Lehman, whirling round in the swivel chair, eyed her belligerently. There was nothing in his manner to indicate that he found in her any trace of that girlish appeal which had so impressed itself on Barmy yesterday afternoon in Madison Avenue. He was still sore from the recent encounter, and to him the lodestar of Barmy's life was merely a handy underling on whom he could work off some of his pent-up feelings.

'Hey, you!'

'Yes, Admiral?'

'Where you been?'

'Lunch, Admiral.'

'You've taken your time about it. And don't call me Admiral. Think I pay you to sit and stuff all day?'

'You don't pay me at all. You owe me two weeks' salary. And listen,' said Dinty, feeling that this sort of thing must be checked at the outset. 'The contract calls for an hour for the midday repast, and an hour's what I've had, no more, no less. So lay off, Simon Legree, and drop that cowhide whip. Don't you know that Lincoln had freed us slaves? Don't you ever read the papers?'

Mr Lehman grunted. With Fanita, the World's Greatest Juggler, he might sometimes hope to hold his own, but when attempting to bandy words with this girl he was always uneasily conscious of an inferiority complex. If it wasn't that he owed her that two weeks' salary, thought Mr Lehman moodily, he would have shot her out on her ear days ago, for she was as fresh, in his opinion, as a certified farm egg.

'All right,' he said, conceding defeat. 'Take a letter.'

Dinty took several letters, for her employer loved dictating them. Presently there was a lull and, as always when these occurred, Dinty became chatty. She was a friendly little soul and liked to make the party go. She sought for a topic that would interest, elevate and amuse. She toyed for a moment with the idea of bringing up the subject of her new hat and explaining how she had got it, but decided – rightly – that this would not grip.

'I saw Mrs Lehman at the rehearsal this morning,' she said, feeling that this was more along the lines required.

'Yah?'

'She's very funny, isn't she?'

'One long scream,' said Mr Lehman, heavily.

'What's the name of the leading woman, the one who plays the heroine?'

'Gladys Whittaker.'

'Gladys Whittaker,' said Dinty meditatively, 'And what a temper *she's* got. Why, Mrs Lehman wasn't even talking to her.'

A horrid thought writhed into Mr Lehman's mind like a snake.

'You mean Fanny let fly with one of them wisecracks at that rehearsal?' he quavered.

'She only asked a question.'

'What was it? What Whittaker's weight was? When she was born?'

'Oh, no. Though she does look kind of stout and elderly for the part, don't you think?'

'No, I don't.'

'Mrs Lehman does. We were watching the bit where Miss Whittaker is climbing up the apple tree, and Mrs Lehman said to the director, "What does she wear in that scene?" And the Director said, "Blue knickerbockers".'

Mr Lehman moaned softly.

'Now it comes! The finger!'

' "She wears blue knickerbockers," the director said. And Mrs Lehman said, "Drop your curtain on that laugh".'

'Miss Whittaker to see you, sir,' said the pimpled office boy, appearing in the doorway.

'Wheel her in,' said Dinty.

Mr Lehman turned on her with the uninhibited warmth of some creature of the wild that has got its foot caught in a trap.

'You get out of here,' he thundered, 'and take them small-time jokes with you. It's bad enough I have to listen to them from Mrs Lehman without having you start.' He turned to the office boy. 'Is she behaving all right?'

'Why, yes, sir.'

'Not crying or nothing?'

'No, sir.'

'Has she got a knife?' asked Dinty.

Mr Lehman repeated his imitation of the trapped creature of the wild.

'Will you get out! Go type those letters.'

'Yes, Massa Legree, sir.'

'Bring her in,' said Mr Lehman. He spun round on Dinty once more. 'What you waiting for?'

'I just want to time her to the desk,' said Dinty.

If Mr Lehman had a suitable reply to this remark, he was forced to repress it, for at this moment the office boy ushered in Miss Whittaker. Dinty, having reached the door of the cubbyhole, paused and turned.

'Yessir, blue knickerbockers,' she said softly.

She went into the cubbyhole, closing the door behind her, and a moment later there came faintly through it the tapping of a typewriter.

'Well!' said Miss Whittaker.

'Don't pay no attention to her,' urged Mr Lehman. 'She's loco. And don't pay no attention to Mrs Lehman. She's loco, too. Sit down. What's on your mind?'

Miss Whittaker sat down. She was a large, spreading blonde, still handsome though a little too Junoesque to be climbing apple trees. Looking at her, one appreciated the significance of Mrs Lehman's advice about the reinforced concrete. She carried in her hand an oblong slip of paper. This she exhibited to Mr Lehman in the manner of a conjurer producing a rabbit from a hat.

'This is that hundred-dollar cheque of yours, Mr Lehman. It just came back to me for the third time. What does that entitle me to? Permanent possession?'

Mr Lehman had been through this sort of thing before.

'Wait a while and put it through again,' he advised.

'I want the money, Mr Lehman.'

'You'll get it.'

'May I say just one word?'

'Go ahead.'

'When?' asked Miss Whittaker, limiting herself to the one word she had asked to be allowed.

Mr Lehman's studied self-control deserted him.

'When I'm good and ready, that's when. Gosh, it's tough,' cried Mr Lehman. 'Here I am, working day and night to get the show in shape, and if I get away for a minute and try to relax, in comes people asking for money. Money, money, money. If you want money, why don't you ask Jack McClure for it? You're his wife's sister.'

'Jack McClure!' said Gladys Whittaker, and it was plain that she held no high opinion of her brother-in-law.

There came belatedly to Joe Lehman the thought that it might be wiser to be more conciliatory. He got up and put an affectionate arm about Miss Whittaker's shoulder. He was still wearing his hat.

'Now listen, baby,' he said. 'You know how it is when you're readying a show. The money's all there, but it's locked up, sort of. Frozen assets, they call it. I'll see that you get that hundred. I'm expecting a rich millionaire in any moment with a big cheque he's bringing. Gimme half an hour.'

'Very well,' said Miss Whittaker, with the manner of a judge pronouncing a suspended sentence. 'But if that money isn't laid on the barrelhead then, I'm going straight to Equity and tell them the whole story. And you know what'll happen then. They'll call out the company.'

She rose majestically and strode from the room, and Mr Lehman, chewing his cigar, stared bleakly before him. He was thinking about Women.

Women! What a sex, what a *sex*! They came badgering you for money and talking about going straight to Equity. They bit the hand which rescued them from Texas honky-tonks. They were flip and disrespectful and looked at you oddly out of the corner of their eyes when you were dictating letters to them. He could see no percentage in the gentler sex. The man who lays a hand upon a woman, save in the way of kindness, is rightly looked askance at and viewed with concern, but Mr Lehman could have named three on whom he would have been delighted to lay the heaviest of hands.

Presently, wincing away from this unpleasant theme, he turned to a more agreeable one. He began to muse on Lester Burdett, and immediately the dark cloud lifted. Sunshine poured into his soul. He ceased to take the dim view which he had been taking of the world because there were women in it. There might be women in the world, far too many of them, but against this you had to set the fact that the good old world also contained men like Lester Burdett, the man who had come in for twenty grand, quick, just like that.

He was still thinking loving thoughts of Lester Burdett, becoming more and more soothed the longer his mind dwelt on that square-shooting garment manufacturer, when there was a confused noise without. The door burst open, and his partner Jack McClure came tottering in, looking like something left over from the Last Days of Pompeii.

'Joe,' said Jack McClure, too agitated to attempt to break the dreadful news gently. 'You know what's happened? Lester Burdett has walked out on us.'

8

JACK McCLURE was the quiet, gentlemanly half of Lehmac Productions. It seems to be a natural law that there shall always be one quiet and gentlemanly partner in every theatrical enterprise. He was a more ingratiating type than Joe Lehman. He was even rather attractive, being tall and well built and with something of the look of the athlete about him. Joe Lehman was a man of the great indoors and at the conclusion of the business day turned his thoughts to drinks at the Astor bar. Jack McClure went off to the New York Athletic Club and played squash, and in the summer months you would find him down at Long Beach on Far Rockaway, cleaving the waves. His attire was up to the minute and a shade beyond it. He wore a fashionable grey soft hat, which, like Mr Lehman's, never left his head.

'Walked out on us,' he repeated, and going to the water-cooler helped himself to a restorative draught from a paper cup.

Mr Lehman, who on Gladys Whittaker's departure had put his feet in their favourite position on the desk, removed them with a jerk which nearly upset the swivel chair. His face had paled. His eyes were staring. He might have been Macbeth watching the ghost of Banquo dropping in to take pot luck.

'What do you mean?'

'Just what I say. He's taking his money out of the show. Every cent.'

'But why?'

'He'll tell you,' said Jack McClure, pointing the paper cup at the door, through which Mervyn Potter, who had stopped to give the office boy his autograph, was now entering.

Mervyn Potter was his customary calm, affable, unruffled self. Last night's hectic doings, which might have taken the bloom off any ordinary man, had left no trace on him. His eyes were bright, his demeanour tranquil. He did not appear to have even a suspicion of a headache.

'Hail to thee, blithe Lehman,' he said genially. 'Quite a time since we met, but you look about the same . . . unfortunately. So does the dear old office. You seem to have put in a peck or so more dust since I was last here, but otherwise conditions appear to be unaltered. This is good dust,' said Mervyn Potter, running a finger over the desk. 'Where do you get it?'

Mr Lehman counted ten, for, oddly enough, his doctor had advised the same precaution as had Mr Anderson's.

'Never mind about my dust,' he said, when the ritual was complete. 'What's all this about Lester Burdett?'

Mervyn Potter shook his head regretfully.

'A hasty man, that Burdett. One who against the advice of the poet lets his angry passions rise. Be slow to wrath, they always taught me at my Sunday School, but apparently no one ever sold that idea to Lester Burdett. I don't think I have ever seen a garment manufacturer a deeper shade of mauve. And all on account of the merest trifle.'

'Trifle?'

'He gave Lester a hot foot,' said Jack McClure.

Mr Lehman raised his hands in agony, and would have clutched his head but for the fact that his hat was in the way.

'A hot foot?'

'And why not? Do be reasonable, my dear Lehman,' said Mervyn Potter. 'From the way you are carrying on, one would suppose that I had been guilty of some tort or malfeasance. I merely did what any other sensitive artist would have done in my place. There was this Burdett asleep in his chair, and I felt – rightly, as I think – that it was an opportunity which might not occur again. The birds, the bees, the breeze, the trees, all Nature in repose seemed to call to me to give him a hot foot, so I made the gesture.'

'Lester was sore,' said Jack McClure, unnecessarily.

'Very,' assented Mervyn Potter. 'I tried to reason with him, strove to get him to see my point of view, but he refused to listen. The man struck me as having deaf adder blood in him. I don't know how well you are up on deaf adders,' said Mervyn Potter, 'but their leading characteristic is a disinclination to hearken to the voice of charmers, charming never so wisely.'

Mr Lehman was a man easily stirred and prompt, when stirred, to express his emotion in burning words. He called Mervyn Potter six derogatory names in rapid succession, and Mervyn Potter said genially that he betted Mr Lehman said that to all the girls.

'Smile on me, Lehman,' said Mervyn Potter. 'A forced bitter smile, if you will, but only smile. Good heavens, I can't see what all the fuss is about. Why, in Hollywood giving a hot foot is just one of the common courtesies of everyday life.'

'To hell with Hollywood!'

'An admirable sentiment,' said Mervyn Potter, 'and one which I have often voiced myself.'

Mr Lehman replaced his feet on the desk. He could think better that way, and if ever there was a time for thinking, and thinking clearly, this was it. Twenty thousand dollars gone, just like that. It served him right, he felt, for ever supposing that anyone outside the violent ward of a lunatic asylum could handle a star like Mervyn Potter. The only bright spot in the whole black business, the only faint suggestion of a silver lining in the cloud that enveloped him, was that Fanita, the World's Greatest Juggler, was not among those present to say, 'I told you so.'

Jack McClure had refilled his paper cup. He sipped at it glumly.

'Well, there goes the ball game,' he said.

Mr Lehman nodded with equal despondency.

'Yah, we'll have to close the show.'

'Why on earth?' said Mervyn Potter.

'Why?' snarled Mr Lehman. 'Maybe you'll tell me where I can find another prospect to pry himself loose from twenty grand?'

'That's what Lester was coming across with,' said Jack McClure. 'Twenty thousand.'

Mervyn Potter seemed amazed.

'Twenty thousand?' he said. 'The merest chicken-feed. Why, in Hollywood we provide free bread and soup kitchens for the poor devils who are down to twenty thousand dollars. We give them our old clothes.'

Mr Lehman shot a baleful look at him.

'Will you stop talking about what you do in Hollywood. This is Broadway, and guys willing to put twenty grand into a show don't grow on bushes.'

'This is the pessimist in you speaking, Lehman. Correct this defeatist attitude. Good heavens, man,' said Mervyn Potter, 'for a play starring God's clean-cut, square-jawed gift to American womanhood, you don't have to go around with a hat, saying "Brother, can you spare a dime?" Big business men with double chins and bags under their eyes will fight for the privilege of paying their tribute to Art. Why, there was a young millionaire at Skeewassett who was pleading to be allowed to invest his all in the venture.'

'What!' said Mr Lehman, leaping.

'What!' said Jack McClure, skipping like the high hills.

'Who is he?' said Mr Lehman.

'Where is he?' said Jack McClure.

'Ah, there you have me,' said Mervyn Potter. 'His name is Phipps, but where he is I could not say. I ran into him yesterday, but omitted to ascertain his address. But you'll find him, you'll find him,' said Mervyn Potter. 'Just hunt around.' And feeling that he had done all that human power could do for these men, he picked up his hat from the desk and withdrew.

Mr Lehman was the first to speak as the door closed.

'Gimme that telephone book,' he said.

Jack McClure handed him the telephone directory, and he turned into pages feverishly.

'There's forty-one Phippses listed,' he announced, having counted.

'Call 'em all,' said Jack McClure.

'I don't have to call 'em all,' said Mr Lehman shrewdly. 'No need to bother about Mrs Anna B. Phipps or Phipps Astor Stationery or Edgar E. Phipps, photographer, or Mrs Edward H. Phipps or Mrs Elsie Phipps or Mrs Florence Phipps or Mrs Grenaline Phipps or the Phipps Guest Agency, Inc.' He took up the telephone. 'Get me Phipps,' he said.

'Sir?' said the pimpled office boy.

'Gimme Phipps.'

'Which Phipps, sir?'

'All the Phippses there are, except Mrs Anna B. Phipps, Phipps Astor Stationery, Edgar E. Phipps, photographer, Mrs Edward H. Phipps, Mrs Elsie Phipps, Mrs Florence Phipps, Mrs Grenaline Phipps and the Phipps Guest Agency, Inc.'

'Yessir,' said the pimpled office boy, alertly dialling the number of Edgar E. Phipps, photographer.

Time passed. Presently a hoarse and exhausted Joseph Lehman leaned back in his swivel chair, mopping his forehead. He had chatted with more Phippses than probably any other man in New York. They included bass Phippses, tenor Phippses, baritone Phippses, three Phippses with colds in the head, two Phippses who stuttered and one final supreme Phipps who appeared to have no roof to his mouth.

'Now what?' he said. A sudden inspiration came to him. He spoke into the telephone. 'Gimme David.'

'All the Davids, sir?' said the pimpled office boy, who was beginning to warm to his work.

'Sol David.'

'Yes sir.'

'Sol might come through,' said Mr Lehman.

'He might,' said Jack McClure.

'This show's a pipe, and any bird that comes in is going to make plenty.'

The telephone rang.

'Is Sol David there? This is Joe Lehman speaking. Oh . . . NO!' Mr Lehman hung up the receiver. 'Bermuda!' he said bitterly. 'Beats hell how far away they can get when you're trying to raise coin.'

Jack McClure had a suggestion.

'Here's a slant. There was two fellows named Levi, in ladies' shirt waists, sunk some dough in a show last year.'

Mr Lehman shook his head.

'They got bit. They're off the stuff for life. So here I am with a compact little drama, up to the minute, and I can't—'

Jack McClure had another suggestion.

'Can't you get it out of Fanny?'

'Fanny!'

'She's got plenty.'

'Don't I know it! I was around at her bank this morning trying to find out what her balance was, but no dice. Fanny won't part. She's so tight she could carry an armful of eels up two flights of stairs and not drop one. There's that damned telephone again. You answer it, Jack. My throat's on fire.'

Mr Lehman, infringing Mr McClure's copyright, went dully to the water-cooler and filled a paper cup.

'WHAT!!!' cried Jack McClure at the telephone.

Mr Lehman dropped the cup. Jack McClure placed a hand over the mouthpiece, and spoke in a trembling voice.

'Phipps!' he said.

'What Phipps? Edgar E., photographer?'

'No, no, no.'

'The Phipps Guest Agency?'

'No, no, no. The right Phipps.'

Mr Lehman tottered like some forest giant beneath the axes of lumbermen.

'The *right* Phipps?'

'Says Mervyn Potter told him we might possibly let him have a slice of the show.'

'Where is he?' asked Mr Lehman tensely.

'Phoning from the Astor,' said Jack McClure, having consulted the instrument. 'Wait in the lobby,' he proceeded, still speaking into the telephone. 'I'll come and fetch you.'

'Yah, do,' said Mr Lehman. 'And hey!' he shouted, as his partner made for the door. 'Keep hold of his arm!'

Mr Lehman's lassitude had left him. He became a thing of fire and energy.

'Moore!' he bellowed.

Dinty appeared from the cubbyhole.

'Yes, Colonel?'

'Clean this place up. There's a big angel coming.'

'Yes, sir.'

'And shake a leg.'

'Yes, sir. Who did you say was coming?'

'An angel. A millionaire. He's going to put money in the show.'

'Three rousing cheers. Does that mean you'll pay me my salary?'

'So you're going to begin now, huh?'

'You owe me two weeks.'

'All right, all right. You'll get it, you'll get it. And look here. When the guy's been here awhile, you make an entrance with a piece of paper, see? A letter – anything – make it busy – put it on my desk.'

'Yes, sir.'

'Don't stop to take no bows. Just exit.'

'Yes, sir. This sounds like one of those new round games that sweep Society like a forest fire.'

'Never you mind what it sounds like. Have you got it?'

'Yes, General.'

'Come in. Bring a paper. Put it on desk—'

'And exit smiling. You couldn't tell me what that's supposed to accomplish, could you?'

'Never you mind what it's supposed to accomplish. It's atmosphere, dammit, if you really want to know. Ain't you never heard of atmosphere?'

'Oh, atmosphere?' said Dinty. 'Excuse it, please,' and went back into her cubbyhole, while Mr Lehman, putting his feet up on the desk, tilted his derby hat over his eyes, lit a fresh cigar and gave himself up to the first really pleasant thoughts he had had today. He was not deeply religious, but he could not but feel that there was something impressive in the way Providence looked after the good man and saw to it that he did not fall by the wayside. The good man might be down, but with Providence in his corner, handling the towel, he was never out.

It is possible that Mr Lehman might have burst into song like a skylark, so uplifted was his mood, but before he could proceed to this awful extreme Jack McClure appeared in the doorway, ushering in the Last of the Fotheringay-Phippses.

He was holding Barmy's arm in an affectionate grip.

'This is Mr Cyril Phipps, Joe,' he said. 'Mr Lehman, Mr Phipps.'

9

THE instant Mr Lehman's eyes rested on Barmy, he realized that he had underestimated the lengths to which Providence was prepared to go when showering its blessings on the good man. 'I seen in a minute he was our oyster,' Mr Lehman would have said, if he had been dictating his Memoirs to a stenographer. 'Built to order,' he would have added. '*With* watercress.' There was an engaging air of innocence about the young man that stirred the senior partner of Lehmac Productions like a bugle.

'How are you, my blossom?' he said. 'Take a seat.'

Barmy settled himself in a gingerly manner in the visitor's chair. Mr Lehman had made a deep impression on him. There was about this theatrical magnate something of J. G. Anderson and a suggestion of Barmy's Uncle Theodore, a man who from childhood's earliest days had always been able to turn a nephew's blood to ice with a glance. He had his hat in his hand, and noticing that Mr Lehman and Mr McClure were wearing theirs, thought for a moment of putting it on his head, but was not quite equal to it.

'Have a cigar?' said Mr Lehman.

'Eh? No, I don't think I will, thanks fearfully.'

'Okay,' said Mr Lehman agreeably. He cocked an eye at Barmy, drinking him in. 'Where you from?'

'Well, London originally.'

'London, England?'

'That's right.'

'Great place. I never played it myself, but they all tell me. So you're interested in the theatre, Mr Phipps? Ever been in show business?'

'Not yet.'

'Well, we've all got to begin. The great thing is to find a great play, like I done. I got a show, my puss, that's the biggest dramatic novelty in twenty years. There ain't never been nothing like it, see?'

'No?'

'Nothing,' said Mr Lehman, and there was an impressive pause while he meditated on the bigness of his dramatic novelty.

Jack McClure broke it by coughing in his quiet, gentlemanly way.

'I was telling Mr Phipps,' he said, 'that providing he acts quick, maybe he could get in on it. We haven't quite completed our financing, have we?'

'Not quite,' admitted Mr Lehman.

'Lucky,' said Jack McClure.

'Very lucky,' said Mr Lehman. 'Well, of course, Mr Phipps, here in New York it's just like Mr McClure says. You got to make quick decisions. Think on your feet. There was a friend of ours could have bought in on *Arsenic and Old Lace* if he'd of snapped it up.'

'He waited till next day,' said Jack McClure sadly, 'and it was too late.'

'That's the show game,' said Mr Lehman, shaking his head.

'That's the show game,' said Jack McClure, shaking his.

Barmy nodded intelligently.

'I see what you mean. Do It Now, as it were. Well, I'm all for quick decisions myself, if it's really a red-hot proposition. Only, of course, I've got to be careful, what? Pretty cautious and wary, if you see what I mean.'

'Just the kind of man I like, sweetheart. I ain't asking you to go in blindfold. I got a great gag and I ain't afraid to show it. I got a play that's going to catch everybody, see? It ain't highbrow, and yet it ain't lowbrow.'

'Sort of medium brow?'

'Yah. It's the first good medium brow show they've had, and it's going to be a knock-out.'

'Going to make a lot of money, what?'

'Money? I'll say! Ask Dick Rodgers and Oscar Hammerstein what they're knocking down out of this *South Pacific*. Ask Oscar Serlin what he made out of *Life With Father*. Ask Max Gordon what he cleaned up out of *Born Yesterday*.'

'You want me to ask them?'

'I'll tell you, sweetheart. Millions.'

'Millions?'

'Millions,' said Mr Lehman.

'Millions,' said Jack McClure.

'Well, that's what I'd like,' said Barmy. 'Only I'd want it to be safe.'

'I'll guarantee it personally. So will my friend here. Won't you, Jack?'

'Sure.'

'So what do you say? Think on your feet. That's show business.'

Barmy fingered his Drones Club tie. Mr Lehman's eloquence had stirred him deeply, but he could not forget that good thing of his Uncle Theodore's which he had heard so often both as a boy and when grown to manhood. 'Look before you leap,' his Uncle Theodore had been fond of saying, for he was a neat phrase-maker.

'Could I read the play or something?' he asked.

'H'm,' said Mr Lehman doubtfully. 'Think we can dig up a script for Mr Phipps, Jack?'

'Afraid not,' said Jack McClure, correctly interpreting that 'H'm'. 'You see, the troupe's in rehearsal, Mr Phipps, and they're using them all.'

'And what the hell! You don't need no script,' said Mr Lehman. 'I'll show you where it's sure fire.' With a sweeping gesture he pushed the litter on the desk out of his way. It was as if a battleship had been cleared for action. Joe Lehman was about to begin. 'Now look,' he said, tilting his hat back. 'It's a play about a feller with a heart of gold, see? Feller who's always trying to do the square thing by everybody.'

'A gentleman in every sense of the word,' said Jack McClure.

'A gentleman in every sense of the word,' said Mr Lehman. 'Mervyn Potter plays the part, and will he play it to the queen's taste? Ask me.'

'Will he?'

'Yes,' said Mr Lehman.

'Yes,' said Jack McClure.

'You betcher,' said Mr Lehman.

'You betcher,' said Jack McClure.

'Well, that's fine,' said Barmy.

Mr Lehman tilted his hat sideways.

'Now look. We open with a Prologue.'

'A Prologue,' explained Jack McClure.

'There's a playwright in the Prologue.'

'Fellow who writes plays,' said Jack McClure.

'And he's in love with a dame, see? And he's asked a bunch of people to come around and hear him read his new drama. Including the skirt. So he starts to read, and he says "The first scene is an orchard". Now!' Mr Lehman juggled briefly with his hat. 'When he says "orchard", we work that cutback trick, like in the movies. Black out, quick change, lights up, and it's the orchard.'

'Just the way he said.'

'Yah. Then all the rest of it is his play. Only he's in it, see, and the dame's in it, see. This doll that's in the orchard is the same doll you seen in the Prologue. Neat?'

'Frightfully neat,' said Barmy.

'She's climbing up an apple tree. On account she's in high spirits,' explained Mr Lehman. 'And along comes this feller that was the playwright in the Prologue, and they gab awhile back and forth, and he tells her he loves her, and she says she loves him, so there they are, all set to get married.'

Barmy blinked. The story, as outlined, seemed to him to lack dramatic complications. A bit on the short side, too. Raise the curtain at eight-forty, Eastern Standard time, and it would fall, he estimated, at about eight-fifty-three.

'Is that the end of the play?' he asked.

'End of the play? Wait!' said Mr Lehman. 'You ain't heard nothin' yet.'

'There's some more coming?'

'You bet there's some more coming.'

'Don't forget the priest,' said Jack McClure.

'Oh, yah. There's a priest comes in, see, an there's some gab with him. Well, orchard scene over, we cut to a big cabaret in New York. Music and dancing. You know.'

'Yah,' said Barmy, risking it.

'And into this cabaret comes the feller, the dame and the dame's brother. The feller and the dame ain't married yet. They're going to be tomorrow. Get it?'

'Yah,' said Barmy, quite confidently this time.

'Now, this brother of the dame's is one of them wild young sons of guns, always cutting up and raising hell, and a feller comes along that don't like him and says "Oh, it's you, is it?", and the brother gives him a dirty look and says "Yah. Want to make something of it?" and the feller . . . well, one thing and another happens, both of them getting uglier every minute, and back and forth and back and forth, and so on and so on, and first thing you know the brother outs with a gun, and *bingo*!' said Mr Lehman, climaxing the episode with an explosive snap of the fingers.

'I say!' said Barmy. 'Hot stuff, what? Shoots him, does he?'

'Deader than a mackerel. Lays him out colder than a stepmother's kiss. Music stops. Waiters yell. Girls scream. Women faint. And in comes the police. "What goes on?" asks the police,' said Mr Lehman, now giving a performance of which Edwin Booth would have been proud. ' "Who dun it?" says the police. And the feller says he dun it.'

'The feller?'

'Yah.'

'But he's dead.'

'Who's dead?'

'The feller.'

'No, no, no,' said Mr Lehman, clutching his hat. 'Not that feller. The other feller. The feller that's nuts on the dame. The hero. He says "I dun it", to save the brother of the woman he loves.'

Barmy was mildly puzzled.

'But weren't there a lot of people in the vicinity?'

'Sure they was.'

'Then don't they see the brother shoot the feller?'

'Naw,' said Mr Lehman, with vast scorn for the novice's ignorance of stage mechanics. 'They're all looking the other way.'

'Oh, I see. Right ho.'

'So the feller's arrested and gets twenty years in the cooler, only you don't know that till the next act. We end at Act One with the arrest. The cops put the bracelets on the feller, and the feller goes out with his chin up and the dame lets out a screech and falls in a swoon as the curtain drops, and that's your Act One. Great start, huh?'

'Oh, terrific.'

'It's called *Sacrifice*,' said Jack McClure. 'He sacrifices himself for the dame, see?'

' "Sacrifice",' said Mr Lehman. 'Good marquee title, huh?'

'Eh?'

'It'll look well up in lights,' said Jack McClure.

'Oh, stupendous,' said Barmy.

Mr Lehman had employed the intermission between the acts by refreshing himself at the water-cooler. He cleared himself for action again.

'Now! Second Act. It's twenty years later, and the feller's out of jail. He's gone to hide his head in one of them South Sea islands, and he's gone down and down, and now he's so far down, he's playing the piano in one of them places,' said Mr Lehman delicately.

'House of ill fame,' said Jack McClure.

'Yah, house of ill fame,' said Mr Lehman. 'He's a broken man playing the piano in a house of ill fame.'

'Don't forget the priest,' said Jack McClure.

'Oh, yah. This priest. Remember him?'

'He was in the orchard.'

'That's him. He's a missionary now, working in this South Sea island, and he comes to close this place up, and you get a big scene. There's a big party going on, everybody cutting up, and he comes in and opens up on them. And suddenly, *zowie*! This feller, the hero, comes back at him. That's where we bring in the strong talk. He calls him all kinds of names. We go the limit. He says, "You missionaries is all alike, you don't give nobody no chance," and back and forth and back and forth and so-and-so and so-and-so and so-and-so, and that's the end of your first scene, Act Two.'

'Lots of action,' said Barmy judicially.

'Nothing to what comes later. Next scene is in the Governor's house.'

'Whose governor?'

'The Governor of the island.'

'Oh, ah.'

'And who's come to visit the Governor in the course of one of them around-the-world cruises but the dame that was going to marry the hero and her husband, because she married this other guy while the hero was in the coop. And the hero's seen her driving to the house, and late that night he breaks in. Feels he must have a word with her, see? So it's her bedroom and she's in a negligay, and in comes the hero through the window and says "Genevieve!", and she says "Harold!", and she says "Is it you?", and he says "Yah, it's me", and back and forth and back and forth, and then it comes out that the brother has died and confessed on his death-bed that it was him that dun it, and she says she loves the hero still but must stick to this guy she's married because she's the soul of honour, see, and they have a farewell scene, and suddenly in comes the husband and he thinks the hero is a burglar and he plugs him with his gun and the hero falls to the ground a corpse and the dame falls on top of him and has a fit and dies on his body. The next act's in heaven,' said Mr Lehman, going to the water-cooler.

Barmy blinked.

'Heaven?'

'Heaven,' said Mr Lehman, emptying his paper cup. 'Here's where we got all those angels coming down the aisles—'

'Long veils over them,' said Jack McClure.

'Everything's all mixed up in this act. The Governor's there, only he's supposed to be God.'

'Is that all right to do?'

'There was a big hit done it,' said Mr Lehman in a tone calculated to lay all doubts. 'Anyhow, we don't really say it.'

'Don't forget the priest,' said Jack McClure.

'Oh, yah. This priest comes in and he's got a rabbi with him, see? And they talk about how everybody's the same underneath and it don't matter what religion they got. And back and forth and back and forth and so on and so on, and then suddenly *bingo*! Black out, quick change, and lights go up on the playwright's home, and the playwright's got the dame in his arms, and she says the bluebird of happiness was at home all the time. Kiss, finish reading the play, everybody says great, the feller and the dame gets married, fade out, and curtain. How do you like it?' said Mr Lehman.

Barmy mopped his forehead.

'Terrific. Who wrote it?'

'Some guy, I forget his name. We bought him out, so of course we don't have to pay royalties. You can't lose with it, sweetheart. Now how much was you thinking of putting up? You can have forty-nine per cent for . . .' Mr Lehman paused, measuring his man. 'For thirty thousand dollars,' he concluded.

'Oh, I say, dash it! Thirty thousand?'

'Can't you shave it a little, Joe, for Mr Phipps?' asked Jack McClure, and Mr Lehman said he thought it might be possible.

'I'll tell you what I'll do. Give me a quick yes and I'll take twenty-five.'

'I'm afraid the binge is off,' said Barmy.

He rose disconsolately, but not for long. Four willing hands pressed him into the chair again.

'This coin of yours,' said Mr Lehman. 'If it was where you could dig it up in a hurry, maybe we can do business.'

'It's in a bank on Fifth Avenue.'

'It is? Well, I wasn't going to of let it go for this,' said Mr Lehman, 'but you give me your cheque for ten thousand and twenty-five per cent of the show is yours.'

'You couldn't have bought in on *Harvey* for that,' said Jack McClure.

'And that was a big hit, too,' said Mr Lehman, handsomely. 'Now what do you say?'

Barmy fingered his tie. A man whose wordly assets consist of twenty-two thousand dollars and eighteen cents may legitimately finger his tie before deciding to invest ten thousand of it in a little drama, however compact and up to the minute.

'Ten thousand?'

'That's the dope.'

'Ten thousand?'

'And it's a bargain. Think on your feet.'

Barmy rose slowly.

'Well . . .'

'Set!' cried Mr Lehman.

'Set!' cried Jack McClure.

The two partners became two live wires. With a quick movement Mr Lehman dipped a pen in the ink and proffered it to Barmy, while simultaneously Jack McClure cleared a space on the desk. Their every gesture showed that immediate action was expected, and Barmy, with something of the emotions of a man who is going over Niagara Falls in a barrel and realizes that it is too late to turn back, slowly began to draw out his cheque-book. Two pairs of eyes followed his every move. It was, indeed, with difficulty that the Messrs Lehman and McClure restrained themselves from taking the book out of his hands and spreading it open on the table. Barmy, still slowly, opened it himself. He took the pen from Mr Lehman's hand, and began to write.

'Guaranty Trust, eh?' said Jack McClure, peering over his shoulder.

'Joe Le-h-m-a-n,' said Mr Lehman helpfully. 'You're a smart baby, Mr Phipps, and you're going to clean up. Now just sign it.'

Barmy poised the pen in the air, and, as he did so, there was a noise outside like the sudden rising of a hundred pheasants and the door was flung open explosively.

The wife of Mr Lehman's bosom strode in.

'Listen, you dog-faced four-flusher!' she said, addressing Mr Lehman, and slammed the door behind her with a devastating bang.

10

WITH a speed remarkable in a man so heavily built, Mr Lehman sprang from his swivel chair and was at her side. He had no means of knowing what was the motive which had caused the moon of his delight to play this return date, but he feared the worst. The look which she was giving him presaged disaster. To say that the World's Greatest Juggler was glaring would be to convey too weak an impression. It seemed to Mr Lehman's fevered imagination that flames were shooting from her eyes. Quaking inwardly, he sought refuge in bluster.

'Ain't you got no sense at all?' he demanded heatedly. 'Get out of here. Get out of here.'

For a moment the emotions with which Fanny was wrestling were too deep for words. Then she found speech.

'Listen!'

'Now, Fanny—' moaned Mr Lehman.

'Fanny, for the love of—' cried Jack McClure.

Fanny was deaf to these appeals. She had a powerful voice, and she raised it to its utmost. The pimpled office boy, who, when the door had slammed, had feared that he was going to be left out of this, experienced a sense of relief and pressed his ear more closely to the keyhole.

'Listen!' said Fanny, all the woman in her flashing from her eyes. 'I just come from my bank. And the paying teller there says there was a guy around there this morning with a check suit and a trick tie trying to find out how big my balance was.'

Mr Lehman shot an appreciative glance at Barmy.

'Now, now,' he said, as soothing as was within his power, 'I don't know nothing about it. Come back after a while,' he urged.

'If you show up around there again,' proceeded the voice of doom, 'they got instructions to shoot on sight. They'll wait till they see the whites of your eyes, then *bong*. That's all I come to tell you.'

'Then get out!'

'I'm not staying. I'm only telling you not to go snooping around my money, because you ain't going to get a nickel of it,' said Fanny. She flung open the door, and the office boy retreated, rubbing his ear. 'No, sir, not a nickel,' concluded Fanny. 'Not for a rotten show like that.'

She went out, and the door crashed shut behind her.

For an appreciable space of time after her departure neither Mr Lehman nor Jack McClure moved. Only their eyes travelled round to Barmy, who was sitting rigidly in the visitor's chair. Then Mr Lehman began to slide back to his place at the desk – slowly, casually, pitifully trying to give the impression that nothing had happened. Jack McClure likewise shifted his position, but neither man allowed his eyes to stray for an instant from Barmy. If Barmy had been the statue of the Winged Victory in the Louvre and they two art-loving tourists, they could not have regarded him with a more single-minded intentness.

Barmy came to life. He raised the pen, then suddenly lowered it and looked up.

'Did she say rotten?' he asked in a low voice.

Mr Lehman was himself again.

'She wasn't talking about this show,' he said quickly.

'It's another one we got,' said Jack McClure.

'She don't even know nothing about this one,' said Mr Lehman.

'Who was it? A friend of yours?'

'It was my old lady. Mrs Lehman. She's loco. Pay no attention to her. She has these spells.'

There was a pause. Barmy's face, both men were distressed to observe, was still sicklied o'er with the pale cast of thought. Mr Lehman addressed him pleadingly.

'Now listen, blossom boy, you got judgment of your own, ain't you? A smart guy like you. I told you about the show. Don't it sound like a wow?'

'Oh, definitely. But . . . on the other hand. You see I'm not so dashed keen on losing ten thousand dollars.'

Mr Lehman achieved an amused chuckle.

'You ain't going to lose it. Did I tell you about the bookings?'

'Bookings?'

'The towns we play in. The theatres.' Mr Lehman reached into the drawer for the route sheet. 'Look. We open in Syracuse, see? A great show town. Then we go to Providence, Worcester, Albany . . . all them soft spots.'

'They're soft, are they?'

'They're great. We got the cream. So just sign that cheque and we'll be set.'

Barmy continued to hesitate. Two voices were ringing in his ears – one the voice of Fanita, the World's Greatest Juggler, the other that of his Uncle Theodore. When he closed his eyes, as he now did, he seemed to see his Uncle Theodore standing warming his ample trousers-seat at the fire in the library at home, fixing him with a fishy gaze and coming through with that look-before-you-leap sequence which was so often on his lips. Useless to attempt to conceal from himself that Uncle Theodore would take a very pale view of what was going on in the office of Lehmac Productions, Inc.

It was as he sat there with closed eyes, wondering what to do for the best, that he heard the click of a door handle. Light footsteps sounded on the office linoleum. He opened his eyes and sat staring, spellbound by what he saw.

A girl of about the tonnage of Betty Grable was leaning over Mr Lehman's desk, laying on it what looked like a letter, and a single glance enabled him to recognize her as the girl who since that romantic meeting in Madison Avenue had never left his thoughts for a moment, except possibly the moment when he was soaring into the boughs of the cedar a short head in front of the dog Tulip. He uttered a wordless cry, and Dinty, looking up, recognized him in her turn. She did not speak, for discipline is discipline, but her eyes widened and she gave him one of her friendliest smiles. Then she went back to her cubbyhole, and Barmy gaped after her, transfixed.

'I say,' he said dazedly.

Mr Lehman was studying the letter frowningly.

'From the Theatre Guild,' he said to Jack McClure. 'They want to buy in on the show.'

'I thought they would.'

'Yah.'

'You were sort of expecting to hear from them after what they were saying Tuesday.'

'Yah. Of course it's too late now. We've promised Mr Phipps.'

'We can't let Mr Phipps down.'

'No, we got to do the square thing by Mr Phipps. It's the same old story. They didn't think on their feet, so they lost out. That's show business,' sighed Mr Lehman.

'That's show business,' sighed Jack McClure.

Barmy was not interested in the misfortunes of the Theatre Guild. He was still gaping at the door of the cubbyhole.

'I say,' he said. 'Who was that?'

'Huh?'

'That girl.'

'Oh her? My secretary.'

'Your secretary?'

'Yah.'

Barmy quivered from head to foot. Soft music seemed to him to be playing in the office of Lehmac Productions and violets to be sprouting from its dusty floor.

'You mean she works here?'

'Sure. All the time.'

Barmy ceased to hesitate. Faintly, as from a great distance, he could still hear Uncle Theodore's warning voice, but he had no leisure to listen to Uncle Theodore now. With a firm hand he signed the cheque, and Mr Lehman jumped at it like a trout leaping at a fly.

'It's wet,' said Barmy.

'I'll dry it. Well, my puss,' said Mr Lehman, 'you're a partner now.' He sprang for the door, where Jack McClure was already standing like a greyhound straining at the leash. 'You wait here, see, while Jack and me go to the bank. You wait here and look after things. I'll tell you what. Hey!' he bellowed.

Dinty appeared.

'Look out for this gentleman till we get back,' said Mr Lehman. 'Come on, Jack.'

The door closed behind them.

11

DINTY was the first to break the silence which followed the exodus of the two partners, for Barmy, confronted at this close range with a girl who would have affected him like a blow from a blunt instrument even if seen through a telescope, was having trouble with his vocal cords. Electric shocks were passing through him, and his toes curled inside their suède shoes.

'So we meet again,' said Dinty. 'Properly introduced this time. Though it wasn't much of an introduction, was it?'

Barmy was now able to articulate.

'Eh?' he said, speaking almost fluently.

'He might at least have mentioned our names.'

'Names? You want to know my name?'

'Well, it would be convenient to have it, so that I could tell whether to address you as Judge or Colonel or Your Royal Highness. Mine, by the way, is Dinty Moore.'

'Dinty?'

'All Moores are called Dinty. Because of the restaurant.'

'What restaurant?'

'Dinty Moore's. Don't you know Dinty Moore's? It's like Lindy's.'

'What's Lindy's?'

Dinty saw that this was going to take some time.

'Suppose we just let it go, shall we?' she suggested. 'What's your name?'

'Mine?' Barmy thought for a moment. 'Oh, Fotheringay – I mean Phipps.'

'Well, which?'

'Eh?'

'Is it Fotheringay or Phipps?'

'It's both.'

Dinty frowned, as if at some smooth sophistry which in her opinion could only cloud the issue.

'It can't be both.'

'There's a hyphen in the middle.'

'That may be your story, but it sounds thin to me.'

'As a matter of fact, it isn't exactly Fotheringay, if you follow me.'

'I don't.'

'It's pronounced Fungy.'

'You can't pronounce Phipps Fungy.'

'No, the Fotheringay.'

'You said it wasn't Fotheringay.'

'No, it isn't.'

Dinty's sternness seemed to deepen. It was plain that she was beginning to feel that she was being played fast and loose with.

'I don't like this shiftiness and evasion,' she said. 'What do you expect to gain by it? Be frank. Be open. Let your Yea be Yea and your Nay Nay, your Phipps Phipps and your Fungy Fungy.'

'My pals all call me Barmy.'

'Now we're getting somewhere.'

'I wish you would call me Barmy.'

'I'd love to. Thank you, Barmy.'

'Not at all.'

There was a pause.

'Well,' said Dinty, 'and how's the arson business?'

'Eh?'

'Been setting any more hats on fire?'

'Oh no, rather not.'

'Bungalows?'

'Oh, no. No bungalows.'

'Turned over a new leaf, have you, and decided to go straight? I was hoping you would. It's just a matter of will power. And what have you been doing since we last met?'

'Me? Oh, nothing much. I was chased up a tree by a dog last night.'

'You do live, don't you? I went to a party up in the Bronx last night, and you'll be glad to hear the new hat was a sensation. I was chased up a staircase by a Television master of ceremonies.'

There was another pause. Barmy sought in his tottering mind for topics that would keep the conversation going. He was aware that his contribution to it so far had not been of an outstanding brilliance, and wished to remedy this as soon as possible. He also wished that the top of his head would stop going up and down like the lid of a kettle, for this interfered with clear thought.

'Lots of dust in here,' he said, hitting on something bright.

'Yes, we're proud of our dust,' said Dinty. 'Mr Lehman has it imported specially. Some of it's got on your face. No, not there. More to the left. Here, let me do it.'

She took the handkerchief from his hand and removed the alluvial deposit.

It was a process which involved a close proximity between them, and it was a dangerous moment for a girl who had made so profound an impression on a Fotheringay-Phipps to come into close proximity with him, for the blood of the Fotheringay-Phippses is notoriously hot. It was Barmy's Uncle Theodore – this can be verified by consulting the family archives – whose hot blood got him into all that trouble with the barmaid at Oxford in the year 1909.

Barmy, moreover, influenced by the remarks of the Gypsy Sybil, had come to look upon this girl as his destined mate, and it is pretty generally recognized by poets of the romantic school that when you meet your destined mate, formalities can be dispensed with and the etiquette book disregarded. A brief 'Hullo, there' and you are at liberty to express yourself.

This may be right, or it may be wrong – poets are uncertain guides – but, wrong or right, it was the view which Barmy took. Whatever it was that was lifting the top of his head suddenly boiled over. Sparks danced before his eyes. He reached out impulsively, folded Dinty in a warm embrace, and kissed her.

He kissed her with all the pent-up passion of a generous nature, and was about to continue along these lines when a hand, whizzing up, smote him on the left ear. Heaven, as is well known, protects the working girl, but Dinty Moore on occasions like this always found it more convenient not to rely solely on help from above. She packed a nice uppercut in both hands and was not afraid to use it. In just such a manner she had smitten a young insurance clerk named Ed one evening at Coney Island when, on the strength of having bought her two hot dogs and a chocolate nut sundae, he had behaved in a similarly impulsive manner.

She stepped back and regarded Barmy coldly. He had disappointed her. She was feeling as she would have felt if she had stopped to fraternize with a dog of amiable aspect, and the dog had turned and bitten her.

Barmy rubbed his ear. He was still not thinking clearly, but he could see that an apology was in order.

'I'm sorry,' he said.

'Don't mention it.'

'I lost my head.'

'If you call it a head. Did I hurt you?'

'Yes.'

'Good,' said Dinty.

Barmy's mind began to work again. He was able to explain.

'It was a bit sudden, I know. I got carried away. You see, a fortune-teller over in England told me I should take a long journey and meet a fair girl, so when I took the long journey and met you, I naturally said to myself "What ho!". I mean, I saw in a second that there you were and there I was. There we both were, if you follow me. I oughtn't to have let myself be carried away like that, but I was sort of leading up to ask you if you'd marry me.'

'What!'

'Marry. M for measles.'

Dinty seated herself on the desk, and eyed him with a bright interest. Hers had been a sheltered life, and this was the first time she had encountered anything like the Last of the Fotheringay-Phippses.

'Well!' she said.

'I know, I know. Of course, you'll want to think it over. I hadn't meant to spring it on you quite so soon.'

'It sort of slipped out?'

'That's right. I fell in love with you at first sight, don't you know, and all that sort of rot, but I had rather intended to hush it up till a more suitable moment.'

'Have you often fallen in love at first sight?'

'Never with the same—'

'Fervour?'

'That's right. Fervour.'

'F for fried potatoes?'

'Exactly.'

Dinty continued to gaze at him, fascinated. She was still doing so, when the door opened and Miss Gladys Whittaker came in, walking grimly and purposefully. Expecting to see Mr Lehman and finding a changeling with butter-coloured hair in his place, she halted, baffled.

'Mr Lehman?' she said, looking about her. 'I came to see Mr Lehman.'

'He'll be back soon, Miss Whittaker,' said Dinty.

'What did he want to go out for? I told him I was coming back, and it's important.'

A consciousness of his new responsibilities roused Barmy from the stupor into which he had fallen.

'Er – is it something to do with the firm?' he said, and wondered if he should have added 'Sweetheart' or 'My blossom'. The technique of being a theatrical manager took some getting into.

'I beg your pardon?'

'I mean to say, if it's something to do with the firm, I could do it, what?'

A questioning graciousness softened the grim intensity of Miss Whittaker's manner.

'I wonder if this is the . . . Mr Lehman spoke of someone who was coming into the company . . . Are you—?'

'That's right. I'm a partner.'

'Then of *course* you can do it,' said Miss Whittaker, letting loose her full battery of charm. 'I don't believe Mr Lehman mentioned your name.'

'Phipps.'

'I'm Gladys Whittaker, Mr Phipps. I'm in the show. You're coming to rehearsals soon, aren't you, Mr Phipps? I'm sure we all want to get your ideas. And I do especially. I'm sure you'll be wonderful. I can't tell you how relieved I am that you've come to take charge of things. Oh, I knew there was something, Mr Phipps,' she said, breaking off as if at some sudden recollection. 'I wonder if you would do me a very great favour. I don't like to trouble you, but I left my cheque-book at home this morning, and just now I saw the darlingest little dress, and they won't hold it for poor me,' said Miss Whittaker, skirting for one terrible second the edge of baby talk.

Barmy produced his cheque-book.

'Why, of course. How much?'

'A hundred. Make it cash.'

'Right ho.'

'Thank you,' said Miss Whittaker, taking the cheque and bestowing it in her ornate bag. 'That's just fine. I think it's wonderful, your coming in with us, Mr Phipps. It makes everything seem different. Now don't forget. You're coming to rehearsals and you're going to tell me just what you think. If you don't like the way I'm doing something, you'll mention it, won't you?'

'Sure you won't mind?'

'*Mind?*' said Miss Whittaker in a sort of ecstasy. 'The one thing a genuine artist wants is advice. Good-bye, Mr Phipps, and thank you again. Such a pleasure to be under your management.'

The door closed. Barmy gaped at it limply. He had found Miss Whittaker, coming on top of that emotional scene, a little overpowering.

Dinty was regarding him with new interest.

'So that's who you are! The angel!'

'Eh?'

'Mr Lehman was telling me all about you. Have you put money in the show?'

'Eh? Oh, yes. I bunged in a certain sum.'

'Well, well. I've often wondered how it would feel to be able to do that. It must be fun being an angel. If I had all the money in the world, like you, I think I'd risk it.'

Her choice of verbs brought to life the qualms and tremors which had never wholly left Barmy since that disturbing scene with the loco Mr Lehman. He quivered as if some hidden hand had thrust a bare bodkin through the seat of his chair.

'Risk it? You don't think it's risky, do you?'

'Well, plays are always a toss-up, aren't they?'

'But this one. With Mervyn Potter starring.'

'Yes of course, his name will be a big draw. But—'

'But what?'

'He's terribly erratic. He might let you down somehow.'

'How?'

'I don't know. Somehow. Have you ever met him?'

'Oh, rather. We're great pals. He was at Skeewassett, at the hotel. He was the fellow I was telling you about, the one I saved from being cooked to a crisp. He had set his bungalow on fire, and I happened to spot the conflagration from my window and nipped across and extracted him.'

'Well, there you are. He set his bungalow on fire. That's the sort of thing he does. I suppose he had been drinking.'

'He was a mite polluted, I fancy.'

'They tell me he generally is.'

'He certainly was last night. He got us chucked out of the Piazza.'

'Well, that's what I mean. Don't you think you're taking rather a chance, putting money in a show where the star drinks?'

Barmy fingered his tie. His jaw had fallen.

'I don't know if you know it, my dear old goddess in human shape, but you're making my flesh creep,' he said.

Dinty apologized.

'I'm sorry. I don't want to cast a gloom on the proceedings. Probably everything will be all right.'

'It will. I've just remembered that Potter's fiancée has made him go on the wagon. So we shan't have any trouble from that source.'

'Well, that's fine.'

'And the play's good, what? I mean medium-brow and full of action and what not. It'll be a hit, don't you think?'

'Oh sure. But—'

'You keep saying But.'

'I hope it will be a hit. But shows do flop, don't they?'

Barmy, who had risen agitatedly, sank back into his chair. He had paled beneath the tan which a summer in Sunny Maine had given him.

'You mean you think this one will?'

'I'm not saying that. I'm only saying it's a contingency, if that's the word, that you have to budget for. You do get an occasional flop, you know, in the course of the theatrical season. Probably Mr Potter's name will put the thing over, but accidents do happen. Still, what does it matter to you? You're a millionaire.'

'Me?'

'Mr Lehman said you were.'

'I'm not a millionaire. I've got twenty-two thousand dollars.'

'What!'

'And eighteen cents.'

A hideous suspicion flashed into Dinty's mind.

'You didn't give it all to Mr Lehman?'

'Good Lord, no. Only ten thousand.'

'Oh!'

'What's the matter?'

Dinty was looking like a mother hearing bad news from her idiot child.

'No wonder you asked me to call you Barmy!' Her manner became urgent. 'Do you know what you've got to do?'

'What?'

'Phone your bank and stop that cheque before Mr Lehman can get there and cash it.'

'Eh?'

'If there's time.'

'But if I do, I shall never see you again.'

'Why not?'

'Because I shan't be working here. I was going to work here, with you at my elbow, so to speak. Lord love a duck, that's what made me go into it. That was the whole idea. I had practically decided to give the thing a miss, when you came sailing in. I ascertained that you were permanently on the premises and immediately signed on the dotted line. I wanted to have you at my elbow.'

'Well, that was very nice of you. But—'

'You do keep saying But, don't you?'

'You must get out of it.'

'But . . . now you've got me saying it . . . but how about seeing you again?'

'You'll see me again, all right. I wouldn't let you go out of my life for a million. You can come and take me to lunch.'

'Every day?'

'If you want to. And on Sundays we'll go and feed the bears in the Bronx Park Zoo. Now get on that phone, quick. Which is your bank?'

'The Guaranty Trust, Fifth Avenue and Forty-Third Street.'

'Oh, heavens! You would pick that one, wouldn't you? The only bank in New York that stays open till four o'clock. I was hoping it was some nice uptown place that closed at three and would be shut when they got there. Hurry, hurry, hurry!'

As Barmy fumbled through the telephone directory, Dinty sat looking at him thoughtfully. She was feeling a little breathless. It was a novel experience to have to regard herself in the role of a *femme fatale*. Like most pretty girls, she had always had a reasonably good opinion of herself, but it had never occurred to her before that there might come into her life men who would count half their fortune well lost in exchange for a smile from her. She felt complimented and gratified. Barmy had ceased to be merely a pleasant young man and had become something portentous. She found that her heart was beating rapidly and that there was a mist before her eyes.

'Oh, gosh!' she cried, as she saw through the mist that the portentous young man had dropped the telephone directory and was groping for it under the desk. Impatience became her dominant emotion.

'Sorry,' said Barmy.

'Is this the time to be practising your juggling?'

'It slipped,' Barmy explained.

He started to scramble out apologetically and, as he did so, the door opened. Mervyn Potter sauntered in.

'Ah, Phipps,' said Mervyn Potter. 'You again? Stap my vitals, your ubiquitousness is simply uncanny. Is there no place where you're not? Next time I take a bath, I shall examine the soap dish very carefully to make sure you are not snuggled up in it.'

'Oh, hullo, Potter.'

'Potter it is, Phipps. First, last and all the time, Potter. So you're taking it easy under the desk for awhile, are you? What a versatile chap you are. Now up trees, now under desks. Tell me, Phipps,' said Mervyn Potter, taking the telephone directory and flinging it with a careless gesture into a distant corner, for it was foreign to his policy to allow men to whom he was addressing his conversation to let their attention wander to telephone directories, 'do you notice anything about me?'

'Eh?'

'My bursting health,' said Mervyn Potter. 'My rosy cheeks. That indefinable air of *bien être*. It all comes from being on the wagon. There's nothing like it. I feel like a new man. But what are you doing here, Phipps? Have you taken my advice and come to see Lehman on business?'

Barmy, who had chased the telephone directory like a retriever, came back with it.

'Eh? Yes, I'm a partner.'

'You are?'

'You are not,' said Dinty. 'Get on that phone.'

The telephone rang. Mervyn Potter took up the receiver.

'Hello?' he said. 'Yes, speaking. What? All right? Of course it's all right. I'm surprised at you for asking such a question.' He replaced the receiver. 'For you,' he said to Barmy. 'Your bank. Wanted to know if it was all right to cash a cheque of yours for a paltry ten thousand dollars or some such sum. I said of course it was. Good heavens, if the stability of the bank balance of a Fotheringay-Phipps is to be questioned by some wretched paying teller probably with watery eyes and spots on his face, things have come to a pretty pass. If that sort of thing is to be allowed to go on, then let the sun be darkened and the moon turned to blood. Hoity-toity, what next?' said Mervyn Potter, summing up.

12

WHEN the late Algernon Swinburne, in his poem *The Garden of Proserpine*, made the statement that even the weariest river winds somewhere safe to sea, he probably had in mind the fact that, though at times it seemed unlikely, the rehearsals of a play do eventually come to an end and that the company does at long last find itself in New Haven, Boston, Philadelphia, or, as in the case of the one partly financed by Barmy Fotheringay-Phipps, in Syracuse.

After four weeks of blood, toil, tears and sweat, the management, director, star, subsidiary actors and camp followers of the Lehmac production *Sacrifice* were distributed about that thriving town, the minor members of the troupe in boarding-houses, the big shots at the Mayflower Hotel.

Barmy, as the man who had made the production possible, had been favoured with ample quarters, Room 726, which had two windows and three armchairs, and already he had made his presence felt. Downstairs in his office Oscar Fritchie, the assistant manager of the hotel, was giving his final riding orders to the waiter who at the conclusion of the opening performance would serve the celebration supper which Barmy had ordered, a supper which was to feature chicken *à la king* and lots of champagne. 'Well iced,' said Oscar Fritchie, and the waiter said, 'Sure.' The word Yah had not penetrated to Syracuse.

During the days which had followed his entry into the firm, Barmy had run what is known as the gamut of the emotions, now soaring to the heights, now sinking into the depths. Sometimes the play had looked to him the wow Mr Lehman had said it was, sometimes it had seemed to justify the trenchant criticism of Mrs Lehman. Sometimes he had hoped, sometimes despaired. But now, with curtain time approaching, doubts had vanished and he was in a glow of optimism. Last night's dress rehearsal had convinced him. It had gone without a hitch, and it was with a light heart that he was donning the dress clothes which he felt an important Syracuse opening justified. When Mr Lehman entered, his derby hat on his head, his manner all eager expectancy and good fellowship, he had just finished tying his tie.

'How are you, my blossom?' said Mr Lehman, then paused, stupefied by the spectacle that met his eyes. 'Say!' he ejaculated admiringly, and Jack McClure, who had followed him into the room, expressed the opinion that Barmy looked like Great Lovers Through the Ages.

Barmy felt a twinge of embarrassment. From boyhood up it had been his constant aim to do the done thing, and he sensed criticism in these observations.

'What's the matter?' he said. 'Aren't you going to dress?'

'No, but that don't make no difference. How's the kid?'

'I thought – being an opening—'

'Sure. And it's going to be some opening. The biggest Syracuse has ever had.'

'Any chance of my having to make a speech, what?'

'I guess not.'

'That's good. I didn't really think there was, but just in case I thought I'd put on the old soup and fish.'

'Sure. Give 'em an eyeful. What room's Moore in, Jack?'

'Down the way. You want her?'

'Yah. And tell Fanny I'm here in twenty-six.'

'Oke,' said Jack McClure.

He went out with a last admiring look, and Mr Lehman explained to what Barmy owed the honour of this visit.

'The reason I come in, my puss, was you got such a fine big room I thought maybe you wouldn't mind if we was to get together up here after the show tonight.'

'You mean, to celebrate?'

'Well, sort of talk things over. There might be some changes or something.'

'Changes in the play?'

'In case there are any.'

Barmy was aware of a slight, but definite, return of the old qualms. He did not like this loose talk about changing the play.

'Isn't it all right?' he asked anxiously.

'Sure, sure. Great. But there might be something, see? Just a line. We'll have to have a conference. I and the wife is cooped up in twenty-eight next door, but this is good and big so we can all get in.'

This puzzled Barmy.

'All who?'

'Well, whoever comes. You see, after a show's opened you always have to do some gabbing back and forth. Back and forth and back and forth and so on and so on,' said Mr Lehman, from force of habit. 'We'll want to know what everybody thinks, see? I'll tell you what you do. You take a wad of paper at the show tonight and put down everything you see that's wrong. Play, acting, scenery, anything. Make a note of it, and then we'll talk it over.'

'What I thought you did after a play has opened is . . . sort of have a spot of supper and celebrate it.'

'We can do that, too. Great.'

Barmy touched his tie coyly.

'Er – could Miss Moore come?'

'You want her right now?'

'No, to the binge, I meant. There's no objection to her joining the revels, is there?'

'Sure not. You invite her. You'd better tell them downstairs.'

'Oh, I did. I saw the assistant manager. His name's Fritchie.'

'That screwball!'

'Eh?'

Mr Lehman's manner became urgent. He might have been a loving father explaining to his adolescent son the facts of life. He had visited Syracuse several times in the course of his career, and the subject of Oscar Fritchie was one on which he held strong opinion.

'You want to watch out for that bird,' he said. 'Don't let him get near you, or he'll talk your ear off. He's a screwball. He's show-crazy.'

'Eh?'

'Off his nut about show business. Give him half a chance and he'll talk your ear off.'

'I thought he seemed a nice sort of chap.'

'Oh, I've nothing against him, except that if you give him half a chance, he talks your ear off. Keep away from him.'

'Right ho.'

There was a pause. A grave look had come into Mr Lehman's rugged face. There was even a suspicion of moisture about his eyes. He held out his hand impulsively.

'Well, sweetheart, tonight's the night. Good luck.'

Barmy shook the hand warmly.

'Good luck.'

'I just want to say,' said Mr Lehman bluffly, 'how swell it's been working with you, Mr Phipps. I don't think you can ever know, Mr Phipps, how much your co-operation has meant to all of us. We're all mighty grateful, Mr Phipps. Thank you.'

'Thank *you*,' said Barmy. 'It's been dashed nice working with you.'

'That's the secret of success in the theatre, my blossom,' proceeded Mr Lehman, now visibly affected. 'Co-operation. Lots of these shows, something goes wrong on the opening night, and everyone's snarling and snacking at everyone, but we're just one happy family.'

'Happy family, that's right.'

'And that's what we'll be right along.'

'Absolutely.'

'Just a happy family.'

'Just a happy family.'

There was another pause.

'Well, good luck,' said Mr Lehman.

'Good luck,' said Barmy.

Silence fell again, as two strong men stood there, wrestling with feelings too deep for utterance. It was broken by the entry of Dinty, followed by Jack McClure.

'Ah!' said Mr Lehman, discarding sentiment and becoming the man of affairs. 'I want you, Moore.'

'Here I am, Field-Marshal.'

'I want you right beside me during the play, see? Take notes as I dictate 'em. Jack, I just been telling Mr Phipps what a help he's been to us.'

'He certainly has.'

'And what a pleasure it was to work with him.'

'It certainly was. Good luck, Mr Phipps.'

'Good luck.'

'Now there was something, Jack, now what was it?' said Mr Lehman. 'Oh, yes, now here's the angle—'

He led his gentlemanly partner out, talking as he went. Dinty, about to follow, was arrested by a passionate cry.

'Hey!'

'Yes, my pet?'

'Don't go,' said Barmy. 'I've got something for you.'

He blushed to think that, overcome by the emotions surging in his bosom as the result of that tender scene with Mr Lehman, he had temporarily forgotten it. He went to the cupboard and returned with a large box of flowers. Dinty tottered.

'For me?'

'Yah. I mean Yes. I got them for you for the opening. They're flowers.'

'That's what I said to myself, the moment I saw them. Flowers, I said to myself, or my eyes deceive me. How sweet of you, Barmy.'

'We Phippses are sweet. We're noted for it all over England.

'You'll make some nice girl a good husband.'

'Exactly. And that brings me to the point I wanted to touch on. How many times have I asked you to marry me?'

'I've lost count.'

'Well, here I go again. Will you?'

'Oh, Barmy.'

'It's no good saying "Oh, Barmy".'

'What else do you expect me to say?'

'You like me, don't you?'

'Of course I do. Who wouldn't?'

'Well, then.'

'If it's no good me saying "Oh, Barmy", it's certainly no good you saying, "Well, then".'

'Why not?'

Dinty became maternal.

'Because this is a tough world, my child, and we've got to be practical. It isn't just a question of whether I like you or not. I think you're as cute as a little red wagon, but the holy state costs money.'

'I've got ten thousand dollars.'

'That doesn't last long these days, if you haven't a job.'

Barmy found her unintelligible. She seemed to him like a goddess in human shape who was talking through the back of her neck.

'What do you mean, haven't a job? I'm a partner in Lehmac Productions, aren't I? And we're going to clean up, aren't we? Listen,' said Barmy, inspired. Mr Lehman's stimulating words at that first meeting had never ceased to remain green in his memory. 'Ask Dick Rodgers and Oscar Hammerstein what they're knocking down out of this *South Pacific*. Ask Oscar Serlin what he made out of *Life With Father*. Ask Max Gordon—'

'Yes, I know.'

'I'll tell you, my blossom. Millions.'

'Yes, I know. But—'

Dinty paused. She had been present at all the rehearsals and they had left her an adherent to the Fanny Lehman school of thought. She had not participated in that emotional scene when Fanny Lehman, speaking of the compact little drama *Sacrifice*, had used the word "rotten", but if she had been, she would have been obliged to admit that Mr Lehman's best friend and severest critic had selected the right adjective. She still clung desperately to the hope that a star of Mervyn Potter's eminence, with all the women in America panting to get a sight of him, would be able to put even *Sacrifice* over, but she was exceedingly dubious.

Still, it was not for her to act as a black frost in Barmy's garden of dreams. There might be a bitter awakening, but she was only too happy to see him in this uplifted mood. She put her hands on his shoulders and kissed him, and Barmy shook like a jelly.

'You've never done that before,' he said, awed.

'And I wouldn't do it now, if it wasn't that I wanted to wish you luck. That was a mother's kiss.'

'Mother's?'

'Mother's,' said Dinty firmly. 'Don't go getting it mixed up with the kiss of unbridled passion. That'll come later . . . maybe. And why I'm hanging around here, dallying with you and giving you motherly kisses, is more than I know. Mr Lehman is probably foaming at the mouth. "She cometh not", he said.'

'That's Shakespeare, isn't it?'

'One of those guys. I wouldn't know. They stopped my education before I was full to the brim. Good-bye, Barmy, dear, and good luck. I'm sure everything's going to be fine. And remember, if it isn't perfect tonight, it can probably be fixed. That's what a try-out's for.'

'Oh, rather. I'm going to take notes of whatever's wrong.'

'That's the way to talk. Up on your toes, boy.'

She hurried out, and Barmy, sinking into one of the three armchairs, gave himself up to rapturous meditation, totting up the score to see where he stood.

Things were moving, he considered. She hadn't said Yes, but, on the other hand, she hadn't said No. She had admitted that he was not wholly distasteful to her, even going so far as to state that she found him as cute as a little red wagon. He had no means of ascertaining how cute this was, but it was apparently quite fairly cute. And, above all, she had kissed him. A motherly kiss, she had said, but he wasn't going to believe that.

'Motherly, my foot!' he said aloud, and Gladys Whittaker, who was entering at the moment, paused and eyed him with not a little astonishment.

'I beg your pardon?'

Barmy sprang to his feet.

'Oh, hullo. I didn't know you were there. I – er – I was sort of soliloquizing. Like those blokes in Shakespeare. Er – was there anything?'

'I was looking for Mr Lehman.'

'He went off to the theatre. Was there something special you wanted to see him about?'

'Yes,' said Miss Whittaker. 'There was.'

Barmy could now see that there was a peculiar expression on this substantial blonde's face. A bleak, austere expression. She was looking more like an aunt than anything human. In his boyhood he had observed platoons of his aunts with their features frozen in a similar rigidity. To name but one, his Aunt Charlotte on the occasion when he had been led into her presence, charged with having broken the curate's umbrella.

'I want him to speak to Mr Potter.'

Barmy was surprised.

'Isn't he speaking to Potter?' he said. He had heard of no rift between the two.

'To speak to him seriously. About his drinking.'

'Is he *drinking*?'

Miss Whittaker looked more like an aunt than ever. 'I am the last person to criticize a fellow artist, Mr Phipps, but I feel it my duty to tell you that I saw Mr Potter in the lobby just now, and he was stinko.'

Barmy reeled.

'Stinko?'

'Stinko,' said Miss Whittaker. 'I only hope he will be able to give a performance tonight. Good-bye,' she said, and went out, looking like Cassandra.

Barmy paced the floor in a fever of disquiet and anxiety. Her words had shaken him to the core. He had so unhesitatingly accepted Mervyn Potter's statement that he was on the wagon, and it is always disconcerting to find that one has been living in a fool's paradise. At what point the blighter's foot had slipped, causing him to fall from the vehicle, he had no means of ascertaining, but that the fall must have taken place was not to be disputed by the most optimistic. A knowledgeable woman like Miss Whittaker would not have employed the adjective 'stinko', had there been any room for doubt in her mind.

This, he told himself, was a nice bit of box fruit. Of all obstacles to the success of a play, a stinko star is perhaps the most serious. Tales he had heard of curtains being rung down and audiences given their money back came flooding into his mind. Little wonder that he paced the floor.

It was as he turned from pacing it in an easterly direction and was about to pace back toward the west that he saw that he had another visitor.

Reading from left to right, Mervyn Potter.

13

BARMY'S initial emotion on beholding this star to which he had hitched his wagon was a profound relief. Miss Whittaker's gloomy words had left him, as we have seen, a prey to nameless fears, and he had had visions of a whooping, yelling Mervyn Potter, a Mervyn Potter behaving more or less along the line of Dangerous Dan McGrew shooting up the Malemute saloon. Privileged, that night of the burning bungalow at Skeewassett and again in the grounds of Mrs C. Hamilton Brimble's mansion at King's Point, Long Island, to observe him when he was going nicely, he knew how animated the Idol of American Womanhood could become in his more relaxed moments. Anticipating a Mervyn Potter who would have to have his head sat on by a posse of strong men while others ran to call out the police reserves, he found the spectacle of him now comforting.

For the Mervyn Potter who came slowly into Room 726 was far from being in the old Skeewassett and King's Point form. His head was bowed, his manner subdued. To all outward appearances, except for a slightly boiled look about the eyes, he might have been a teetotaller who had just received bad news from home.

'Ah, Phipps,' he said, in a low, toneless voice, like a spirit whispering into a trumpet at a *séance*.

Barmy became managerial. No theatrical manager likes to see his star loitering in hotel bedrooms with the curtain due to go up at any moment.

'I say!' he said. 'Aren't you dressed?'

'What's missing?' said Mervyn Potter, still in that same toneless voice, squinting a lack-lustre eye down at his costume.

'I mean, aren't you going to dress? The show will be starting soon.'

'Never mind the show,' said Mervyn Potter, becoming more animated. 'You leave the show alone, and it'll leave you alone. I have something serious to say to you, Phipps. As the Walrus said, the time has come to speak of many things.'

He lowered himself into an armchair, and after seeming to experience a difficulty in getting him into focus stared owlishly at Barmy.

'Phipps,' he said, 'we are old friends.' He paused, and looked questioningly at Barmy from under his eyebrows. 'Aren't we old friends, old friend?'

'Oh, rather.'

'Don't qualify it with any "Oh rathers",' said Mervyn Potter with a touch of that sternness which had come into his manner on the occasion when Barmy had suggested going off and having dinner. 'Either a man is an old friend or he is not an old friend. There is no middle course. You and I, Phipps, are very old friends. I will go further, extremely old friends. Through every peril, every adversity, in fair weather and foul, we two have stood shoulder to shoulder. Like the Boys of the Old Brigade. Are you familiar with the habits of the Boys of the Old Brigade?'

'Eh? No, I don't think I am.'

'They stood shoulder to shoulder, and, though I would not tell this to everyone, steadily blade by blade,' said Mervyn Potter, and fell into a light sleep. And there the scene might have concluded, had not Barmy, who had begun to pace the floor again, tripped over his visitor's feet.

Mervyn Potter opened his eyes.

'Where were we?' he asked.

'Eh?'

'We were discussing some subject replete, as I recall, with interest. What was it?'

'You were saying that we were old friends.'

'So I was. And so we are. You don't dispute that?'

'Oh, no, rather not.'

'I should be hurt and disappointed if you did. People sometimes come to me and say "Tell me, Potter", addressing me, you understand. My name is Potter. "Tell me, Potter, to settle a bet, are you and Phipps old friends?" and I reply, "Yes, Griggs or Freylinghausen or whatever the name may be, you are perfectly correct. Phipps and I are excessively old friends. Some friends are young friends, but Phipps and I are old ones. Who ran to help me when I fell and would some pretty story tell and kiss the place to make it well? Phipps. Between Phipps and myself," I tell these people, "there exists a perfect trust and confidence, so that we are able to speak our minds to each other frankly and openly and without offence. If, for example, prompted by the thought of our old friendship, I find myself compelled to talk to Phipps like a kindly elder brother, pointing out that he is hovering on the brink of a precipice, Phipps takes it in good part." Don't you, Phipps?'

'Oh, definitely.'

'No umbrage?'

'None.'

'Good. Then I will talk to you like a kindly elder brother now. Phipps, as I was coming along the corridor, I saw that secretary of Lehman's, young Dinty Moore, leaving your room, the inference being that at some earlier point she had sneaked into it. I dozed off for a moment or two, leaning against the wall, and when I opened my eyes, I saw Gladys Whittaker leaving your room, the inference again being that she had previously entered it. How many other females of the species entered your room during the interval when I was taking my siesta, I cannot say. Even now, for all I know, there may be women in every nook and cranny, hiding under the bed, tucked away in closets, peeping out from behind armchairs and nestling in the bath tub. I don't like it, Phipps. I don't like it, old friend. You may try to argue that your heart is young and that you are merely following in the footsteps of Casanova and Charles the Second, but I repeat I do not like it. Cut women out of your life, Phipps, and you will be a better, brighter man. It is the secret of a happy and prosperous career.'

Having said which, Mervyn Potter fell asleep again.

Barmy looked at him, bewildered. The sentiments he had just heard expressed were the last he would have expected from one who in previous conversations had always exhibited a rather noticeable enthusiasm for the other sex. He was still seeking vainly for a solution of this *volte face*, when Mervyn Potter woke up and immediately began where he had left off.

'What mighty ills have not been done by Women! Who was't betrayed the Capitol? A woman. Who lost Mark Antony the world? A woman. Who was the cause of a long ten years' war and laid at last old Troy in ashes? Woman. A sex I strongly disapprove of,' said Mervyn Potter severely, and added that there ought to be a law.

Barmy's bewilderment increased.

'I thought you liked women.'

'No longer, Phipps. Not any more. There was a time when my heart was an open house with Welcome on the mat, but now that heart is broken, Phipps, into a thousand pieces. It has become a crumbling ruin, through the cracks in which the chill winds of despair and disillusionment blow like nobody's business. A woman has done me dirt, Phipps. She has proved as false as she was fair. I allude to my fiancée. Or, rather, my ex-fiancée.'

'Well, I'll be blowed. Is she ex?'

'Ex to the last drop. You never saw anything Ex-er. By this morning's mail I received a letter from her, handed in at Nassau in the Bahamas, severing diplomatic relations and giving me the heave-ho in no uncertain terms. Yes, Phipps, she has thrown me out on my little pink behind, and life has become a blank. From sport to sport they hurry me, to stifle my regret, and when they win a smile from me, they think that I forget. But do I, Phipps? No, Phipps, I do not. Not that I've had much time to so far, of course,' said Mervyn Potter reasonably.

Barmy sought for words to comfort this broken man.

'I say, I'm frightfully sorry.'

'Thank you, Phipps.' Mervyn Potter thrust out a hand to clasp Barmy's, missed it by about two feet six inches, over-balanced, fell, picked himself up with an encouraging 'Upsy-daisy' and resumed. 'Your sympathy touches me. I don't say it mends my broken heart, but it touches me. Thank you, old friend. Well, that's how matters stand. I pray you, in your letters, Phipps, when you shall these unlucky deeds relate, speak of me as I am; nothing extenuate, nor set down aught in malice. Then must you speak of one who loved not wisely but too well . . . You haven't got a drop of whisky anywhere, have you?' said Mervyn Potter, changing the subject.

'I'm afraid I haven't.'

'Scotch? Rye? Bourbon? I'm not particular.'

'I'm afraid not.'

'Ah, well. That's Life, isn't it?'

'But what on earth happened?'

Mervyn Potter brooded for a moment.

'It is a long, sad story, throwing a blinding light on Woman's treachery and general skulduggery. Do you know what that girl did, Phipps? No, don't tell me, I'll tell you. Throw your mind back to that night when we dropped in at the Brimble residence, and you climbed all those trees. Do you recall my telling you that she bade me cut out all alcoholic stimulants?'

'Yes, I remember. You did it, didn't you?'

Mervyn Potter heaved a heavy sigh.

'I did. I kept my trust faithfully and well. She had a way of sniffing at me suddenly which rendered any other course impossible. For three long, weary weeks nothing passed my lips but barley water and an occasional lemonade. And then what happened? In company with her father, C. Hamilton Brimble of King's Point, Long Island, and her mother, Mrs C. Hamilton Brimble, oddly enough also of King's Point, Long Island, she went off to Nassau for a change of air, leaving me alone . . . alone in New York.'

Mervyn Potter sighed again, even more heavily than before. It was plain that whatever the story was that he was about to relate, it was one that racked him to his foundations, and Barmy felt a pang of pity. He also felt a cold tremor down his spine as he snatched a surreptitious glance at his watch and read the position of its hands. Long ere this the stricken man should have been in his dressing-room, slapping on the grease paint.

'The parting,' resumed Mervyn Potter, 'was agony. I felt like one of those fellows in the early nineteenth-century poems who used to go around losing dear gazelles. Still, in every cloud wrack the experienced eye, if it peers closely enough, can detect some sort of a silver lining, and the horror of my predicament was mitigated by the reflection that, now that she was no longer there to sniff suddenly at me, I would be able to start ingurgitating once more. The man of honour,' said Mervyn Potter, putting in a nutshell his philosophy of life, 'keeps his word to the woman he loves while she's around. When she's not around, conditions alter. To cut a long story short, Phipps, she was scarcely on the boat when I proceeded to line up at the Lambs Club bar with all the enthusiasm of a camel which, after toiling for days through the hot sands, finds itself at an oasis. I also lubricated the system at many a restaurant and night club. I had leeway to make up, and I made it up.'

'And she found out?'

Mervyn Potter sighed for the third time, the sigh of a man who has drunk life's bitter wine to the lees and whose faith in woman is dead.

'How could she help but find out, old friend? You would scarcely believe that a pure-minded girl, a product of Miss Finch's school and Vassar University, could be capable of such a thing, but before leaving for Nassau she had put herself in touch with the Day and Night Detective Agency, and my every move, though I did not know it, was being closely followed by Private Eyes complete with book and pencil. They tailed me up, Phipps, making copious notes, and handed in their report to Hermione, only daughter of C. Hamilton Brimble (and, of course, Mrs C. Hamilton Brimble) of King's Point, Long Island, with the results which you now see before you. So there you have the whole story. Well, good-bye, Phipps, old friend. I must not trespass on your time. No doubt you have a hundred things to do.'

'And you'll be getting along to the theatre, what?'

Mervyn Potter stared.

'Theatre?'

'It's awfully late.'

'Theatre?' said Mervyn Potter, amazed. 'Getting along to the theatre? I'm not going to any theatre. They'll have to put my understudy on. Good heavens, Phipps, you don't seriously suppose that I could play an exacting part, handicapped by this broken heart of mine? I'm going to have another drink or two and then go off and join the Foreign Legion, that cohort of the damned where broken men toil and die and, dying, forget. Good-bye, Phipps,' said Mervyn Potter, and with a kindly word of warning to his old friend not to take any wooden nickels, walked heavily from the room, dragging his feet and giving little jumps from time to time, as though vultures were gnawing at his bosom.

14

If the Lithuanian chambermaid who at half-past nine that night came to turn Barmy's bed down had been at all psychic – which, of course, very few Lithuanian chambermaids are – she would have sensed, as she went about her work, a strange, almost eerie atmosphere in Room 726, as of a room in a haunted house that is waiting for its spectre to clock in and start haunting. It is an atmosphere which always clings about those hotel apartments in New Haven, Syracuse and other try-out towns where before long haggard men will be meeting to conduct the post-mortem on a newly opened play. It was as though Room 726 were holding its breath, anticipating it knew not what.

From nine-thirty till shortly after eleven it continued in this painful state of suspense. Then a key clicked in the lock, and Barmy entered, whistling gaily. Leaving the door open behind him, he switched the lights on and advanced into the room, still whistling, his whole aspect such as to create the impression that he had found the bluebird. A spectre, had one been present, would have recognized him at a glance as a young man, financially interested in a theatrical production, who had just witnessed that theatrical production laying them in the aisles and massacring them, and would probably have resolved to dig down into its ectoplasm for the price of a ticket.

A few moments later, however, it would have found itself changing its mind and deciding to keep the money in the old winding-sheet. For it was now that Joseph Lehman made his appearance, and there was that about Mr Lehman's manner which would have chilled the spine of the stoutest spectre. Followed at a respectful distance by a dejected Jack McClure, he looked like someone who has come to lay a wreath on the tomb of an old friend. His back was bowed, his eyes cast down. He still wore his derby hat, but even that had lost its jaunty tilt and seemed to droop on its stem. With a sigh that came up from the soles of his feet, he sank heavily on to the bed, while Jack McClure, with a similar sigh, slumped into a chair.

Barmy regarded the two mourners with bewilderment. Tonight of all nights he wanted to see smiling faces about him and judging from their appearance and behaviour it looked as though, like a famous English king, Joseph Lehman and Jack McClure would never smile again. It puzzled him. Easily pleased as a theatregoer, it had seemed to him that the performance which had just concluded had gone with a swing. For the first time, he began to entertain doubts. Gloom like this was surely not the usual thing after a first-night success.

'I say,' he said. 'Is something the matter?'

He received no reply. Mr Lehman was picking at the coverlet, Jack McClure drumming on the arm of his chair. He tried again.

'I thought it went awfully well, what?' he said. Then, observing Mr Lehman's convulsive start and seeing Jack McClure's head jerk back as if someone had struck him between the eyes, he qualified the statement a trifle. 'Well, except here and there, I mean to say. In spots, as it were.'

Again neither of his two business colleagues spoke. It was as though they had taken Trappist vows, and his uneasiness deepened. He was not, as has been indicated, a highly intelligent young man, but even he could see that there was a possibility that he had been mistaken in supposing that all was for the best in the best of all possible worlds. He was still trying to correct a growing disposition to shake like a blancmange, when he heard a cough, one of those dry, unpleasant coughs, and perceived Mrs Lehman sailing in like a battleship going into action.

'Oh, hullo,' he said. 'What ho, there.'

Fanny, her eyes fixed on Mr Lehman, ignored the greeting. She was fond of Barmy and generally enjoyed chatting with him, but she was busy now arranging her thoughts preparatory to addressing her husband. Victory was so completely hers that she hardly felt that words were necessary. Nevertheless, she proposed to speak a few. She came well into the room, picked a prominent spot and settled herself to begin.

'*First!*' said Fanny.

Life returned to Mr Lehman's rigid limbs. He sprang to his feet.

'Now one thing we ain't going to have none of is wisecracks,' he thundered. 'Get me?'

Fanny laughed. A light, tinkling laugh.

'You could have used a few wisecracks in that charade tonight,' she said. 'Yessir, you could have used lantern slides. You could have used acrobats and performing dogs.'

'Now, listen—'

'*And* trained seals,' said Fanny.

Mr Lehman's hat quivered.

'Does that trap of yours ever close?' he inquired with strained politeness.

'From time to time.'

'Then close it now,' urged Mr Lehman. 'I don't want to hear no more of all that. They can't nobody tell me we ain't got a great show . . . when it's fixed. Just because this bunch tonight didn't like it don't prove nothing. Syracuse is the worst show town in America.'

This news surprised Barmy, who had been told otherwise.

'I thought you said—'

'Never mind what I said. Shut up.'

'Oh, right ho. Still, you did remark—'

'Shut *up*, I tell you.'

Barmy subsided, his feelings wounded. Was this, he was asking himself, the man who had clasped his hand and, with tears as near as a toucher in his eyes, thanked him for his co-operation and told him how swell it had been working with him? His limited acquaintance with the theatre had not yet taught him that between the demeanour of a manager on the eve of a production and that of the same manager immediately after the failure of that production there is a subtle but well-marked difference, generally more wellmarked than subtle.

Mr Lehman resumed his remarks.

'If it didn't go just right tonight, what of it? What can you expect when your star walks out on you half-an-hour before the opening and you have to put on a lousy understudy?'

Fanny would have none of this specious reasoning.

'Don't talk to me about lousy understudies. That guy Spender gave a damn sight better performance than Mervyn Potter would ever have done. It's the play that's wrong.'

'What's wrong with it?'

'Let me tell you,' said Fanny, licking her lips. '*First!*'

It was perhaps fortunate, for Mr Lehman was a man with a high blood pressure, that at this moment there was an interruption. A waiter entered, bearing a folding table and other supper accessories. He was short and stout and probably the friendliest waiter in Syracuse.

'This where the party's going to be, folks?' he asked genially.

Barmy came out of his reverie.

'Oh, thanks. Yes, right ho,' he said. He turned to Mr Lehman. His feelings were still hurt, but one must overcome wounded feelings at a time like this. 'I say, it's just a little thing, isn't it, what? The matter, I mean? I mean to say, the play's a success, isn't it?'

Mr Lehman gave him a long, lingering look, but did not speak. The waiter unfolded the folding table.

'Mr Fritchie says he'll be up later to see if everything's all right,' he said, and Mr Lehman quivered like a harpooned whale.

'All I need is that screwball!' he moaned. 'Get out!'

'Yes, sir.'

'Fritchie!' said Mr Lehman. The way he spoke the name made it sound like one of those robust Elizabethan oaths, the sort of thing rare Ben Jonson in a testy moment might have flung at Beaumont and Fletcher over the sherris sack in the Mermaid Tavern. 'At a time like this . . . Fritchie!'

Silence fell once more on Room 726. It was broken by Fanny.

'I wonder if I might ask a question?' she said with a meek sweetness which affected Mr Lehman like the touch of a red-hot poker. He leaped feverishly, his hat swaying.

'Lay off!' he urged. 'Lay off me, I'm telling you.'

Fanny was not to be diverted. It was her duty to be helpful, and helpful she intended to be.

'I was only going to ask if you were planning to put anything in that five-minute spot where Whittaker couldn't think of the next line,' she said, all gentle wifely solicitude. 'Because if she's going to wait like that every night, I figure it would be a great place for a specialty. A ballet of some kind. Or I could come on with the clubs—'

'Lay off!' said Mr Lehman, fermenting visibly. 'Lay off, lay off, lay off!'

'We're all working for the good of the show,' said Fanny virtuously. 'There's a troupe of Swiss bellringers I saw at—'

'Will you stop it!' roared Mr Lehman. He turned to Jack McClure. 'Did you tell that director we was meeting here?'

'Be here any minute.'

'How about Bernie?'

'I give him the room.'

'And where's Moore with those notes of mine?'

Barmy became helpful.

'Here are my notes, Mr Lehman, if you would care to—'

'Better give Bernie a ring. Get him up here.'

'Right,' said Jack McClure. 'I didn't see him at the show.'

'I saw him,' said Fanny.

'What did he say?' asked Mr Lehman. 'Don't tell me,' he added quickly, as he observed his wife's face light up.

Barmy was still persevering.

'Here are the notes I bunged down, Mr Lehman, if you would care to take a dekko. There's one with ref. to the orchard scene which I am particularly anxious to draw to your—'

'Ah!' said Mr Lehman.

Dinty Moore had come in, bringing with her the script of the play, an ample sheaf of Mr Lehman's obiter dicta and an assortment of well-sharpened pencils. Her manner was subdued, lacking all trace of its customary brightness. She looked like one of those characters in ghost stories who have seen some awful sight, as of course she had. Barmy's welcoming 'What ho' brought no answering smile to her lips. Nice girls do not smile at funerals.

'Gimme them notes,' said Mr Lehman, seating himself at the writing-table. 'Gimme the script. Gimme a pencil.'

'Gimme Mr Sampson, Kitty,' said Jack McClure at the telephone. 'He's in four-thirteen. Oh, say, how did you like the show, Kitty?'

'Now then,' said Mr Lehman, opening the script.

'Oh!' Jack McClure's exclamation was one of pain. It was evident that he had received a none too cheering reply from the lady at the switchboard. 'Well, I wouldn't go as far as that,' he said, having winced a little. 'You got to understand it's still new yet. It needs work, of course. But by the time we hit the big town it'll be clicking all along the line.'

'Ah!' said Barmy, encouraged. This, he felt, was more the old bulldog spirit.

Mr Lehman motioned Dinty to the chair at his side.

'Now you take down anything that comes up, see? And I don't want . . . Oh, my God, he's in again!'

The waiter had returned, this time laden with bottles of champagne. Fanny's eyes followed him bulgingly as he crossed the room.

'Well!' said Fanny, lost in admiration of this lavishness. 'Your birthday?'

'Eh?' said Barmy. 'Oh, it's to celebrate the success of the play.'

Fanny's eyebrows rose.

'The what of the which?'

'The success of the play.'

'I thought that was what you said.' Fanny walked across and took up a bottle. 'Do they open?'

'Oh, rather.'

'Soon?'

'Oh, I see what you mean. Waiter, will you open a bot or two?'

'Pardon me for seeming in a hurry,' said Fanny, 'but you see I saw all three acts.'

Jack McClure, at the telephone, had established communication with the mysterious Bernie.

'Bernie? Mac.'

'Tell him to hurry up,' said Mr Lehman, chafing.

'We're getting together up here in 726, Bernie, whenever you're ready,' said Jack McClure. 'Okay.'

He hung up. The waiter was lingering in the doorway.

'Mr Fritchie says how soon do you want the food served?'

'Oh, yes,' said Barmy, recalled to his duties as a host. 'Would you like the garbage lugged in right away?'

'I don't care,' said Mr Lehman, his mind still above mundane matters. 'All I ask is keep that Fritchie away from here.'

'You wish to see Mr Fritchie?' said the waiter brightly.

'No, I don't wish to see Mr Fritchie. Scram!'

'Yes, sir. Remember what MacArthur told the Japanese when they pushed him out of the Philippines?'

'No.'

' "I shall return",' said the waiter.

Two measures of champagne had given Fanny the party spirit. She proposed a jolly toast.

'To Gladys Whittaker, queen of the deaf mutes!' she said, raising her glass.

Mr Lehman banged on the table.

'Shut that door!' he bellowed. 'And where is everybody? I pay a director the earth. Where is he? I bring Bernie Sampson up from New York. Where is he? Aren't I ever to get no co-operation? Ah!' said Mr Lehman. 'And about time.'

Cecil Benham, the director, was coming into the room.

15

CECIL BENHAM was calm, reserved, well stricken in years and very dignified. There were those, though Mr Benham was not among them, who considered him a fossil, a back number and an anachronism. He had been at his best as a director many years ago in the great days of the New York stage, when motion pictures were in their infancy and Television a horror still in the mists of the future. As he came placidly into the room, giving the impression, though this was not actually so, that he had a scarlet-lined opera cape about his shoulders, he brought with him something of the atmosphere of those spacious times.

Many men, meeting Cecil Benham, felt a sort of nostalgic reverence, as if they were in the presence of some noble old public monument. Mr Lehman did not belong to this group.

'Hey!' he barked, getting right down to it without wasting time on courteous preliminaries. 'What happened to that scenery?'

Mr Benham gave him the calm, dignified look which he might have given a bumptious young actor at the Players' Club.

'I beg your pardon?'

'I said, what happened to the scenery? It was crooked, all through the show.'

'That was one of the things I bunged down,' said Barmy, helpful as ever, 'particularly with ref. to the orchard scene. I don't know if you happen to know it, but in a real orchard—'

Cecil Benham's calm was disturbed by the faintest suggestion of annoyance.

'My dear Mr Lehman, I was hardly in a position to prevent that. A director cannot be everywhere. I was holding book all the evening.'

'Well, if you were holding book, where were you during that stage wait of Whittaker's in the second act? Couldn't you give her the line?'

'I gave Miss Whittaker the line four times, but it appeared to make no impression on her. She seemed nervous.'

Barmy had light to throw on this.

'She wasn't feeling well, poor soul.'

'What?'

'So she told me.'

'When did you see her?'

'In her dressing-room after the first act. I was giving her some suggestions.'

'*You* were?'

'That's right. I was telling her that in the big scene with the hero in the bedroom she ought to do some of her best acting, really pull up her socks, don't you know.'

Mr Lehman swelled. He looked like a minor prophet of the Old Testament about to curse the people for their sins.

'Well, for—'

He broke off. There had come a knock on the door. Barmy was in the fortunate position of a pugilist who has been saved by the bell.

'Come in!' shouted Mr Lehman.

'Maybe it's Bernie,' said Jack McClure.

It was Bernie, and not only Bernie, but a young lady.

Bernie Sampson was a sallow young man who wore that air of desiccated sophistication which can be acquired only through long service on Broadway. He was what is known in theatrical circles as a fixer. Once, several years before, he had made a suggestion for the improvement of a comedy which was in its death agony out of town. The suggestion was misunderstood by the producer, and the mistaken suggestion saved the play. Ever since then Bernie Sampson had been a recognized dramatic doctor. A sort of vulture hovering over the theatrical scene, he had witnessed a vast number of plays open and close, and with each one he had participated in just such a bedroom conference as this.

As for the young lady whom he was escorting, her name was Peggy Marlowe, and she was not unknown to the choruses of Broadway. It was her custom to appear for about a month in one of the most prominent musical comedies of the town and then to desert abruptly for Florida. She was smartly dressed and extremely good-looking.

'Hello, people,' said Bernie, tossing his hat on to the bed. 'Hello, Joe. How are you, Mackie?' He waved a hand in the direction of Peggy. 'I just happened to have a young lady with me. This is Miss Marlowe, folks.'

'How are you?' said Miss Marlowe, blowing a cloud of smoke from the long cigarette-holder which was as permanent a decoration of her shapely lips as was Mr Lehman's derby hat of Mr Lehman's head.

Jack McClure did the honours.

'Mrs Lehman . . . Mr Benham . . . and Mr Phipps.'

'Pleased to meet you, Mrs Lehman. Hey, Mr Benham. Hi, Mr Phipps. Ah, mucilage,' said Bernie, sighting the champagne.

Mr Lehman stuck doggedly to the agenda. He frowned at the champagne, holding the view that it struck a frivolous note out of keeping with the solemnity of the occasion.

'Now, Bernie, I want you to tell us just what you think of it.

Mr Sampson here,' explained Mr Lehman, addressing Mr Benham, 'come up from New York to see the show and maybe do some work if it needs it.'

'If?' said Fanny. 'What do you mean, if?'

'Indeed?' said Cecil Benham, none too pleased. He regarded the fixer with a wary eye. There had been Bernies back in the old days and he had never liked them.

'Now we're all going to give our frank opinions, see?' said Mr Lehman. 'We're going to say just what we thought of the show.'

Fanny rose obligingly, a little unsteady on her feet.

'Well,' she began. '*First!*'

'That's enough,' said Mr Lehman quickly. 'Go ahead, Bernie.'

The portentous manner of the seasoned fixer enveloped Bernie Sampson like a garment. He went into his opening speech with the confidence of one who is on familiar ground.

'Well, of course there ain't no doubt but what it needs some work.'

'Hard labour,' suggested Fanny, busy with the champagne. 'If not the death sentence.'

'Ah, shut up,' said Mr Lehman.

'Now, when I watch a show,' proceeded Bernie profoundly, 'I don't look at the show so much, I look at the audience. They'll tell you every time. Now, your Prologue is great. It's a great idea, him reading the play. And it held them. But after that they begin to slip away from you.'

'I'd like to ventilate just that point,' said Barmy, full of zeal, 'with particular ref. to the orchard scene—'

'Who's this?' asked Bernie. 'Phipps did you say his name was?'

'That's right,' said Barmy. 'I'm—'

'If you don't mind, Mr Phipps—'

'Oh, right ho. I only wanted to say that in the orch—'

He broke off, startled and intimidated by Mr Lehman's glare. Mr Lehman allowed his eyes to dwell on him for perhaps ten seconds, then turned to Bernie.

'Yah? You were saying?'

Mr Sampson resumed.

'Well, like I'm telling you, it needs work. Some of them scenes, they don't quite click. Now I got a scene that I done in a show called—'

Miss Marlowe's roving eye had discovered Barmy.

'Hello, cutie,' she said affectionately.

'Oh, hullo,' said Barmy.

'You're English, aren't you?'

'Yah.'

'Don't you mean "Right ho"? Nice hair you've got.'

'Oh, thanks.'

'Kind of butter-coloured, isn't it?'

'Butter-coloured in spots, no doubt.'

'It does something to me,' said Miss Marlowe, with that same affectionate note in her voice.

Bernie Sampson had lost the thread of his remarks.

'Say, what goes on here?' he asked suspiciously.

'Mind your own business,' said Peggy Marlowe.

Mr Lehman flung his hands heavenwards. His voice shook the ceiling. He had conceived a violent antipathy to Miss Marlowe.

'Bernie, can't you get rid of this beazel?' he pleaded.

'Let him try!' said Miss Marlowe equably. 'What I got on him!'

'Are we going to get anything done?' demanded Mr Lehman. 'Or aren't we?'

'I vote no,' said Fanny.

'What I vote,' said Miss Marlowe, 'is that somebody slips me a tankard of that juice. I'm surprised you haven't offered me any before, dreamboat,' she went on, addressing Barmy reproachfully. 'Who do you think I am? Volstead or someone?'

'Give her a glass of that stuff,' said Mr Lehman imperiously, jerking his chin at Barmy and his thumb at the champagne, and Barmy sprang to the task with the alacrity of a man doing a job at which he knows he is good. He was beginning to get the impression that the other members of the conference, notably Mr Lehman, were bad listeners, but even if he was unable to secure attention for his views, he could pour champagne. He filled Miss Marlowe's glass, and Miss Marlowe drained it and said: 'Boy!'

'Yah?' said Mr Lehman, having caught Bernie Sampson's eye, which had been showing a tendency to wander in the direction of his young lady. 'You was saying you got a scene.'

'Yah. You got to put something in the place of that cabaret thing. If ever I seen a Kiss of Death!' said Bernie, shuddering. 'Of course,' he went on, in the manner of one who looks at a problem from every angle, 'it may be the way it was put on. I don't know who done it for you, but of all the lousy directing—!'

Cecil Benham rose to his full height.

'I beg your pardon, Mr Jackson?'

'Bernie Sampson is my name.'

'Indeed? Mine is Cecil Benham.'

'Is that so?'

'Possibly you do not know who I am.'

'That's only part of it.'

'I was associated for ten years with David Belasco. I have directed Nazimova. I have directed Edmund Breeze. I have directed Lowell Sherman, Cyril Scott and Jeanne Eagels.'

'And where are they now?' said Fanny, waving her glass.

'And I am not accustomed to having my direction described by the adjective which you have employed.'

Bernie Sampson bridled.

'Listen. I come up from New York as a favour to Joe here—'

'Nevertheless, I must insist—'

'Now don't let's get scrapping,' pleaded Mr Lehman.

'But if he is to be permitted—'

'There's no use flying off the handle.'

'Yes, but—'

'He didn't mean anything. Just kidding, see? That's the stuff,' said Mr Lehman, as the injured director slowly resumed his seat.

'Is that going to be all?' inquired Miss Marlowe. 'Well, call me for the next round,' she said, and stretched herself restfully at full length on the bed, ignoring the fact that Mr Lehman was giving her one of those looks of his which up to the present he had been reserving for Barmy and the partner of his joys and sorrows.

'Go on, Bernie,' said Mr Lehman, with the air of a man of high blood pressure who, following his doctor's recommendation, has just counted ten slowly. 'What's this scene you've got?'

'Well, I'll tell you. It'll drop right in where your cabaret is, see? It was a wow scene, but the show never come into New York, so it'll be new. It was a hop joint in Hong Kong.'

'It would not possibly do,' said Cecil Benham with great dignity.

Even Mr Lehman seemed a little dubious.

'We got to stick to the story, Bernie. We can't throw away the whole play.'

'Why not?' said Fanny.

'What we got to do is start at the beginning . . . Who's this?' said Mr Lehman, as a knock sounded on the door.

'The police, if there's any law and justice in Syracuse,' said Fanny. 'Do a dive through the window, I would if I was you. Don't let them take you alive.'

'Open that door,' said Mr Lehman.

'Me?' said Barmy.

'Yah.'

'Right ho,' said Barmy. He had the feeling that all he needed to make him a commissionaire was a peaked cap and the uniform of a Ruritanian admiral, but his was a sweet and obliging disposition, and he had been ordered about by his Uncle Theodore too much in his youth to take offence at a little peremptoriness now.

He went to the door and opened it.

16

IT was Gladys Whittaker who entered, a Gladys Whittaker plainly in defiant mood and prepared to counter possible attacks on her artistry. She got a round of applause from Fanny, but appeared not to appreciate it. She took up her stand in the precise centre of the room and burst into speech.

'Before anything is said,' began Gladys Whittaker in a low, thrilling voice, 'the stage wait was not my fault. Mr Spender gave me the wrong cue, a cue out of the third act. So of course I had to stop and think.'

'You certainly had a lovely evening for it,' said Fanny sympathetically.

'You'd think there would be someone in the wings to throw me a line. But no.'

Cecil Benham swelled ominously. The Benhams did not war on women unless the women asked for it. This he considered, Miss Whittaker was now doing.

'I gave you the line distinctly.'

'Well, I didn't hear it.'

'That is scarcely my fault.'

'Oh, goody!' said Peggy Marlowe, sitting up on the bed. These raised voices promised well for one of those battles of which she was so enthusiastic an *aficionado*.

'I've had a raging headache all day,' said Miss Whittaker, her voice quivering with self-pity. 'And if you suppose,' she went on, suddenly switching her attack to Barmy, 'that it is easy for an artist to give a performance of a big part with people coming back into your dressing-room all the time, making idiotic suggestions—'

Barmy felt like Caesar stabbed by Brutus.

'But, dash it all,' he cried, aghast at this ingratitude, 'you told me you wanted me to make idiotic suggestions . . . I mean—'

'Well, really, Mr Phipps, I've been longer in the profession than you have—'

'And *that's* no fairy tale,' said Fanny.

Miss Whittaker drew herself up.

'I beg your pardon?'

'Oh, stop it, you two,' bellowed Mr Lehman. 'Now – we're going to begin at the beginning and go right through the show.'

Jack McClure had a brain wave.

'Joe, do you want some good straight dope? A fresh viewpoint?'

'Who?'

'There's a little girl down on the switchboard, smart as a steel trap. She sees everything that comes here, and I slipped her a couple tonight.'

'Good idea. Get her up. Anybody but that Fritchie.'

Miss Marlowe, who had turned on her side and appeared to be about to go to sleep, rolled over and sat up. There was a rather intent look on her face, like that of a leopardess preparing for the kill.

'Did he say on the switchboard?'

'Now, baby,' pleaded Bernie. He had heard that note in her voice before.

Jack McClure was talking into the telephone.

'Kitty? This is Mr McClure. Say, can you leave there for a minute and come up to 726? . . . I'll tell you when you get here. That's right. Good-bye.'

Miss Marlowe was still brooding.

'Is there more than one operator in this hotel?'

'Now, baby,' said Bernie.

'Because I just had a run in with one of them and I'd like to know.'

Mr Lehman raised his voice.

'Bernie, can't you get this dame to—'

'Some other time, baby.'

'Well, just in case she is the one,' said Miss Marlowe, 'I'll take another drink.'

'Now come on,' said Mr Lehman, calling the meeting to order. 'We ain't going to have no more interruptions. We're going to take up the scenes as they come along. Now. We're set on the Prologue. Okay?'

'Okay,' said Bernie Sampson.

'Okay,' said Jack McClure.

'How about you, Benham? Prologue okay?'

'Oh, I am quite satisfied. Perfectly.'

'Well, don't get sore about it. Put that down,' said Mr Lehman to Dinty. 'Prologue okay.'

'Prologue okay,' said Barmy, making a gratuitous endorsement, and catching Mr Lehman's eye dived at the nearest champagne bottle, embarrassed. Odd, he was thinking, not for the first time this evening, how greatly changed the other's manner toward him was tonight. Not the same old hearty friendliness at all. What had become of the big-hearted crony who had so often addressed him as 'my puss' and 'blossom boy'?

Miss Whittaker had a suggestion to offer.

'What's wrong with this play is that the heroine doesn't have sympathy. I'm fighting the audience all the time. I feel it. They don't like me.'

Fanny went to all the trouble of getting up.

'Well, I think you were fine. I really do.' She resumed her seat. 'That'll give you some rough idea of my condition,' she said, reaching out for her glass.

Miss Whittaker, after one icy glance, ignored her – as far as it was possible ever to ignore Fanita, the World's Greatest Juggler.

'No sympathy. That's the answer. Something ought to be put in to show that I'm really all right at heart and not just a frivolous Society butterfly.'

'How about giving out pamphlets?' said Fanny.

'If I could have a scene early in the play that would show me in a more sympathetic light . . . maybe a scene with a baby.'

'We'll come back to it,' said Mr Lehman. 'Make a note,' he said to Dinty. 'Baby for Miss Whittaker.'

'Not if it's early in the play, though, what?' said Barmy. 'She isn't married.'

'All right, all *right*!' There was a knock. 'Open that door.'

'Me?'

'Yah.'

'Right ho,' said Barmy.

It was the waiter, laden with chicken *à la king*.

'The chow,' announced the waiter cheerily. 'I told you I would return.'

'Bung it on the table.'

'Yes, sir. Come an' get it, folks, come an' get it,' said the waiter, with the same chummy air of a kindly soul who wants to make everybody happy.

Mr Lehman glowered at the chicken *à la king*. Chicken *à la king* meant nothing to Mr Lehman. He lived only for his art.

'Come on, come on, come on,' he shouted. 'We can't stop here all night. We're going ahead from the Prologue. The next is the orchard scene.'

Barmy's face lit up. This was his big moment.

'I want to say something with ref. to that, Mr Lehman.'

'You don't tell me!'

'I was just waiting till you reached it. You see, my dear old companion—'

'Would you mind letting *me* talk for a minute? And don't call me your old companion.'

'Right ho, old egg.'

It is possible that Mr Lehman might have made some comment on this alternative form of address, but at this moment there was another knock on the door, and Barmy, once more directed to open it, found himself confronted by a small girl in a neat black dress, at whom he gazed inquiringly.

'Oh, here's Kitty, Joe,' said Jack McClure, supplying the necessary footnotes. 'Kitty from the switchboard. This is Miss Humphreys, everybody. Now, here's the angle, Kitty. We want you to tell us just what you thought of the show tonight, see? Straight from the shoulder. You see all the shows that come here. We want to know your real opinion.'

Miss Marlowe, seated on the bed, was regarding the newcomer with a speculative eye.

'Well, I'll tell you, Mr McClure,' said Kitty. 'You see, Syracuse is a funny town.'

'Oh, *that's* it?' said Fanny.

'It's a hard town to please, sort of,' proceeded the oracle, speaking the speech of every small-town playgoer, 'because you see we get all the new shows. The managers all bring their shows here, because they know if it goes here, it'll go any place. You see, the people here are funny, sort of. If they like a show, they'll go to it, but if they don't like it, they won't.'

'That's a hot lot of news,' said Mr Lehman unpleasantly.

'Listen, folks,' said the waiter. 'I can tell you what's wrong with your show. I wasn't there, but the chambermaid on Number Four was, and she—'

'Just a minute,' said Jack McClure. 'We want this young lady to—'

'Oh, I beg your pardon,' said the waiter. 'You have the floor, Miss.'

Peggy Marlowe had risen from the bed. Her manner was quiet but menacing.

'Are you the operator that took a New York call out of four-thirteen this evening?' she inquired in a cold, level voice.

'Now, baby,' said Bernie.

'Are you?'

'Yes, I am.'

'You were pretty fresh, weren't you?'

'I don't think so.'

'Well, I do. Are you or are you not supposed to be respectful?'

'I'm always respectful, madam, when I'm speaking to a lady.'

There was a pause.

'I'll tell you what you want,' said Miss Marlowe, struck with an idea. 'You want your ugly little face pushed in.'

The words were spoken casually, easily. Peggy Marlowe, veteran of fifty dressing-room fights, was not even mildly excited. Her statement, however, came close to breaking up the meeting. Fanny uttered an encouraging 'Whoopee!'. Mr Lehman gave a wordless cry. Bernie said 'Now, baby!'. Mr Benham clicked his tongue and murmured 'Really, really!', and you could see that he was feeling that this sort of thing could never have occurred under the auspices of David Belasco. Jack McClure did the clever, practical thing. In his quiet, gentlemanly way, he pushed Kitty out of the room and closed the door, and there was a moment of complete and grateful calm.

Mr Lehman was breathing heavily.

'Lock that door!' he said.

'Me?'

'Yah.'

'Right ho,' said Barmy.

'You'll only have to unlock it again,' the waiter pointed out, 'to permit me to make an egress. Well, folks, I was going to tell you what this chambermaid said, the one on Number Four. She said to me, "Rupert," she said to me, "what the theatregoer today wants is entertainment".'

Mr Lehman howled like a banshee.

'Get out!'

'Okay, sir. You're the boss. Good night, folks.'

'Good *night*!' said Mr Lehman.

Barmy was feeling bewildered. This was the first after-opening-performance conference at which he had assisted, and it was completely unlike anything his imagination had pictured. He had envisaged a group of genial people – what Mr Lehman in a moment of inspiration had so well described as a happy family – exchanging amiable small talk as they sipped their champagne. He had expected something on the lines of one of those eighteenth-century salons of which he had read at school, and he appeared to have been plunged into the middle of a cage of rather exceptionally short-tempered wild cats. It perplexed and confused him. There was nobody to tell him that the current get-together had been, by normal theatrical standards, almost unusually urbane.

Mr Lehman called the meeting to order once more.

'Come on, now, come on, come on,' he said in that forceful way of his. 'We're here to decide about this show, and we're getting nowheres.'

'I move we make this a permanent organization and meet every week,' said Fanny.

'Shut up!'

'I didn't open my mouth.'

'Gab, gab, gab . . . We were up to the Prologue.'

'Prologue okay,' said Barmy sagely.

Mr Lehman favoured him with another of those incandescent looks. On these occasions when all has not gone well with an opening performance, it is theatrical custom for the presiding manager to select from the little group about him a single individual on whom to expend his fury. Lacking the author who as a rule automatically gets the nomination, Mr Lehman had chosen Barmy. Barmy, though innocent of actual literary composition, was the nearest thing to an author in sight.

Having gazed his fill, Mr Lehman proceeded.

'Now. The next is the orchard scene.'

This, as has been said, was where Barmy had opinions to express. He revived like a flower in the rains of spring.

'Ah, yes, the jolly old orchard scene,' he said briskly. 'I'll tell you about the good old orchard scene. The trees aren't planted right.'

Mr Lehman rose from his seat, and Jack McClure, always one for pouring oil on troubled waters, begged him to take it easy.

'Oh, they aren't, huh?'

'No, laddie. I mean my blossom. In a real orchard—'

A ghastly calm fell upon Mr Lehman, the sort of calm which falls upon a volcano just before it starts scattering molten lava while thousands flee.

'Now listen! I'm pretty near fed up with you, get me? You been butting in all night long, one fool idea after another, and I had all I can stand.'

'But this isn't a fool idea. It's the goods.'

'Well, I don't want to hear it, see? Who's producing this show, anyhow?'

'I'm part producer—'

'Yah? Well, I'm the main producer, see? And I'm going to do the talking. Twenty-five per cent, that's what you got.'

'Yes, I know, but, dash it, you told me to take notes—'

'You're going to keep on, are you?'

'But, Lord love a duck, if I see that something's wrong, I mean to say, surely I can bung in the word in season? An orchard isn't planted that way. Years ago, when a slip of a boy,' said Barmy, becoming reminiscent, 'I used to go and spend my summer holidays with an old aunt of mine in the country – to be exact, my Aunt Ysobel at Lower-Smattering-on-the-Wissel in the county of Worcestershire – and she had an orchard and, believe me or believe me not—'

The volcano erupted.

'Sweet suffering soup spoons!' cried Mr Lehman, clutching at his hat, the only stable thing in a whirling universe. 'It's too much. You half wreck the show, prowling around backstage and annoying artists, and then you come here shooting your head off about trees and orchards and your Aunt Agatha.'

'Ysobel. Spelled with a Y.'

'What in blazes do you know about show business? I'm running this show, see, and I want you to butt out of it, see? I had all I can stand, and I want you to keep out. When bigger half-wits are born, they'll have twice the sense you have. Stop talking and save the wear and tear on your tonsils. Get me?'

Dinty rose from her seat. She was pale, but composed. She had observed Barmy's lower jaw droop like a dying lily, and the sight had aroused all that was maternal in her.

'Don't talk to him like that! I won't stand for it.'

Mr Lehman turned a red eye on this mutineer in the camp.

'Oh? Now it's your business, is it?'

Dinty was a Moore from County Kerry, and you can push County Kerry Moores only so far. Her lips tightened, her eyes glowed. It seemed for a moment as if she was about to handle Mr Lehman as she had handled the insurance salesman named Ed at Coney Island.

She fought down the impulse.

'Yes, it is. You take his money – all that you could chisel out of him – for a play you must have known hadn't a dog's chance, and every time he opens his mouth, you shout at him. You listen to switchboard girls and waiters, but—'

'Is that so? And who asked you to say anything?'

'I've kept quiet as long as I could.'

'Yah? Well, now suppose you try keeping quiet somewheres else. You can get to hell out of here, and you needn't come back.'

Barmy spoke. He had been intending to intervene in the debate earlier, but the nobility of Dinty's outburst had stunned him and rendered him incapable of speech.

'Just a minute,' said Barmy, realizing too late that the first two words should have been pronounced 'Jussa'. 'Not so damn quick, my puss. This jolly old room happens to be *my* jolly old room, and what I mean to say . . . Well, to cut a long story short and get down to the nub, you can't go about the place ordering people out of it.'

'I can't, eh?'

'Definitely not. That's official.'

'I warn you to lay off me.'

'I'm dashed if I'll lay off you.'

'Oh? So besides running the show, you're trying to run me? To hell with you. Go on back to London or whatever Limey town it was you said you come from, and take her with you, because she's fired.'

Barmy's voice, which had climbed well into the higher register, rose higher.

'Fired, eh?' He laughed a harsh and mocking laugh. 'Let me tell you, my old sport, that she wouldn't work for you any longer, anyhow. Do you want to know why?'

'I'd love to.'

'Because she's going to work for me, my blossom, that's jolly well why. You think I don't know anything about show business. I'll show you whether I know anything about show business. Do you want to sell the rest of it to me . . . the play?'

'Do I *what*?'

'You heard. How about it? Think on your feet, sweetheart.'

A certain thoughtfulness had replaced the belligerency of Mr Lehman's manner. He looked at Jack McClure, and noting on that gentleman's face the expression of one who had just become convinced that there is a Santa Claus, saw his way clear before him.

'I might,' he said slowly. 'For a price. It's a valuable property. What do you say, Jack?'

'Up to you.'

'McClure and me is in together. Give us . . . ten thousand apiece, and the show's yours.'

'I'll give you five thousand apiece.'

'Seventy-five hundred.'

'Five thousand.'

'Cash?'

Dinty uttered a wail.

'Barmy, you can't!'

Barmy ignored the interruption. One keeps the women out of these things.

'Cash,' he said. 'Ten thousand dollars, cash down, for Lehman Productions – all of it.'

'Set!' said Mr Lehman.

'Set!' said Jack McClure.

Barmy went to his suitcase. His faithful cheque-book was there. As he groped for it, it seemed to him to shrink away, as if it were trying to hide. He wrote the cheque, and handed it with a flourish to Mr Lehman, who took it devoutly and said he guessed that was that. And Jack McClure said he guessed that was that.

'And now,' said Barmy, 'if you wouldn't all mind leaving—'

The room emptied itself. Only Fanny lingered. Her face wore a look of gravity, as if she were preparing to do seven clubs instead of six for the wow at the finish. She hesitated for a moment, as if about to say something, then seemed to change her mind.

She shrugged her shoulders, and went out.

17

'OH, Barmy,' wailed Dinty. 'Why did you do it? Why?'

To Barmy, still breathing fire through his nostrils, the question seemed a foolish one. It was as if a damsel in distress, rescued from a two-headed giant by a knight errant, had called upon the latter to give a brief explanation of his behaviour.

'Why?' he snorted. 'What else could I do, dash it, when he started giving you the old raspberry like that? Had to put the blighter in his place, what?'

'But your last ten thousand dollars!'

'Eh?'

'The last ten thousand dollars you had in the world.'

Barmy sat down heavily, as if his legs had been mown from under him. The heady exhilaration which comes from making a great gesture had buoyed him up so far, but its aid had suddenly failed him. He felt as though his spine had been withdrawn from his body and a cheap spaghetti substitute inserted in its place.

'I see what you mean,' he said. 'Yes, you have a point there. Still,' he went on, brightening, 'I own the play now.'

'But how are you going to run it?'

'Eh? Why – I suppose – er – just run it, as it were.'

'But what *with*? Oh, Barmy, I hate to be such a crêpehanger, but it's no good not facing it. Don't you know what happens to shows on the road before they come into New York? They never make a cent. They always lose money. Thousands of dollars unless you have the most tremendous luck. You'll need at least another ten thousand to cover expenses and keep the thing going.'

'I will?'

'Otherwise you'll just have to close and cut your losses.'

A delicate green had begun to steal into Barmy's face. He looked like a passenger on a Folkestone to Boulogne boat who had just become sensitive to the vessel's motion.

'This opens up a new line of thought,' he said. 'You really mean that? There positively is no hope of navigating under our own steam and paying the weekly bills as we go?'

'None, I'm afraid.'

'Then shall I tell you something,' said Barmy, becoming greener.

'I'm ruined. I'm a spent egg. I'm a . . . What was that thing I used to sing in my bath quite a good deal? Ah, yes. "I'm a worthless cheque, a total wreck, a flop." Possibly the wisest course would be to end it all. You don't happen to have a fluid ounce or two of cyanide on you, do you?'

'You mustn't talk like that. We'll get through this somehow. Something will happen, I know. I just feel that something is going to happen.'

'So do I. And I wish it wasn't.'

The telephone rang shrilly. Barmy took up the receiver with a weary gesture.

'Hullo? . . . Yah, this is Mr Phipps . . . What do you mean? Of course there isn't . . . Oh, sorry, yes, there is . . . All right. Yes, I see what you mean. Right ho.' He hung up and moodily announced the bad news. 'That was the office, accusing me – with some show of justice, I admit – of having a member of the gentler sex in my room. You aren't allowed on the premises, apparently. It's against the rules.'

'Oh, damn the rules!'

'I couldn't agree with you more wholeheartedly, but I suppose we shall have to humour the sons of bachelors. We don't want a bevy of stern-faced men coming up and leading you out with gyves upon your wrists. You'd better buzz off.'

'But we must talk this thing over.'

'True. Lots of stones to turn and avenues to explore. I see that.'

'How are you going to get some money?'

'Ah! You may well ask. That's the very problem I was turning over in my mind myself.'

'Do you think there's anyone in Syracuse with ten thousand dollars?'

'I don't think there's anyone anywhere with ten thousand dollars.'

'You told me once you had a rich uncle in England. Couldn't you cable him?'

'And try to bite his ear for the sum needed?'

'Yes.'

'Ha!'

'What?'

'I merely said "Ha!". Did you ever read *Alice Through the Looking-Glass*?'

'Yes, years ago.'

'Remember the Jabberwocky?'

'Of course.'

'Uncle Theodore. The jaws that bite, the claws that catch! One move on my part to try to separate him from ten thousand of the best and brightest, and he would come whiffling through the tulgey wood and burble as he came. At the moment, I don't mind telling you, I am not high up on the list of his favourite buddies. One of these days

I must show you the letter he wrote me on receiving the information that J. G. Anderson had given me the bum's rush. It was a fruity letter, full of good stuff. No, if you had been entertaining any idea of Uncle Theodore as a promising prospect for the quick touch, abandon same. I've about as much chance of tapping him for the needful as I have of strolling into Fort Knox with a spade and bucket and helping myself to contents.'

Dinty bit her lip.

'It's a mess, isn't it?'

'A Grade A mess. But with one bright spot in it, if messes have bright spots. I may be down among the wines and spirits – I will go further. I *am* down among the wines and spirits – but at least I met you.'

'If only you hadn't!'

'What do you mean, if only I hadn't? Lord love a duck, it's the one aspect of the whole bally affair that you can't find a flaw in. I may be down to my last bean, I may have to starve in the jolly old gutter, but at any rate I've known you. It makes up for everything. Purified in the holocaust of a mighty love, I shall wander out into the bread line a finer, deeper man. Gosh, how I love you, young Dinty.'

'And I love you, Barmy.'

Barmy reeled. He stared at her incredulously, and noted that her eyes were shining like, as he put it to himself in a happy flash of inspiration, twin stars.

'You do?'

'Of course I do. I always did, right from the beginning.'

'Not when I set your hat on fire?'

'Not then, perhaps, but next day, when you told me you had put that money in the show just so as to be near me. I suddenly realized that you were the most wonderful man in the world.'

'Would you go as far as that?'

'There's nobody like you.'

'That's what my Uncle Theodore has often observed. Only he didn't say it the way you do. More with a sort of nasty rasp in his voice, if you know what I mean. Dinty, you don't really love me, do you? You're kidding me, aren't you? What they call ribbing over here.'

'Of course I'm not kidding you.'

Barmy swelled like a balloon.

'Then to hell and blazes,' he cried, 'with ruin and gutters and bread lines and what not! Nothing else matters but that. If you love me, I laugh at ruin,' said Barmy, doing so. 'And I'll tell you something,' he proceeded, all fire and enthusiasm. 'I'll get that money. I'll get it somewhere . . . somehow, if I have to burgle a bank. And the play. It might be a success in New York, don't you think?'

'Well—'

'I mean, I know it isn't frightfully good, but that isn't supposed to matter much in New York, is it? If I can just get that money . . . enough to keep us going—'

He broke off. An unseen hand had knocked on the door.

'Gosh!' he said, suddenly deflated. It had sounded like the hand of doom. He looked at Dinty, and Dinty looked at him. Here, they both were thinking, was that bevy of stern-faced men with the gyves.

'Who's there?' quavered Barmy.

'It's Mr Fritchie, Mr Phipps.'

'Oh, what ho, Mr Fritchie. It's the screwball,' said Barmy in a hoarse aside. He opened the door. 'It wasn't locked,' he said defensively.

'I was just leaving,' said Dinty.

'Huh?' Mr Fritchie looked about him. 'Oh, broke up early, eh?'

'This is . . . Mr Fritchie. Miss Moore.'

'How are you, Mr Fritchie?'

'Well, I'll tell you. My throat's not too good—'

Barmy resumed the speech for the defence.

'The door wasn't locked, and Miss Moore was just going out.'

'Huh?'

'Isn't that what you came about? Someone just telephoned from the office, beefing about Miss Moore being here.'

'Oh, that was only Mr Hemingway. He's a dope. Don't pay any attention to Mr Hemingway.'

'Well, that's fine,' said Barmy, relieved. 'Come in and take a chair.'

Oscar Fritchie took a chair. He was a stoutish young man with a vacant face and large, myopic eyes. He looked like a sheep with horn-rimmed spectacles. Anyone who had ever seen a sheep wearing horn-rimmed spectacles would have recognized immediately its resemblance to the assistant manager of the Mayflower Hotel, Syracuse. His rather bleating voice increased the illusion.

'How was everything?' he said. 'All right? The supper?'

'Oh, terrific, thanks.'

'I see you got the champagne.'

'Yes, rather.'

'I told the waiter to be sure to ice it. Did he?'

'Absolutely. Like billy-o.'

Oscar Fritchie explained his policy.

'You see, we get show-troupes right along up here, and I know they got the habit of getting together, sort of, so I kind of make a point of seeing that everything's all right. I'm sorry your party's broken up.'

'Yes, too bad.'

'I'd have liked to meet them. I've always had a kind of liking for theatrical people,' said Oscar Fritchie, starting to converse easily, 'and of course they stop here at the hotel a lot, and some of them sort of let me come around.'

'I see.'

'Ian Keith was here last year. We had quite a long talk. You know how it is,' said Oscar Fritchie. 'You get a liking for something. The theatre, I mean. All my life I've . . . just kind of liked to talk to theatrical people. I guess maybe it's because I've always had a sort of feeling I might get into the theatre myself some day. Pardon?' said Oscar Fritchie, looking inquiringly at Dinty, who had leaped some inches into the air with a sharp cry.

'Cramp,' said Dinty.

'Huh?'

'I got a touch of cramp.'

'Is that so? I get a touch of cramp sometimes. Comes on sudden.'

'Yes, doesn't it,' said Dinty, and gave Barmy the sort of look which in Keats's poem the soldiers of stout Cortez directed at one another when standing silent upon a peak in Darien. It was almost identically the same look which Barmy had shot at her. Here, one would have said, and in saying would have been a hundred per cent correct, were two minds with but a single thought.

Barmy cleared his throat.

'Would you mind repeating that?' he said in a low voice.

'Huh?'

'About the theatre.'

'I like it.'

'And you think that some day you might get into it yourself?'

'That's what.'

There was an awed silence.

'You mean . . . as a producer?' said Dinty.

'As a producer, do you mean?' said Barmy.

'That's what I'd like.'

'Sit down!' cried Dinty.

'Sit down!' cried Barmy.

'I am sitting down,' said Oscar Fritchie.

'Oh, yes, so you are. Silly of me.'

Dinty drew a deep breath.

'Do you own this hotel, Mr Fritchie?'

'Me? No, I'm the assistant manager. Mr Hemingway owns it.'

'Still, I suppose that's a pretty good position, assistant manager? You must make a lot of money.'

'Oh, I don't suppose you folks would call it much.'

Barmy, noticing a speck of lint on the visitor's coat sleeve, flicked it off in a loving manner.

'Have you . . .' He paused, searching for the right words. 'Have you been able to . . . Have you got any saved up?'

'Huh?'

'Mr Phipps worked in a hotel, too, before he went into the theatrical business,' explained Dinty brightly. 'He has known so many hotel men who didn't save. He just hopes you're different.'

Oscar Fritchie nodded in a rather superior manner. He was proud of his thrift.

'That's right. A lot of them don't.'

'But you do?'

'You bet your life I do. What's the matter?'

'Not a thing. Just another touch of cramp.'

'You got it, too?' asked Mr Fritchie, looking at Barmy.

'The merest twinge. I say, would you care for a stoup of champagne?'

'That's not a bad idea. You know, I like you folks. You make a fellow feel nice.'

'Some more?'

'I'm not robbing you?'

'Not a bit.'

Oscar Fritchie sipped at his glass.

'Yes, sir,' he said, 'I always say theatre folks are nice people. Not stuck up . . . You know . . . Make a fellow feel at home. I guess that's why I've always liked it . . . sort of . . . the show business.'

'There's no business like show business,' said Dinty. 'You remember the song?'

'You betcher. I can sing it.'

'Go ahead.'

'Well, not right now. Some other time.'

'Any time that suits you.'

Barmy had found another piece of lint, and was busy removing it. His hand being so conveniently placed for the gesture, he patted Oscar Fritchie's arm.

'Er—'

'Huh?'

'Nothing yet,' said Barmy, his nerve failing him.

Oscar Fritchie regarded him with a perplexed frown.

'Say, what's up?'

Dinty leaped into the breach. Women are braver than men.

'I know what Mr Phipps was going to say, Mr Fritchie. He has a proposition to make to you.'

'He has?'

'He's going to give you the chance to invest in this play of his that opened tonight. It's going to make an awful lot of money.'

'Millions,' said Barmy, himself again now that his path had been made straight. 'Millions, my blossom, millions. And you've only to say the word, and you get your slice.'

Oscar Fritchie scratched his left eyebrow. The proposal attracted him, but as so often happens on these occasions, he was conscious of a certain coldness about the feet. It made him waver. If Shakespeare had happened to enter the room at this moment with a friend, he would have said to the friend: 'Don't look now, but that fellow in the horn-rimmed spectacles over there will give you some idea of what I was driving at when I wrote that stuff about letting "I dare not" wait upon "I would", like the poor cat in the adage.'

'Oh . . . now . . . er—' said Oscar Fritchie.

Dinty pressed him hotly.

'Now wait! Wait! It's a wonderful opportunity, Mr Fritchie. You didn't see the show tonight, did you?'

'No.'

'That's fine. It's going to be much better. There was an understudy playing the leading part tonight.'

'And you know what that means,' said Barmy. 'Before I bring it into New York, I shall get a regular star. Someone big.'

'Maurice Evans, perhaps,' said Dinty.

'Or the Lunts,' said Barmy.

'The Lunts wouldn't be bad,' Dinty agreed. 'Or Clark Gable.'

'Yes, Gable might do,' said Barmy.

'Someone big, anyway,' said Dinty.

'Yes, someone big,' said Barmy.

Dinty had now attached herself to the lapel of Mr Fritchie's coat, and was twisting it.

'Mr Phipps will tell you what a wonderful play this is, Mr Fritchie. It's simply marvellous. And he has bought his partners out and has got hold of the whole thing.'

'Lock, stock and barrel,' said Barmy.

'Yes, lock, stock and barrel. It's a real chance, the chance of a lifetime.'

'It sounds kind of good,' admitted Oscar Fritchie. 'But on the other hand—'

'What an amazing coincidence,' said Barmy, flicking off some more lint. 'That's exactly absolutely what I said myself, when I was offered a slice of the thing. I don't mind telling you I hesitated at first, quite a bit. One's got to be careful. But once I'd been told the story—'

'Oh, baby!' said Dinty.

'Precisely,' said Barmy. 'Oh, baby! I could see it was terrific. I knew it was going to be a knock-out. There's a priest in it, and a rabbi, and they come in and gab back and forth, and the feller shoots the feller, only he doesn't really, it's the brother. And so on and so on and back and forth and back and forth, and then off you go to Hong Kong. A great big scene instead of where it's a cabaret. It's wonderful. It's a hop joint and the priest comes in, only he's a missionary now, and he wants to close up the place and the hero comes back at him with the strong talk and so-and-so, and so-and-so, and the girl gets more sympathy because we're writing in a baby. And then they all go to heaven in the last act and put on wings and there's a fat part for God. There's absolutely never been anything like it. It's going to be the biggest thing there ever was in the theatre. So how about it, my puss?'

Oscar Fritchie, having done all that was possible to his left eyebrow, had started to scratch the other one. It was plain that he had been swayed, as who would not have been, by Barmy's eloquence.

'Go into the theatrical business?' he murmured musingly. 'It would be sort of fun.'

'Oh, it's an awful lot of fun,' said Dinty. 'You haven't any idea.'

'Would it cost much?'

Barmy reassured him.

'Practically nothing. You can have twenty-five per cent of it for thirty thousand dollars.'

'Thirty?'

'Twenty-five.'

'Twenty-five?'

'Twenty.

'Twenty?'

'Fifteen. Or, putting it another way, ten.'

'But that's the very lowest, Mr Fritchie,' said Dinty, giving the coat lapel another loving twist.

Oscar Fritchie scratched his chin.

'It's a lot of money.'

'No, no. A bargain. Only you've got to decide quick, because so many people are after it. You see, that's how theatrical business is. You have to make quick decisions.'

'Absolutely,' said Barmy. 'I mean Yah. The bimbo who decides right away – standing up – he's the bird who drags home the gravy. Why, there was a fellow we know who could have bought in on *Arsenic and Harvey*, only he didn't think standing up, so look at him. Didn't get a smell of it. That's show business.'

'That's show business,' said Dinty.

There was not much more of Oscar Fritchie's exposed portions left to scratch, but he scratched what there was.

'I – I don't know what to say. I been getting kind of tired of the hotel lately—'

'Of course you have,' said Dinty sympathetically. 'You're not the kind of man to stay cooped up in a hotel all his life. Look at Mr Phipps.'

Oscar Fritchie looked at Mr Phipps.

'He's got out, and where is he now?'

'Ah!' said Barmy, waving a spacious arm and upsetting the visitor's glass.

Oscar Fritchie found that he had not scratched the tip of his nose. He repaired the omission.

'I'd love to quit and tell Mr Hemingway what I thought of him.'

'That's the spirit!' said Dinty. 'Why don't you?'

'I'm scared.'

'You won't get another chance like this to leave this old hotel behind you. You'll be sorry if you let it go.'

'Yes,' said Barmy, thoroughly concurring. 'I should imagine that if a man had to look back at a colossal opportunity he'd missed, as it might be this one, it would make him pretty bitter, pretty bitter. He'd brood a bit, I bet.'

'He'd be eaten by remorse,' said Dinty.

'To the bone,' said Barmy.

Oscar Fritchie quivered. No man likes to think that he is going to spend a lifetime of vain regrets, brooding on what might have been.

'It wants thinking about.'

'Do it on your feet.'

'You say it's a good play?'

'Terrific.'

Oscar Fritchie started in again on his left ear. His defences were crumbling.

'There are certainly some things I'd tell Mr Hemingway, the big stiff,' he murmured, like a man communing with his immortal soul.

'Write a receipt,' said Barmy.

'Okay, boss.'

'Now wait,' said Oscar Fritchie. 'Wait a moment.'

'You can't wait in show business. Unless you can give us your cheque on the spot,' said Barmy, 'the whole thing's off. Can you?'

'I haven't said I was going to at all, yet.'

Dinty smiled her bright smile. That suggestion of the maternal came into her manner. She conveyed the impression that if she had not been busy writing the receipt, she might have patted Oscar Fritchie's head.

'Just think, Mr Fritchie. If you sign this agreement, you can go to Mr Hemingway tonight and tell him all those things.'

'He's in bed.'

'Pull him out of it.'

Oscar Fritchie considered this. It was an alluring idea.

'I suppose he makes you work very hard?'

'Twelve hours a day.'

'Awful!'

'Monstrous!' said Barmy. 'In the theatre you don't have to work at all. It's just fun. We're just one happy family. And look,' said Barmy.

'There's no reason why we have to produce just this one show. We could go ahead and do a lot more. When this is a big success. Why, we can be the biggest producers there are. All kinds of shows . . . Shall I open this for you?' said Barmy, clutching at the cheque-book which had stolen almost imperceptibly from Oscar Fritchie's pocket.

'No, no. I can do it.'

'Well, here's ink and everything, and here's the pen of the gardener's aunt. You make the cheque out to me. Cyril Phipps. C-y-r-i-l.'

'What's your first name, Mr Fritchie?' said Dinty. 'And how do you spell this one?'

'Oscar Fritchie. F-r-i-t-c-h-i-e. But I haven't made up my mind yet.'

'Here's the receipt,' said Dinty. 'It says you're giving Mr Phipps ten thousand dollars for twenty-five per cent of the show. Is that all right?'

'Well . . . say . . .'

'Perfectly all right,' said Barmy. 'Couldn't be better. Now all you have to do is to write the good old cheque, and all will be joy and laughter.'

'Do you think I ought to?'

'Of course you ought to. It's a great big drama, not highbrow, not lowbrow, just medium-brow, and a feller shoots a feller and the priest and the rabbi gab back and forth and there's an orchard in it and Mr Hemingway comes in . . . Ah!' said Barmy, grabbing at the cheque.

'Look out,' said Oscar Fritchie. 'It's wet.'

'I'll dry it.'

'I wonder if I done the right thing.'

'Or course you done the right thing. You've set yourself on the broad highway that leads to wealth and fame and, in a nutshell, what not. It's going to be a whale of a hit, sweetheart, a whale of a hit!'

'That's my old Phipps! That's the Phipps I used to know! You never spoke a truer word, my old friend Phipps.'

It was not Oscar Fritchie who said this. The voice was the voice of Mervyn Potter. The errant star was standing in the doorway, supporting himself with a hand on either side.

A great change had taken place in Mervyn Potter since Barmy had last seen him, a change very much for the better. Before, he had been in the depths, a broken man headed for the nearest recruiting station of the French Foreign Legion. Now he seemed quietly happy. His wide, pebble-beach smile betrayed intoxication but it was a gay light-hearted intoxication. Still stinko, he had become joyously stinko. The vultures which had gnawed at his bosom appeared to have downed tools.

'You bet it's going to be a whale of a hit,' he proceeded, recklessly removing his hands from their support and zigzagging to a chair, into which he fell like a sack of coals. 'And I'll tell you why. I am going to star in it, Phipps, old friend. Back to the army again, sergeant, back to the army again. Mervyn Potter reporting for duty,' said Mervyn Potter, rising, saluting and immediately falling back again into his seat, like another sack of coals.

'What!' cried Barmy.

Mervyn Potter, who had closed his eyes as if about to drop into one of his refreshing sleeps, opened them.

'Phipps,' he said, 'when we had that last stimulating little chat of ours, I think – correct me if I am wrong – I told you that my fiancée – Hermione, only daughter of C. Hamilton Brimble of King's Point, Long Island, assisted by Mrs C. Hamilton Brimble of King's Point, Long Island – had given me the brusheroo.'

'That's right.'

'I fancy – again correct me if I am wrong – that I mentioned that my heart was broken.'

'That's right.'

'Mended,' said Mervyn Potter, patting the left side of his waistcoat. 'Sound as a bell. Not a crack in it. Mervyn Potter is himself again.'

'That's good.'

'Not good,' corrected Mervyn Potter. 'Colossal. Yes,' he proceeded, 'for a time Hermione's heartless inhumanity upset me quite a little. The sun seemed darkened. Life appeared to be at an end. But mark the sequel. I stepped around to an excellent bar at no great distance from this hotel, and there shot perhaps half a dozen quick ones down the hatch. I then subjected the whole affair to a close review, analysing every facet of it. And all of a sudden a remarkable change came over my mood. I perked up and saw that all had been for the best and that, so far from wallowing in the soup, I had been saved from the scaffold at the eleventh hour, precisely like those fellows in the historical novels, who, as the hangman is adjusting the noose, perceive a horseman riding up on a foaming horse, waving a paper.'

He sat for a while musing.

'This whole business of getting married, Phipps,' he resumed, 'is a thing you have to look at from every angle. What suddenly struck me like a blow was the reflection that a girl like Hermione Brimble would have insisted on a fashionable wedding with full choral effects. There would have been a Bishop, possibly two Bishops, and assistant clergy and bridesmaids and choir boys and reporters and photographers and about eleven hundred guests of assorted sexes. And as I tottered up the aisle, these Bishops, these assistant clergy, these bridesmaids, these reporters, these photographers and these guests would have laughed their fat heads off at me, making me feel like a piece of cheese. Add vergers, sextons, beadles, pew-openers, first and second gravediggers and what not, and take into consideration the fact that after the ceremony would have come the reception at the home of the bride, and can you wonder that I felt that I had had a merciful escape? I tottered from that bar, Phipps, ashen to the lips but with my heart singing within me. I realized that the guardian angel of the Potters, instead of being, as I had supposed, asleep at the switch, had in reality been working like a beaver in my interests, saving me from an experience so terrible as to make the imagination boggle. And as I walked along the street, I met a baby.'

Mervyn Potter paused, and a strong shudder shook him.

'I don't know,' he went on, his voice trembling, 'if all babies in Syracuse are like that, or whether this one was sent especially to warn me. It was one of those bulging babies. It looked a little like Boris Karloff and a little like Winston Churchill. Our eyes met, and it was as though a voice from above had whispered in my ear, 'See, Potter! But for excellent staff work on the part of your guardian angel, something like that might have happened to you!' You may say that a thing like that would not have happened to me, but how do you know? Better men than I have produced babies of an even greater repulsiveness. Some of my best friends are the fathers of the world's leading gargoyles, and who shall say that I would have escaped unscathed? At any rate, be that as it may, my last doubts as to the wisdom of Providence in foiling my matrimonial plans were removed. A heavy burden seemed to fall from my shoulders. I inflated my chest. I gloried in my youth. I abandoned all idea of joining the Foreign Legion and decided to come back to you and resume my place in the troupe. So here I am, Phipps, up and doing with a heart for any fate. Standing shoulder to shoulder like, as I believe I once mentioned to you before, the Boys of the Old Brigade, we will take this play into New York and knock their ruddy eyes out. I've had a great idea. Do you know what we are going to do, Phipps, old friend? We are going to play this charade for laughs. We're going to kid the pants off it and have the customers rolling in the aisles. This opus is not a drama, it's a farce. And when you reflect that if I had remained on the wagon, I should never have thought of that, it makes you realize what a great big wonderful world it is, does it not? Is that a bottle which I see before me, its handle toward my hand?' asked Mervyn Potter, interested. 'Or is it but a bottle of the mind, a false creation proceeding from the heat-oppressed brain?'

'Eh? Oh, yes. One bot as per memo. Champagne.'

'Come let me clutch thee,' said Mervyn Potter.

A stunned silence, the silence of happiness too deep for speech, had fallen on Room 726.

It was broken by Oscar Fritchie.

'Say, could I have your autograph, Mr Potter?' said Oscar Fritchie.

18

INASMUCH as the compact little drama *Sacrifice* had opened in Syracuse toward the end of September and had then gone on to play Albany, Worcester and Providence, it was not until nearly the end of October that it completed its preliminary tour and had what in motion picture circles is known as its preemeer on Broadway. To be exact, October 27th.

As Dinty Moore entered the office of Lehmac Productions on the morning of October 28th, she had a sudden illusion that joy bells were ringing through the world. It was, however, only the telephone, and she hastened to answer it.

'Lehmac Productions,' she said in her official voice, the one with the rising lilt. 'Noo, Mr Phipps has not come in yet. Yace, it looks like a very big hit does it not? . . . Oo, well, I don't knoo. I believe Mr Phipps was thinking of producing it himself in London. Maybe if you give him a ring later. *Good*-baye,' said Dinty and, hanging up, executed a few dance steps across the floor.

The success of *Sacrifice* had probably not come as a surprise to whoever it was who had been speaking at the other end of the wire, for there are no surprises in the theatre today. Thirty years ago it was possible for a play to steal quietly out into the hinterland and arrive in New York still an unknown quantity, but nowadays *Variety* has its spies everywhere, and the chances of even the most modest enterprise are weighed week by week. The fierce light that beats upon a throne is a mere glimmer compared to that which beats upon a new theatrical production.

To any knowledgeable citizen of Broadway such headlines as:

SACRIFICE NEAT $15,000 ALBANY

SACRIFICE SOLID WOW WORCESTER

and, above all,

SACK SWEET SOCKO 20 G. PROVIDENCE

had told the story. The word had gone around that – unless, of course, these out-of-town triumphs failed to repeat themselves under the more testing conditions of the metropolis – Sack was in. And so it had proved. Unquestionably, indubitably, uncontrovertibly and past all dispute, as Mr Roget would have put it in his *Thesaurus*, it was a sweet socko.

Time marched on. There were further telephone conversations. Two callers arrived, asking to see Mr Phipps, and Dinty promised that their visits should be drawn to the attention of the man up top, if and when he put in an appearance. And eventually Barmy came in, on his face the awed look of one who has seen visions.

'What ho, queen of my soul,' he said in a hushed voice.

'Pip-pip, maestro,' said Dinty, returning civility for civility.

'I say,' said Barmy, 'did you come here past the theatre?'

'I did.'

'Was there really a line of people at the box office?'

'There was, my poppet. A long line. And they all had their four-eighty clutched in their hot little hands, bless them.'

Barmy drew a deep breath. If Dinty, too, had observed the spectacle, it could be accepted as official.

'I could hardly believe it. I thought I saw them, but I couldn't help feeling that it was just a beautiful dream. Didn't you think they looked extraordinarily attractive?'

'Fine fellows.'

'The salt of the earth. I don't know where you can find more splendid specimens of humanity than in the line waiting at the box office of a show you've bunged a lot of money into. Talk about fair women and brave men! Oh, Dinty!'

Barmy seemed to expand, as if a load had been removed from his shoulders. There had been times during the past four weeks when doubts had assailed him and melancholy had marked him for its own, principally on the occasions when his partner, Mr Fritchie, had been suffering from one of those attacks of cold feet which were so frequent with him. Moody, wavering, irresolute, Oscar Fritchie was the sort of man who would have got on well with Hamlet. He seemed to find it impossible to look on the bright side. Tell Oscar Fritchie that the house was all sold out for tonight, and he would reply, 'But who'll come tomorrow night?', and this kind of thing cannot but have a lowering effect on the most ebullient.

But now that a Broadway first-night audience had received the show rapturously, now that eight critics out of nine had submitted excellent notices (and the ninth not too dashed bad), now that long queues of charming and intelligent playgoers were lining up at the box office, eager to shower their money on the autocrat behind the window, Barmy had blossomed like some lovely flower. His eyes gleamed. His butter-coloured hair seemed to shine. He held himself jauntily and gave the impression of being three inches taller than he actually was. It was with the air of a conquering knight coming home to his lady after a successful couple of years at the Crusades that he now folded Dinty in a close embrace, covered her upturned face with burning kisses and told her that of all the outstanding eggs that ever drew perfumed breath, she was the most pre-eminent.

'I love you, young Dinty.'

'Not so much as I love you.'

'Much more than you love me.'

'You couldn't. Still, let's not quarrel about it. Isn't it wonderful, Barmy, that all this happened? Do you realize that we shall be rich?'

'Rolling.'

'We'll live on Park Avenue.'

'With a butler.'

'Two butlers. And we'll get a really good car.'

'Several really good cars. How about a yacht?'

'I wonder if we could buy the *Queen Mary*?'

'We'll have a jolly good try. And now, touching on this business of converting you into Mrs C. Fotheringay-Phipps, what's the procedure? Give me the lowdown straight from the horse's mouth. I say,' said Barmy, in sudden alarm, 'you don't want a fashionable wedding with full choral effects, do you? And that stuff Potter was talking about . . . the Bishop and assistant clergy and bridesmaids and choir boys and sextons and beadles and first and second gravediggers and all that?'

'Of course not. I want to be married in the Little Church Round the Corner.'

'Where's that?'

'Twenty-ninth Street.'

'Quiet sort of place?'

'We shall have it all to ourselves.'

'Except for the parson.'

'I don't see how you could keep him out.'

'No, admit the parson. And possibly a brace of witnesses?'

'I suppose so.'

'But that's the lot.'

'That's the lot.'

'Then ho for the Little Church Round the Corner. Come on, grab your hat and let's go.'

Dinty regarded him maternally.

'My poor child, you can't rush things like that. You've got to get a licence.'

'Couldn't we dispense with all that sort of thing?'

'I'm afraid not. If you blew in without a licence, the minister would throw you out on your ear. And, anyway, you've work to do.'

'Work? At a time like this?'

'This is just the moment. All sorts of people have been telephoning and calling. You'll have to spend the rest of the day thinking on your feet and making quick decisions.'

'Perhaps you're right,' said Barmy. 'Yes, I suppose there is man's work to do.'

He seated himself in the swivel chair, tilted it back, put his feet on the desk, reached for his hat and placed it on his head.

'Now!' he said. 'Tell me all, my puss, omitting no detail, however slight, for one never knows how important the most seemingly trivial detail may be. What's been happening?'

Dinty consulted her notebook.

'There have been two or three telephone calls. One was from someone who wanted to buy the play for London. I told him you were probably going to do it in London yourself.'

'Of course I am. And in Paris and Berlin and Moscow.'

'You can't do it in Moscow.'

'Well, Brussels, then. Where the sprouts come from. Brussels is just as good. Proceed,' said Barmy, putting the tips of his fingers together.

'There were two callers. One of them wouldn't leave his name. He was rather mysterious, and said he would be back.'

'Did he state his business?'

'No.'

Barmy frowned. Laxity here. It would be necessary, he saw, to ginger up the office staff.

'Always ask them to state their business,' he said, rebukingly. 'And bring their cards in first, to see if I'll see them.'

'Yes, sir. I will, sir. Thank you for telling me, sir.'

Barmy blushed.

'Was I putting on dog?'

'You were.'

'I'm sorry. I keep trying not to, but the fact of the matter is, this thing has given me the most frightful swelled head. I find myself chucking my chest out and jostling people off the sidewalk and being in two minds whether or not to pop round to Lee Shubert's office and call him Lee. Deflate me from time to time, will you? If you see it coming on, just say "Hoy!" '

'I will.'

'Hoy! Sharply, like that.'

'Okay, professor.'

Barmy mused.

'And yet, dash it all,' he said, feeling cheated of his dues, 'why shouldn't one stick on a bit of the haughty seigneur and swank around somewhat after a hit like this one? Did you read the notices?'

'I know them by heart. They were wonderful.'

'*The Times*?' said Barmy dubiously.

'It wasn't bad?'

'Not bad, no, but . . . I didn't like that bit about the brothel being merely adequate.' A stern look came into Barmy's face. 'I don't think I'll let *The Times* critic come to my next one. Teach him a sharp lesson.'

'Hoy!'

'Hoy it is. Notice how it comes on me in a flash, like a stroke or something? I'll be buzzing along quite all right, and suddenly – *bingo!* – the old head swells up like a poisoned pup. I'll have to see a doctor. Who was the other bird?'

'Which other bird?'

'The other bird who presented himself *chez* Phipps. You said there were two of them.'

'Oh yes. It was your former boss, Mr Anderson.'

Barmy stared.

'J. G. Anderson? Are you sure?'

'I've only his word for it, but that's who he said he was.'

'Well, I'll be dashed.'

'He said he wanted to see you about something important.'

'He did, eh? Then do you know what must have happened? He must have come up to New York on a toot and gone to the show last night and read the papers this morning and seen that I've got a whale of a hit, and he's going to have another try to get me to buy that hotel of his. In Bessemer, Ohio. A fat chance!'

'Why? Why don't you buy the hotel?'

Barmy laughed derisively. The idea amused him.

'Me? What do I want with hotels? If Lee drops in and suggests my taking over half a dozen of his theatres, that's another matter. But hotels!'

'Hoy!'

'Not a bit of it. Hoys don't enter into the thing at all. How could I run a hotel in Ohio when I'm in the legit?'

'Get out of the legit.'

Barmy gaped. He could hardly believe that he had heard her aright.

'What, chuck show business just when I'm sitting on top of the world?'

'But it's so precarious, my pet. You're up today and down tomorrow. *Sacrifice* is a hit but your next one might be a terrible flop. And the next one after that, and the next one after that. A hotel's different. It's solid. I'd love to help you run a hotel, and I know I'd be happy in a place like Bessemer. I'm sick of Broadway.'

Again Barmy found himself doubting his ears.

'Sick of Broadway?'

'Sick to death. Oh, Barmy—'

She broke off. The door had opened, and Oscar Fritchie was coming in.

Externally, Oscar Fritchie looked about the same as he had always done, which was not much, but with his opening words it became evident that internally he was a mere mass of quivering ganglions.

'Say, what are all those people doing over at the theatre?' he asked anxiously, not even waiting to say Good morning. 'I came by the theatre just now, and there was a whole bunch of them milling around the lobby.'

Barmy tilted his hat and uttered a short laugh. These novices!

'They're buying tickets.'

'Tickets?'

'Yah.'

'For the show, you mean? Why?'

'It's a big success.'

'Who says so?'

'Everybody says so. Didn't you read the notices?'

'What notices?'

'Of the play. In the papers.'

'I hadn't the nerve to look at the papers.'

'Dinty, have you got the papers?'

'Not here. Shall I go out and buy them?'

'Do so, and with all speed.'

'I will,' said Dinty. 'And later on, if you have a moment, Mr Shubert, I'd like to go on with what I was saying when we were interrupted. I have much to say to you on a certain subject.'

Oscar Fritchie waited anxiously while the door closed. Then he turned to Barmy and spoke in a hoarse whisper.

'Now, on the level, how are things?'

'It's one of the biggest hits ever produced.'

'No, no,' said Oscar Fritchie. 'She's gone. You can tell me.'

'Mobs of eager men are calling up wanting to buy it for London and everywhere.'

Oscar Fritchie started.

'How much did you get?'

'I didn't sell it.'

'What?'

'Of course I didn't. Sell it, foolish! What the dickens would I want to sell it for?'

Oscar Fritchie clutched piteously at his partner's coat sleeve. His manner was agitated. He bleated like the sheep he so closely resembled.

'Now look. I think if we can get any money, we ought to, huh? . . . because . . . I don't feel just right yet, see?'

Barmy's jolly laugh ridiculed his fears.

'When we go ahead and produce a few more, you'll feel all right.'

'Do you think we ought to do that?'

'Of course I do. This is not an end, but a beginning. I'm planning to do a big musical, to start with, with ten comics and a hundred lovely girls.'

Oscar Fritchie reached for his hat.

'I think maybe I ought to get out.'

'Out of the firm? Right ho. I can handle it myself.'

'Would you buy my share?'

'Like a shot.'

'Oh?' said Oscar Fritchie, putting his hat down. 'Well . . . then . . . I don't know,' and you could see Hamlet patting him on the back and telling him he knew just how he felt.

'Do you know what I'm going to do, my blossom?' said Barmy, tilting his hat. 'I'm going to get hold of all the big playwrights there are in this country and put them under contract, and then I'm going to buy up all the foreign plays. Make what they call a corner.'

Oscar Fritchie's adam's apple was leaping up and down.

'You are?'

'And when I've got all the plays tied up, I'm going to get the theatres.'

'The theatres?'

'Yah.'

'Buy up a whole lot of theatres?'

'Got to have somewhere to put the plays, what?'

Oscar Fritchie's adam's apple did another quick exercise gallop.

'But look. Suppose something happens? Suppose something goes wrong some place?'

'How can it?'

'It might.'

'Not a chance. Shall I tell you the secret of show business? Just give the public what they want.'

'But how do you know what they want?'

'They always want the same thing.'

'Sure as I went into it,' said Oscar Fritchie, shaking his head lugubriously, 'they'd change their minds.'

Dinty appeared with the papers under her arm and a card in her hand.

'Hoy!' she said, speaking immediately from the doorway.

Barmy eyed her with a touch of guilt.

'Why the Hoy?'

'I'll bet it was needed while I was out of the room.'

This was so true that Barmy hastened to change the subject.

'I see you have a card on your person,' he said, rather distantly. 'Does someone wait without?'

'He does.'

Barmy waved a managerial hand at Oscar.

'You see? Not a moment passes but some eager beaver comes muscling in, wanting to do business. Who is he?'

'He's one of the two birds.'

'Two birds? Ah, yes. The two birds who called, you mean.'

'That's right. This is the first bird. The one who wouldn't leave his name and said he would be back.'

'I don't know why,' said Oscar Fritchie, beginning to show the early symptoms of palsy, 'but I've got a feeling that this is bad news.'

Barmy glanced at the card. It held no message for him.

'The bimbo under advisement is a complete and absolute stranger to me. Man and boy, I've knocked about the world quite a bit in my time, but I've never heard of J. Bromley Lippincott.'

'Attorney-at-law,' said Oscar Fritchie, looking over his shoulder. 'That's the part I don't like, that attorney-at-law.'

'Did he say what he wanted?'

'Not a word. The silent tomb.'

'He must have come to make an offer.'

Oscar Fritchie shook his head.

'Not an attorney-at-law. They don't make offers. It wouldn't be something you did before this, maybe, huh?' he said hopefully.

Barmy became the brisk executive.

'Well, I can give him five minutes and hear what he's got to say. Bung him in, young heart's delight.'

'Yes, my king.'

Oscar Fritchie was now trembling like a leaf.

'You know what?' he said. 'I'll bet we've got the show in the wrong theatre.'

Before Barmy could comment on this unpleasant thought, Dinty returned, escorting the visitor. And the moment Barmy set eyes on him, he saw that this was a visitor of no common order.

One of those visitors who mark epochs.

19

J. BROMLEY LIPPINCOTT was a tall, dark cadaverous man who looked about sixty, as he had probably looked at the age of ten, and gave the impression, not unusual with attorneys-at-law, of having seen so much of life's murky side that he now automatically suspected everyone he met of nameless crimes. Formidable was the word for J. Bromley and sinister the word for the bulging briefcase which he bore with him like a warrior's shield. Too small to contain a corpse, except possibly that of a Singer midget, it was large enough to hold the guilty secrets of half the population of New York, and the nervous beholder, eyeing it, had visions of documents suddenly popping out of its interior which would prove him, the nervous beholder, to be legally debarred from being a feoffee of any fee, fiduciary or in fee simple or something of that nature. It was that sort of briefcase.

He laid it on the desk with the air of an executive of the Black Hand checking a bomb at a restaurant cloakroom, and for a moment stood facing Barmy and Oscar, allowing his gaze to bore deep into their sensitive persons. Like the Ancient Mariner, he held them with a glittering eye.

'Good morning,' he said.

Simple words, but he uttered them so much in the manner of a detective unmasking the murderer in the final chapter of a mystery thriller that Oscar Fritchie, who had been staring at him with wide, horrified eyes, started convulsively, as if he had been lolling in an electric chair and some practical joker had turned on the juice. It was plain that Oscar Fritchie feared the worst.

Nor was Barmy feeling as nonchalant and lighthearted as he could have wished to be. There was an indefinable something about this attorney-at-law which chilled the spirits. Scattered throughout the United States of America there were probably men, friends of his boyhood days or old cronies who had gone through law school with him, who looked on J. Bromley Lippincott as one of the gang and got a pleasurable kick out of his society, but Barmy was not of their number. He was definitely allergic to Mr Lippincott. Meeting Mr Lippincott's pale grey eye, he found himself understanding what the Gypsy Sybil had meant when she had spoken of trouble coming from a dark man.

'Did you want to see me?' he said, plucking at his tie, and J. Bromley Lippincott gave him a quick, short, sharp, unpleasant look.

'Which is Mr Cyril Phipps?' he asked in a voice of steel.

'He is,' said Oscar Fritchie with vast relief. It was the first suggestion he had had that the bluebird might be among those present.

His relief was short-lived.

'Is this Mr Oscar Fritchie?' asked the visitor keenly.

The jig was up.

'Yep,' said Oscar, commending his soul to God. Nothing could save him now.

'Ah,' said Mr Lippincott, and was silent for a space, his thoughts probably busy with replevin or something of that sort. Then his eye fell on the briefcase and, recalled by the sight of it to the fact that he was here on a mission, he resumed, still speaking in that steely voice which reminded Barmy of his bank manager in London regretting that in the circumstances it would be inconvenient – nay, impossible – to oblige him with the suggested overdraft.

'I called on you gentlemen earlier and left word that I would return.'

'Yah? I wish I'd known,' said Oscar.

'You have my card?'

Concealment was useless. Barmy confessed to having his card.

'My name is Lippincott.'

'That's right. J. Bromley, what?'

'Of Lippincott, Lippincott, Cohn, Mandelbaum and Lippincott.'

'A lawyer, huh?'

This was Oscar Fritchie, breezily endeavouring to establish friendly relations. Try for a chummy atmosphere right at the outset, that was the policy of Oscar Fritchie.

'An attorney-at-law,' corrected Mr Lippincott with cold severity. 'May I—?' he said, indicating with a gesture that he wished to use the desk.

'Oh, rather,' said Barmy, suppressing a desire to rush from the room and escape to Nova Scotia, and with a hideous, menacing slowness Mr Lippincott went to the desk and took up the briefcase, holding it lovingly in his hands like a mother dandling her first-born. He opened it and extracted from it a bundle of documents. He put the bundle on the desk, at the same time shooting a keen glance at Barmy and Oscar. He took out a second bundle and placed it beside the first, giving Barmy and Oscar another glance. A third bundle, a third glance, and the preliminaries were completed. He removed his glasses, produced a second pair, adjusted them on his nose, cleared his throat, took up one of the documents and unfolded it. A ray of sunshine peeped in at the window, and he inspected it coldly for a moment, as if warning it to be up to no tricks with *him*.

'Now, gentlemen,' he said, and it was evident that he was about to get down to the *res*.

He gave the briefcase an affectionate tap, for he loved the little thing, and cleared his throat again.

'You are the owners,' he began, 'of Lehmac Productions Incorporated, of Fourteen Hundred and Sixty-Eight Broadway, New York, New York.' He paused for a moment, then, as if the words constituted deadly evidence which would strip the mask from their faces once and for all, added in a rasping whisper, 'A New York corporation.'

Oscar Fritchie, vaguely recollecting films he had seen at Syracuse picture palaces, raised his right hand solemnly.

'We are. But he owns most of it,' he said, still hoping for the best.

Mr Lippincott had not shot his bolt. There was more to come.

'Said corporation being the producers of a dramatic composition – or play – entitled *Sacrifice*.'

'Yah,' said Barmy, fogged, but helping the thing along. 'It opened last night. At the Broadhurst.'

Mr Lippincott cleared his throat again. From the briefcase, out of which Barmy felt that practically anything could emerge now, he took a magazine with a brightly coloured picture on the cover showing a gentleman in a black mask and correct evening dress insinuating a knife into a lady with nothing much on but step-ins and blood.

'In November, Nineteen Hundred and Forty-Seven,' he resumed, 'there appeared in this magazine, *Peppy Tales*, published in New York City, New York, an article of fiction – or novelette – entitled *A Man's Honor*. Said article of fiction having been written by my client, Mr Rodney Rich, of Worcester, Massachusetts.'

He paused again. A deadly pause, like that of a cobra preparing to strike.

'And, as we shall duly prove in court—'

Oscar Fritchie leaped.

'Court?'

'Court.'

'I thought you said court,' said Oscar Fritchie.

Mr Lippincott resumed his tale to a flatteringly attentive audience. The minstrel was infirm and old, but he was putting his stuff across.

'And, as we shall duly prove in court, the said novelette was made the basis of a dramatic composition – or play – by one Harley Thompson, since deceased.'

'Dead,' explained Barmy for Oscar Fritchie's benefit. He had been acquainted with Oscar Fritchie long enough to know that anything over one syllable bothered him.

'Subsequently, as we shall prove, the said play was purchased or acquired by one Joseph Lehman, trading – in association with one John McClure – as Lehmac Productions Incorporated of Fourteen

Hundred and Sixty-Eight Broadway, New York, New York, a New York corporation, and by him duly produced.'

Mr Lippincott paused again. The sternness of his manner had become tempered by a touch of sadness. It was as though he were telling himself that he was pretty tough, by golly, prepared for anything and not easily shocked, but that he had now come up against something so revolting, so sickening to anyone who, like himself, believed in Man's kinship with the divine, that he could hardly find words with which to continue. Confront him with double burgage, he seemed to be saying to himself, and he could accept it. He might not like it, but he could make allowances for erring human nature and accept it. And the same thing applied to heirs taken in socage.

But this! My God!

With a strong effort he fought down his feelings, and forced himself to the nauseous task.

'It will be shown,' he said, pausing for an instant and eyeing the briefcase as if debating the possibility of a rabbit coming out of it, 'that the said dramatic composition – or play – is similar to the aforesaid novelette at one hundred and forty-six points.'

Barmy sprang toward the ceiling. An adagio dancer could not have got off the mark more nimbly.

'One hundred and forty-SIX?'

'One hundred and forty-six. And that no fewer than seven characters in the aforesaid play bear the same names as those in the aforesaid novelette.'

'Oh, my sainted aunt! But listen—'

'One moment, please.' Mr Lippincott had overcome that touch of sadness. He was now all steel and menace once more. 'My client, Mr Rodney Rich, has received no payment for this play, nor has his permission been sought in any way. It is, in short, a clear case of plagiarism, and one of the most flagrant that it has ever been my privilege to encounter,' said Mr Lippincott, and stopped abruptly, as though, yielding to the influence of the surroundings in which he found himself, he had been about to say, 'It's a whale of a case of plagiarism, sweetheart, a whale of a case of plagiarism!'

Barmy looked at Oscar. Oscar looked at Barmy. Neither seemed to derive any great pleasure or solace from what he saw.

'But . . . But . . . But . . .' said Oscar.

'But listen, my dear old minion of the Law,' said Barmy. 'We didn't know anything about it, dash it all. I bought it from Mr Lehman, I mean to say, and then Mr Fritchie here chipped in and took a slice. We never dreamed there was dirty work at the crossroads.'

'Possibly not. I acquit you of any deliberate malice aforethought. Unfortunately—'

'That's a bad word,' said Oscar, wincing.

'Unfortunately my client cannot take that into account. His composition has been produced in dramatic form without his permission. Not unnaturally, he seeks redress.'

'Seeks what?' said Oscar.

'Money,' said Barmy.

Mr Lippincott, who now seemed to have abandoned all hope of a rabbit coming out of the briefcase, replaced the documents bundle by bundle and snapped the catch. In the stillness its click sounded like one of those explosions which slay six.

'My purpose in laying these facts before you gentlemen, prior to bringing suit, is to afford you the opportunity, if you so desire, of adjusting the matter outside of court.'

'Settle it, you mean?'

'Precisely. Here is the proposition I am authorized to lay before you. My client will accept sixty-six and two-thirds per centum of all profits derived from said play, when, if and as produced, and in those circumstances will permit the play to continue. Failing to receive sixty-six and two-thirds per centum—'

'That's money, too,' said Oscar, whose brain was working well this morning. Well, that is to say, for Oscar Fritchie.

'—he will apply for an injunction and cause the play to be closed at once.'

Barmy uttered a sharp, agonized cry.

'He'll close it?'

'He will close it.'

'Close it?' said Oscar.

'Close it,' said J. Bromley Lippincott.

A loud gulping noise broke the impressive silence which followed his words. It proceeded from Oscar Fritchie. He had started to totter toward the door, his horn-rimmed spectacles registering anguish and despair. He was a child in theatrical matters, but he knew enough about conditions in the world of the drama to be aware that if you put money into a play and someone comes along and closes it, you cannot hope for substantial returns on your investment.

An abstemious man as a rule, he was conscious of an imperious desire for a drink, and a strong one, at that, and he intended to have it immediately.

'Look,' he said, addressing Barmy in a low, hollow voice. 'Most of it's yours, see? I don't know much about lawyers. You do something and I'll go over and see if the theatre's burned down.'

He passed from the room, and silence fell again upon the office of Lehmac Productions Incorporated of Fourteen Hundred and Sixty-Eight Broadway, New York, New York, a New York corporation. Barmy was robbed of speech, and Mr Lippincott, his task completed, was now preparing to relax like an executioner in some Oriental court taking a breather after strangling a few odalisques with his bow-string. He opened the briefcase, once more paused as if giving the rabbit a last chance, then put a hand in and produced a bar of nut chocolate, which he proceeded to nibble, explaining that he had had a light breakfast.

Barmy turned to Dinty. All this while she had been standing by the water-cooler, a silent spectator of the tragedy unfolding itself before her horrified eyes. He felt that if anything constructive was to be accomplished, she must be the one to point the way.

'What do you think we ought to do, Dinty?'

Dinty came forward. Her face was pale and her eyes round. She looked at J. Bromley Lippincott as if trying to detect in his granite features some evidence of human feeling. But Mr Lippincott, though he seemed to be enjoying the nut chocolate, remained the same impregnable figure of doom whose mere glance, before he had even begun to speak, had taken the sunlight out of this sunny morning.

'Must Mr Phipps give an answer immediately?'

J. Bromley Lippincott finished the nut chocolate and wiped his fingers daintily on his handkerchief.

'I regret that he must.'

'But dash it, I haven't had time—'

'Can't we even talk it over? asked Dinty.

Mr Lippincott removed his reading-glasses, took out the pair which he used for distance, wiped them, placed them in position and examined Dinty carefully, as if she had been a knotty point of law.

'This young lady is your adviser?'

'Yah.'

'H'm,' said Mr Lippincott. He subjected Dinty to another scrutiny. Possibly something about her reminded him of his mother when a girl. Possibly her appearance recalled some home town belle of his youth whose memory he had laid aside in lavender. At any rate, he softened. That is to say, instead of looking like a First Murderer, he looked like a rather kindlier Second Murderer. 'At best,' he said, 'I could allow but a brief time.'

'Well, that's better than nothing.'

'Shall we say half an hour?'

'Shall we?' said Barmy.

'Yes,' said Dinty.

'Very well. I shall return for your decision in half an hour or,' said Mr Lippincott, making it clear to the meanest intelligence, 'thirty minutes.'

He picked up the briefcase, licked a morsel of chocolate from the corner of his mouth, and withdrew.

20

IN spite of the fact that a room without J. Bromley Lippincott in it was unquestionably a much jollier place to be in than a room full to overflowing with J. Bromley Lippincott, there was nothing in Barmy's demeanour, as the door closed behind the attorney-at-law, to suggest that he had experienced anything in the nature of a sudden burst of high spirits. In Mr Lippincott's presence, notably during the concluding stages of the interview, he had looked like a corpse which has been several days in the water, and it was such a corpse that he still resembled. Falling into the routine of his predecessors in this office when things were not going quite as planned, he walked sombrely to the water-cooler and filled himself a paper cup. Only when he had drained this, rather in the manner of Socrates drinking the bowl of hemlock, did he speak.

'We won't buy the *Queen Mary*,' he said.

'Oh, Barmy!'

'And one more word. We won't live on Park Avenue. We won't have those cars. And those two butlers of whom we spoke will have to pull up their socks and look around for other situations. Yes, I know,' he said moodily, as Dinty flung her arms about his neck and kissed him. 'Awfully sweet of you, old bean, and delicate attention much appreciated, but, getting remorselessly down to the nub, no amount of kissing and womanly sympathy can alter the salient fact that I am in the soup and sinking for the third time. And just when everything looked so juicy, dammit.'

'You mustn't get discouraged.'

Barmy eyed her wanly.

'Did you say "get"? Was the word you employed "get"?'

'He may be wrong.'

'Those fellows are never wrong.'

'You didn't make him show you his proofs.'

Barmy shuddered.

'I couldn't bear to look at them. No, he's got the thing all taped out. If he states that the said dramatic composition – or play – is similar to the aforesaid novelette at one hundred and forty-six points, you can put your shirt on it that one hundred and forty-six points is the precise total at which it is similar, and that his client, Mr Rodney

Rich of Worcester, Massachusetts, is going to scoop in sixty-six and two-thirds per centum of all profits derived from said play, precisely as indicated. Sixty-six and two-thirds per centum! And I was going to do such big things.'

'You still will.'

Barmy shook his head. Oscar Fritchie himself could not have been more despondent.

'Not a chance. I see now that I'm not the sort of bird who does. There are birds who do big things and birds who, in sharp contradistinction, don't. I'm one of the birds who don't. The brain power isn't there. There is a shortage of little grey cells. I remember my Uncle Theodore – it was on the occasion when I broke his meerschaum pipe while endeavouring to do the home a bit of good by swatting a fly which was chucking its weight about in the library – saying that I had as much sense as a village idiot. He was a trifle stirred at the moment, for he loved that pipe passionately and used to spend hours a day colouring it, and it seemed to me that he was letting generous wrath run away with his cool judgment, but I now realize that he was quite right. In fact, he was giving me the breaks. I'm no good. I'm hopeless. I'm just poor old Barmy, the village idiot.'

'I love village idiots.'

Barmy stared.

'Don't tell me you're still toying with the idea of marrying me?'

'Get that licence, and watch my smoke!'

Into the depths which covered Barmy, black as the pit from pole to pole, there crept a faint ray of sunshine. He did not smile, for much would have to happen before he smiled again, but his V-shaped depression perceptibly lightened. He kissed Dinty with something approaching animation.

Then despondency returned. He released her with a heavy sigh.

'You don't know what you're letting yourself in for. A nice breadwinner I should be under present financial conditions. I doubt if I could win a single slice, let alone support you in the style to which you have been accustomed.'

'A one-room flat in Astoria.'

'My resources won't even run to a one-room flat.'

'You can get a job.'

'I doubt it. We Phippses are not easy to place.'

'You had a job before.'

'True. I held a portfolio as desk clerk under J. G. Anderson. But I got the post not by merit but through influence. My Uncle Theodore, who breeds Siamese cats, happened to be in New York, paying his annual visit to my late grandfather, and learning that Siamese cat breeders were collecting in gangs at Bessemer, Ohio, decided to join the party. He put up at J. G. Anderson's hotel, met J. G. Anderson, got pally with him, and took advantage of this burgeoning of a beautiful friendship to shove me off on him in the capacity, as I say, of a desk clerk. Came the dawn, and J. G. Anderson gave me what Potter calls the old heave-ho.'

'Wouldn't he take you back?'

Barmy laughed a faint, weak laugh. He had not supposed that he would ever again be capable of laughter, even of the faint, weak type, but this artless question succeeded in producing it.

'If I read aright the message in his eyes when we parted, no. But, dash it, we mustn't waste time talking about jobs and the distant future. We've got to decide what to tell J. Bromley Lippincott. He'll be back in about two shakes, all agog to know what the score is. We shall have to tell him something.'

Dinty reflected.

'Suppose you gave him what he wanted?'

'It wouldn't leave much to split up.'

'That's true.'

'Half of thirty-three and one-third per centum per me per Oscar per person.' Barmy paced the floor feverishly. Remorse was searing him. 'It makes me feel such an abysmal louse, having got Oscar into the thing. There he was, poor broken blossom, perfectly happy, with a good job and all that money in the old sock, and I come barging in and . . . Holy smoke!' said Barmy, as knuckles rapped on the door. 'That can't be J. Bromley already, can it?'

'Come in,' said Dinty. 'No, of course it can't. He won't be here for another twenty minutes. It's probably . . . Oh, hello, Mr Potter.'

'Oh, hullo,' said Barmy.

Although the party given in his honour on the previous night by a few friends and admirers had not broken up till six in the morning, Mervyn Potter was looking extraordinarily spruce and debonair. His eye was not dimmed nor his natural force abated. He was one of those fortunate persons who seem to thrive on a shortage of sleep. If there was any criticism that could have been made of his appearance, it was that though the day was well advanced, it being now nearly lunch-time, he was still wearing the white tie and tails more conventionally allotted to the dinner hour. And the bizarre note was further stressed by the circumstance that some loving hand had written the words 'Oh, baby!' across his shirt front in lipstick.

But Mervyn Potter was never the man to attach too much importance to the trivialities of dress. If you had asked him, he would have said that it was the soul that mattered. 'Get the soul functioning in mid-season form,' he would have told you, 'and the outer crust can take care of itself.' He beamed upon his old friend Barmy, and his young friend Dinty, and asked if they had read the notices.

'A genuine triumph,' said Mervyn Potter, 'reflecting great credit on all concerned. We shall run a year. But I didn't come simply to tell you that, gratifying though it admittedly is. I am here, Phipps, old friend, in the capacity of an ambassador. I'll sit down, if you don't mind. Is anybody except the great white chief allowed to use that swivel chair? Throw me out if I'm breaking the rules.'

He seated himself at the desk, and put his feet on it.

'Yes,' he resumed, 'I am a plenipotentiary. One of those boys who go in for pourparlers. I have been asked to treat with you in a matter of considerable importance. I was curled up on the floor of my bedroom at the Lambs this morning, sleeping like a little child,' explained Mervyn Potter, 'when the telephone rang from downstairs and I was informed that I had a visitor. "Strangle him with your bare hands," I said. They doubted whether this could be done. "Then send the hellhound up," I said, and they sent up the hellhound. And who do you think it was, this hound of hell? None other than our old crony, J. G. Anderson, of the Skeewassett Andersons. And after the customary civilities had been exchanged, he asked me to plead with you to buy that hotel of his. I gather that at a previous meeting you found yourself unable to ante up, but now that you have made this colossal hit, pulling in millions weekly, he feels that the conversations can be resumed. He'll take seventy-five thousand, he says.'

'Ha!'

'I beg your pardon? What did you say?'

'Just Ha!' said Barmy.

Mervyn Potter was puzzled.

'You say Ha! thereby placing yourself in a limited class with the war-horse which, if you recall, made the same observation among the trumpets, but what does it *mean*? Enlarge on that simple ejaculation.'

Barmy went to the water-cooler and filled a paper cup.

'When he said seventy-five thousand, did he mean dollars or cents?'

'Dollars, I understand.'

'Well, it doesn't much matter,' said Barmy, 'because even seventy-five thousand cents would be beyond the scope of the privy-purse.'

'We've had bad news, Mr Potter,' said Dinty. 'Tell him, Barmy.'

Brokenly, Barmy told the story, and Mervyn Potter, shaking his head, agreed that 'bad' was a neat description.

'What are you going to do?' he asked.

'We don't know. We were just talking it over when you arrived.'

'I fear you will have to give him his pound of flesh. Lawyers,' said Mervyn Potter, 'are the devil. Back in Hollywood I moved in a morass of them. They were about my board and about my bed, spying out all my ways. I remember once—'

What it was that Mervyn Potter remembered was not destined to be revealed, for at this moment the door flew open and Fanny Lehman swept in with that confident stride of hers which always gave the impression that she was taking the stage preparatory to wowing an audience with six clubs at the finish. She seemed in the highest spirits. Her eyes were bright, her face aglow. She looked like a woman about to slip something over on somebody.

'Hello, children,' she said. 'Hello, Mr Potter.'

'Good morning, madam.'

The last thing Barmy wanted at this moment, with problems to be threshed out and vital decisions arrived at, was an interruption, even from a woman of whom he had always been fond. But if short on the little grey cells, he was courteous.

'Oh, hullo, Mrs Lehman,' he said, and hoped that the words had not sounded like a death-rattle.

They had. Fanny's eyebrows rose. Her eyes shot from him to Dinty and back again. She was a quick observer, and even a slow observer would have sensed a strain in the atmosphere.

'For heaven's sake!' she said. 'What's all this about? You ought to be peppier than this. Don't you know you've got a hit?'

'Oh, rather. Yes, I know that all right.'

'Well, I'm here to tell you that you've got about three times as big a hit as you think you have. It's that brothel scene that's rung the bell. The police are going to try to close the show on account of it, and you know what that means. You'll have 'em hanging on to the rafters.'

Barmy gasped. What with J. Bromley Lippincott and the New York police force, he was feeling like an electric hare pursued by an army corps of greyhounds.

'But suppose they do close it?'

Fanny laughed indulgently.

'Not a chance. Not in this town.'

'No,' said Mervyn Potter. 'New York isn't Boston. We got our rights here, boy. All that will happen is that there will be a lot of front-page stuff in the papers and you'll have to cut out a couple of 'Hells' and a 'Damn' or two tomorrow night. You will then put them back on the following night and carry on as before.'

'And meanwhile,' said Fanny, 'every single individual person in the city with four dollars eighty in his kick will come burning up the sidewalks to get at the box office window.'

'While those who haven't four dollars eighty,' said Mervyn Potter, 'will run around in circles till they've borrowed it somewhere.'

'I tell you,' said Fanny, 'it's going to be a landslide. And I'll tell you something else. You've got company coming.'

'Eh?' said Barmy. 'Company?'

'Mr Lehman.'

Dinty uttered a cry.

'Mr Lehman.'

'None other. He's smoked out a bankroll,' said Fanny, giving full weight to the announcement, 'and he wants to buy the show back. He raised the money on that tip about the police, and he's got it with him in certified cheques.'

If she had expected the news to make a sensation, she was not disappointed. Barmy gasped, and looked at Dinty. Dinty gasped, and looked at Barmy. To both of them simultaneously a thought had come like a full-blown rose, flushing the brow. And it was plain from his demeanour that the same thought had come to Mervyn Potter.

'Golly!' said Dinty.

'The happy ending,' said Mervyn Potter.

'It will be if he doesn't get here in less than about a quarter of an hour,' said Barmy. 'Will he get here in less than about a quarter of an hour?' he asked tensely.

Fanny looked puzzled.

'What's all this?' she asked. 'What's going on?'

Barmy pressed his point.

'Will he, do you think?'

'I guess so. He's on his way. I just shot ahead of him to give you the low-down. I got a kind of fool liking for you, brother Phipps. Somehow, suckers always appealed to me. And I don't think Joe Lehman ought to be encouraged to slip the harpoon into the young and innocent. Joe's swell, and I love him, but I don't like some of his ways.'

'How true,' said Mervyn Potter. 'They do invite criticism. I don't know where Joe got his early education, but it was in some school or college where they forgot to teach him the difference between right and wrong. There is a difference, so they tell me, but nobody ever straightened Joe out on it.'

'No,' said Fanny. 'He's planning the steal of the century, bless his impetuous old heart, and I raced ahead to warn you. When he arrives and goes into his act, don't weaken for a single instant. If you let that robber baron sweet-talk you into parting with this show, it'll be a crime.'

Somebody banged on the door. Fanny smiled a gentle smile.

'Ah! Up goes the curtain!'

'Yes,' said Mervyn Potter. 'Here, if I mistake not, Watson, is our client now.'

21

WHEN Mr Lehman came lumbering in, a man in a hurry, the first emotion he experienced was one of surprise at finding himself a unit of what appeared to be some sort of convention. The magnitude of the crowd in his old office plainly took him aback. He looked at Barmy. He looked at Dinty. He looked at Mervyn Potter. Then his gaze fell upon Fanny, and he started like one who finds tarantulas in his bath tub.

'You!' he said, speaking hoarsely. 'What are you doing here?'

'Just visiting.'

'Get out!'

Barmy raised his eyebrows. One cannot have this sort of thing.

'Hoy!' he said, with quiet rebuke. 'You're not going to start putting people out of places again, are you? This is *my* office,' said Barmy. 'Fourteen Hundred and Sixty-Eight Broadway, New York, New York, a New York corporation, and any putting out of people that's required I'll attend to – by my halidom.'

'Well spoken, Phipps,' said Mervyn Potter.

'The word in season, what?'

'Right plumb spang in season,' said Mervyn Potter.

Barmy seated himself in the swivel chair which Mervyn Potter had gallantly vacated on Fanny's entrance, and put his feet on the desk.

'Sit down, sweetheart,' he said, 'and let's hear what's on your mind.'

'Such as it is,' said Mervyn Potter.

'Precisely,' said Barmy. 'Such as it is. What brings you here this bright, sunny morning, my blossom?'

Mr Lehman, who during these exchanges had been glowering at the wife of his bosom, turned to him with a passionate gesture.

'Listen,' he said. 'I don't know what she's been handing you, but don't start believing it.'

'You speak in riddles, laddie.'

'Look,' said Mr Lehman. 'I come around to give you your coin back – let you out clean.'

'You mean you want to buy the show?'

'I'll give you what you paid for it – twenty thousand. You won't lose a thing.'

'You won't either, will you, what?'

'What?'

'That's what I said. What?'

'I don't get you.'

Barmy had never expected that the time would come when he would be glad to have met J. Bromley Lippincott, but he was conscious now of a marked thankfulness that he had been privileged to see the attorney-at-law in action, for there was much which a young theatrical manager could learn from the dark, cadaverous man in the matter of deportment. He could not make himself dark and cadaverous, but he could borrow some of the steel and thrust of J. Bromley Lippincott's manner, and he did so.

'Let me explain,' he said. 'You talk airily—'

'Or glibly,' said Mervyn Potter.

'Or, of course, glibly,' assented Barmy, always open to suggestions. 'You talk airily or glibly of buying the show, but let me remind you that the aforesaid dramatic composition – or play – is a dashed valuable property. It's the greatest dramatic novelty in twenty years. It starts with a Prologue—'

Mr Lehman exploded.

'You're going to believe that stuff of hers, huh? Listen, my blossom –'

'I'm listening, my puss.'

'I'm an old hand at this game. Huh?'

The 'Huh?' was addressed to Fanny, who had uttered the words 'Vaudeville agent'. On request, she repeated them, and Mr Lehman, scorching her with a malignant stare, said, 'That's all right about Vaudeville agents, we aren't talking about Vaudeville agents, we're talking about running shows.'

'I'm an old hand at this game,' he said again, striking the palm of his left hand with the clenched fist of his right, 'and I can make something out of this show, but you can't.'

'I can't?'

'No.'

Barmy uttered a light laugh. J. Bromley Lippincott in a similar situation would, he was aware, have frowned, but he preferred the light laugh. It did not tinkle quite so musically as he could have wished, so he tried it over again, and this time it tinkled splendidly.

'I can't, eh? Step round to the theatre and take a look at the mob of pleasure-seekers trying to buy tickets. It's a whale of a hit, sweetheart, and under my management—'

'It's the management that counts,' said Mervyn Potter.

'Yessir, it's the management that counts,' said Barmy. 'Absolutely. You need the expert hand, and that's what this dramatic production's got nothing else but of.'

Mr Lehman was breathing in a stertorous manner which would have caused his doctor to purse his lips and reach for the sedatives.

'Look,' he said. 'I'll give you thirty, and I've got the certified cheques in my pocket. Set?'

Barmy shook his head.

'It can't be done, old son. For your own sake I couldn't do it. If you had it on your conscience that you had sweet-talked me into selling a big dramatic novelty like this for thirty thousand dollars, you'd never have a moment's peace. You wouldn't sleep at nights. There's a cabaret scene—'

'Forty.'

'Sorry.'

'I only got fifty. Do you want it all? Do you think I'm trying to gyp you?'

'No, no. I acquit you of any deliberate malice aforethought. Unfortunately—'

At this point, there was a sound like a mighty rushing wind, the door flew open, and Jack McClure came whirling in, not stopping to knock. Like his late partner, he appeared to be in a hurry. Seeing Mr Lehman, he rocked back on his heels, shocked and astounded.

'So!' he said, with a wealth of emotion in his voice.

'Aha!' said Fanny. 'The boy friend!'

'I thought so!' said Jack McClure, and not even J. Bromley Lippincott, appalled by a whale of a case of plagiarism, could have put more horror and indignation into three short words. 'Trying to doublecross me, eh?' said Jack McClure. His burning eyes rested on Mr Lehman for a long moment, then he wrenched them away and turned to Barmy. 'Have you sold it to him yet?'

'The big dramatic novelty?'

Jack McClure, generally so quiet and gentlemanly, raised his voice to a shout.

'If you haven't, don't. Because he's out to skin you.'

'Mr Lehman?' said Barmy, amazed.

'He didn't tell you about the police, did he?'

'I did,' said Fanny, and Mr Lehman gave her a look which J. Bromley Lippincott, had he been present to observe it, would have been the first to admit surpassed by a long way anything in his own *repertoire*.

'Just a pal!' he said thickly. 'Just a pal!'

Jack McClure was getting down to business.

'Look here. I'll give you fifty thousand dollars. I've got it right here.'

'Fifty thousand?' Barmy risked the tinkling laugh again. 'Why, even Mr Lehman offered that.'

'He did?'

'Do you want to go any higher? It's a terrific dramatic composition. A priest comes in with a rabbi, and they gab back and forth – and so on and so on—' Jack McClure fingered his chin.

'Fifty thousand? That's a lot of dough.'

'How about you, Mr Lehman?'

Mr Lehman's attention had been momentarily detached from the discussion. He was telling his wife in a low, confidential undertone that he intended to brain her. It was Mervyn Potter who took it upon himself to offer a suggestion.

'I think—' said Mervyn Potter, and paused. For the first time this morning he had caught a glimpse of his shirt front and read its message. He stiffened, and there came into his handsome face a keen, accusing look. 'Lehman,' he said, 'is this your handiwork? Was it you who crept up on me like a thief in the night and wrote the words 'Oh, baby!' on my wishbone?' Then, softening, he went on: 'No, of course you didn't. You don't use lipstick, do you? I imagine the thing will have to remain one of those insoluble historic mysteries like the man in the iron mask. But I was saying I think I see the way out. I don't know if you have had much to do with the world of finance, but I believe that on these occasions when two tycoons, call them Tycoon A. and Tycoon B., are desirous of putting through some important deal and neither will yield to the other, they frequently settle the difficulty by resorting to what is known as a merger. They, as it were, if you follow me, merge. It seems to me that this would be an admirable way of adjusting the present problem. You, my plutocratic old Lehman, have fifty thousand dollars. You, my wealthy old McClure, possess the same. Why don't you pool your pieces of eight and buy the show together?'

Barmy was lost in admiration. King Solomon, he told himself, was a fool to this clear thinker. Right from the moment when Jack McClure had mentioned that fifty thousand, he had had a feeling, watching Mervyn Potter out of the corner of his eye, that the motion picture star was about to come forward with an idea of some kind, a notion of sorts, a ruse of some description. And now he had done so, and every word that had fallen from his lips had been an Orient pearl of purest rays serene.

'That's the stuff!' he cried buoyantly. 'Hats off to M. Potter, the man with the bulging forehead. One hundred thousand is the price, Mr Lehman. How about it?'

Mr Lehman sank into a chair. Jack McClure did the same.

'A hundred thousand?' said Mr Lehman.

'A hundred thousand?' said Jack McClure.

'And think on your feet,' said Barmy.

Mr Lehman rose like a rocket. So did Jack McClure.

'Is that . . .' Mr Lehman gulped. In the past minute or two he appeared to have aged a good deal. He might have been the elder brother of the man who had burst into the room so short a while before, an elder brother who had led a hard life and seen a lot of trouble, and was wearing a collar some sizes too small for him. 'Is that final?'

'Absolutely final.'

'Five-star,' said Fanny, and received from her mate another look which would have extorted generous admiration from that specialist in dirty looks, J. Bromley Lippincott.

'Of course, I must know right away,' said Barmy. He snapped his fingers. 'That's the show game!'

Mr Lehman tottered to the door of Dinty's cubbyhole.

'Come in here a minute, Jack.'

'Okay.'

'We'll be right back,' said Mr Lehman.

The cubbyhole door closed behind them. Fanny drew a deep breath.

'And I came here to look after you!' she said.

Dinty went to her, her face glowing.

'We couldn't have done a thing without you, Mrs Lehman,' she said. 'We do appreciate it . . . enormously. Don't we, Barmy?'

'I'll never forget it, dear old present help in time of trouble,' said Barmy fervently. 'You will receive favourable mention in my prayers night and morning from now onward, and the first Phipps issue shall be named after you. If a girl of course. If male, Mervyn, after Potter.'

'You could find no nobler label for a bouncing baby,' said Mervyn Potter.

'Issue?' said Fanny.

'Just peeping into Vol. Two,' Barmy explained. 'Dinty and I are going to be married.'

'Is that so?'

'Well, well,' said Mervyn Potter. 'So you're getting married, eh? Starting out on the new life together, you two young things, are you? I wish you every luck and happiness. But it is a very moot point,' he proceeded, striking a graver note, 'whether a girl who marries a man with two names isn't committing bigamy. I see certain embarrassments ahead of you, young Dinty Moore. You may feel a bit silly one of these long winter evenings when you are sitting on Fotheringay's lap and Phipps suddenly comes in, or vice versa. Still, that is entirely your own affair, entirely your own affair. I just thought I would mention it.'

Fanny was eyeing Barmy with open admiration.

'And to think that I ever took you for a sucker! You've certainly put it over. You must have had second sight when you insisted on buying that play. But how it ever turned out to be a hit will always be a mystery to your Aunt Sadie. If you see what I mean, Mr Potter.'

'I see precisely what you mean,' said Mervyn Potter. 'But we must never forget that not only was it presented by Cyril Phipps, with all the advantages of the inimitable Phipps touch, but it had as its star one whom, did not modesty forbid, I would describe as—'

'A ham?'

'You take the words out of my mouth, dear lady. And talking of mouths, mine is so singularly dry that if I do not immediately lubricate it, I shall have another of those dust bowls on my hands. You would not care to accompany me around the corner and hoist a few?'

'It's a lie,' said Fanny. 'I would and will.'

'I always say that there is nothing like a little something at about this hour of the morning to pick one up,' said Mervyn Potter. 'Good-bye, young Dinty. Good-bye – for the present – my old friend Phipps. I shall inform J. G. Anderson that he will shortly be seeing you. He is awaiting me at a certain bar not far from here. Give me half an hour, and I think I can get him so oiled that he will slice the price of that hotel of his practically to nothing. When you are through in here, if you wish to talk business with our Anderson, turn to the left as you leave the building, walk down a couple of blocks till you come to a bistro called Mike's Place, and wait outside till you hear rowdy drinking songs proceeding from its interior. That will be J. G. Anderson, and that will be the moment to strike.'

And with an old-world courtesy Mervyn Potter escorted Fanny from the room. As the door closed, they could hear him explaining to her that the words 'Oh, baby!' on his shirt front were in his opinion probably the work of an international gang and that he thought he knew the ringleaders.

'What a man!' said Dinty.

Barmy did not reply. A reaction had come upon him. Dominant a moment ago, he was suffering now from those unmanning tremors which so often poisoned the day for Oscar Fritchie. Once, visiting Monte Carlo, he had placed his last hundred francs on the red at the roulette table, and it was with the emotions with which he had watched the wheel begin to spin that he now gazed at the door behind which the two tycoons were holding their conference. For comfort and moral support he turned, as he was always to turn for the rest of a long life, to Dinty.

'Do you think they'll do it?'

'Of course they will.'

'But suppose that lawyer comes back before they decide?'

He broke off. Oscar Fritchie was sliding in in that odd, crablike way of his which always suggested that he was expecting something – the ceiling, as it might be, or possibly a thunderbolt – to fall on his head. Oscar had had three quick ones at Mike's Place, but though filled with the old familiar juice he was still the timid, palpitating rabbit which might have come – though actually as we have seen it, it did not – out of J. Bromley Lippincott's briefcase. Looking about him and seeing no sign of Mr Lippincott, he perked up for an instant. Then, as a booming voice came through the door of the cubbyhole, he sagged again.

'He's in there, is he?' he said despondently.

'No, Mr Lippincott's gone,' said Dinty. 'He's coming back again—'

'Oh?' said Oscar, even more despondently.

'—but he's not here now. That's Mr Lehman and Mr McClure in there.'

'Lehman and McClure? What are they doing here? Gosh!' said Oscar Fritchie, seeing it all. 'There was something wrong with those papers we signed and they didn't sell us the show.'

'Yes, they did,' said Barmy. 'And now they want to buy it back. I'm asking a hundred thousand.'

'What!'

'Yah.'

'A hundred thousand *dollars*?'

'Yah.'

'Jiminy Christmas!' said Oscar Fritchie.

Barmy's momentary weakness had passed. Once more he was the man who thought on his feet and made quick decisions.

'Listen, my quivering aspen,' he said. 'What you might call the whole aspect of the fruity old situation has changed. Lehman and McClure have come here with certified cheques clutched in their hot little hands, and it is but a matter of time before we shall have a hundred thousand of the best and brightest at our disposal. And my late employer, J. G. Anderson, is waiting for me down the street to sell me his hotel in Bessemer, Ohio. You and I'll buy it together, what? We can make it one of the greatest dramatic hotels in the world, anywhere. You don't want to be in show business. Does he?'

'Of course not,' said Dinty.

'Don't I?' said Oscar. 'Certainly not,' said Barmy. 'A man like you should be in the hotel business. Shouldn't he?'

'Of course he should.'

'But last time you said I ought to get out of it.'

'Oh, that was different,' said Barmy. 'You'll like Bessemer. It's a wonderful place. Look! I'll sell you twenty-five per cent of the hotel for your share of the hundred thousand. Set?'

'Well . . . now . . .'

Barmy rapped the desk.

'Come on, come on. Think on your feet. It's a deal?'

It would have taken a better man than Oscar Fritchie to resist this high-powered salesmanship, particularly at a moment when Dinty was clutching the lapel of his coat and looking yearningly into his eyes.

'Well, if you say so,' he said weakly.

'Right!' said Barmy, and Mr Lehman and Jack McClure came out of the cubbyhole. They had the air of men who have arrived, not perhaps without reluctance, at a decision.

'Oh, hello,' said Oscar. 'Hello, Mr Lehman. Hello, Mr McClure.'

'How are you?' said Jack McClure.

'Not bad. I've a funny kind of buzzing feeling in my head and my throat's sort of—'

'Please!' said Barmy, rightly considering that these details should more properly be reserved for Oscar Fritchie's medical adviser. 'Well?' he said, turning to Mr Lehman.

Mr Lehman seemed to have a lingering hope that something might be accomplished by a last appeal to Barmy's better feelings.

'Now, look here a minute—'

He stopped. An authoritative knock had sounded on the door. Barmy and Dinty exchanged an agonized glance. They did not need to be told who was on the other side of that door. The half-hour was up, and J. Bromley Lippincott, of Lippincott, Lippincott, Cohn, Mandelbaum and Lippincott, attorneys-at-law, was with them once again. He might have dallied over a drink at the Astor bar, he might have sauntered up Broadway, seeing the sights, he might have done a hundred things which would have made him late at the tryst, but no. He had returned at the appointed time, punctual to the second.

'I'll go,' said Oscar, ever obliging, heading for the door.

'No, no!' cried Barmy in agony, seizing his coat.

'Huh?'

Barmy swallowed.

'It's . . . it's only . . . I know who it is.' He reached the door in a single bound and turned the key. A moment for mopping the brow, and he was back with Mr Lehman again. 'What were you going to say?' he asked, his fingers busy with his tie.

Oscar Fritchie was not the man to give up easily. He had seen a chance of being helpful, and he hated to let it go.

'But if there's somebody out there—'

'There isn't anybody out there.'

The knock was repeated, louder and more authoritative than ever.

'Well, I'll take your word for it,' said Oscar Fritchie doubtfully, a puzzled eye on the door.

'Who's out there?' said Mr Lehman.

'It isn't anybody,' said Barmy, whose tie was now a mere tangle. 'It's just a book agent or something, I expect. Well, do you want the show or don't you?' he demanded desperately. 'Well, now, look here, sweetheart. A hundred grand, that's a big bundle of coin. You can't expect us to . . .' Mr Lehman broke off as the echoes of a third knock boomed through the room. 'For heaven's sake,' he barked irritably, 'why don't you send that pest away?'

Dinty took over the conduct of affairs with the quiet, efficient smoothness so characteristic of women when they are about to embark on a course of action not scrupulously honest. It was plain to her that her Barmy was unequal to coping with the situation, and it was a situation which, with a little feminine manipulation of the truth, could so easily be handled.

'Mr Phipps can't send him away,' she said. 'Would you like to know who he is?'

'I don't care who he is, as long as he stops his racket.'

'It's a man who wants to take over most of the show,' said Dinty carelessly.

Mr Lehman tottered.

'What!'

'You'd be surprised if you knew his name. He's a man who does things just like that,' said Dinty, snapping her fingers. 'So if you don't want the show, just say the word and I'll let him in.'

'Wait!' cried Mr Lehman. 'Wait! Wait! Wait! Wait!'

With a feverish haste he pulled out his certified cheque, but no more rapidly than Jack McClure produced his. With a simultaneous movement, as if they had been rehearsing for weeks, they thrust them upon Barmy, and Barmy dutifully handed them to Dinty, who had been busily scribbling on a piece of paper.

'Now it's ours!' said Mr Lehman.

'And here's your receipt,' said Dinty.

'And I get my money back?' said Oscar anxiously.

'My dear old prune,' said Barmy, who had made another of his quick recoveries and was now at the peak of his form again, 'you get a lot more. I explained it carefully to you a moment ago, but I suppose it didn't penetrate. The Lehman-McClure comedy duo have paid a hundred thousand dollars—'

'For thirty-three and one-third per centum of the show,' said Dinty.

Mr Lehman started violently.

'For *what*?'

'This gentleman will tell you all about it,' said Dinty, throwing open the door, and J. Bromley Lippincott entered, looking, if possible, taller and darker and more cadaverous than ever.

'He's a lawyer,' said Barmy. 'At law. And he wants sixty-six and two-thirds per centum of all profits derived from aforesaid play, when, if and as produced, because aforesaid play was pinched bodily from a novelette written by his client, Mr Rodney Rich of Worcester, Massachusetts, a Massachusetts corporation. It's a clear case of plagiarism, and one of the most flagrant that it has ever been Pop Lippincott's privilege to encounter. Correct, my old crumpet?'

'Perfectly correct,' said his old crumpet. 'Who are these gentlemen?'

'Mr Lehman and Mr McClure. They've just bought the show back again.'

'Indeed?'

'Yes, indeed,' said Oscar Fritchie emphatically. He wished for no misunderstanding on this point. On others, possibly, but not on this one.

Mr Lehman, gallant in defeat, was making a Custer's Last Stand.

'I know all about this phony case,' he said. 'You ain't got no more grounds than a rabbit.'

J. Bromley Lippincott did not smile. Attorneys-at-law do not smile. But a quick muscular spasm at the corner of his tight-drawn lips seemed to indicate that he had come as near to smiling as an attorney-at-law ever comes.

'We have a perfect case,' he said composedly.

'Yah? Well, come in here and tell us all about it,' said Mr Lehman, 'and see how quick I'll turn that perfect case of yours inside out. There ain't been a hit produced in twenty years that some guy ain't said it was swiped from him.'

He led the way into the cubbyhole, his whole air that of a good man wronged. Jack McClure, about to follow, lingered for an instant, giving Barmy a reproachful look.

'You have disappointed me,' said Jack McClure.

He went into the cubbyhole, and the door closed behind him. As it shut, J. Bromley Lippincott could be heard saying, '. . . at one hundred and forty-six points'.

Barmy had become brisk and executive.

'Hey!' he said.

'Me?' said Oscar Fritchie.

'Yah. Do you know the Guaranty Trust Company, Forty-Third Street? Rush along there and deposit these cheques without the loss of a single instant. Fly like a youthful hart or roe over the hills where spices grow. Lehman might take it into his head to stop them. By bunging them in like a flash of lightning, we avoid all rannygazoo.'

'And one does so wish, does one not,' said Dinty, 'to avoid rannygazoo. Why don't you deposit them yourself, *maître*?'

'I have one or two letters, cables and telegrams to get off,' said Barmy. 'Got that clear? Tell me in your own words what you're supposed to do.'

'Go to the bank—'

'—and deposit the cheques to account of Cyril Phipps. Right. And now do you know a joint called Mike's Place?'

'I just come from there.'

'Good. After you've been to the bank, go to Mike's Place. You will see there, in company with Mervyn Potter, an elderly man with a face like a passport photograph. His name is J. G. Anderson. Tell him I'll be along in a minute. He's the bloke who owns the hotel we're going to buy. Set?'

'Okay,' said Oscar. He would have preferred to remain and ask a lot of questions, but even he could see that this matter of depositing the cheques was one of urgency. He left the room at what for him was a rapid pace.

'And I'll tell you something more about this show,' Mr Lehman was shouting in the cubbyhole. 'There was a fellow called George Bernard Shaw—'

Barmy turned to Dinty, as brisk as ever.

'Can you do shorthand?'

'The shorter it is, the better I like it.'

'Take a cable,' said Barmy curtly. 'To Theodore, Lord Binghampton, Binghampton Hall, Binghampton, Norfolk, England. "Letter received and torn into a thousand pieces. Go and boil your bally head, sweetheart. Cheerio. Cyril".'

'Is that all?'

'That's all. Now a telegram. To the Rector, or Vicar or whatever he is, Little Church Round the Corner . . . where?'

'Twenty-Ninth Street.'

'Twenty-Ninth Street. "What ho, vicar, or rector as the case may be. Clear decks for big wedding in near future, my puss. The Phippses are coming – and I may add with bells on. Regards, Phipps".'

'You do write such lovely telegrams.'

'And now a letter. To the President, White Star Cunard Line. Where do we find the President, White Star Cunard Line?'

'Somewhere down at the bottom of Broadway.'

'Right. To the President, White Star Cunard Line, somewhere at the bottom of Broadway. "Dear Sir. Kindly quote me your lowest terms for the liner Queen Mary . . .".'

Barmy paused. He blinked like an awakened somnambulist.

'I'm crazy,' he said. 'We aren't buying ocean liners, we're buying hotels. Omit letter to President, White Star Cunard Line, somewhere down at the bottom of Broadway, slip me one quick kiss for the road, then ho, for the great open spaces!'

In the cubbyhole, Mr Lehman was making a telling point.

'And another thing. The man in that novelette was named George. In the play he's Harold . . .'

But Dinty and Barmy missed this. They were already on their way to Mike's Place.

POEMS

The Audience at the Court Theatre*

They're the Pioneers of Progress, they're the Devotees of Art,
They're the men with bulging foreheads, they're a race of souls apart;
No ordinary drama can rely on their support –
It is Culture – yes, sir, Culture that they ask for at the Court.

Lesser men may like the plays that are produced for vulgar gain;
Lesser men may laugh at Huntley or be charmed by Edmund Payne;†
But the audience would crush you with one vast, indignant snort,
If you showed such plays or mummers any evening at the Court.

But you must not think that every form of fun would come to grief;
They enjoy tuberculosis as a humorous relief.
And a really comic death-scene will infallibly extort
Tears of unaffected laughter from an audience at the Court.

Ah, but what they really revel in is something dark and grim.
If the hero kills his mother, or his mother murders him;
If loud shrieks ('off left') suggest that blood is flowing by the quart,
Then a placid satisfaction soothes the audience at the Court.

How they love it when a character brings out a gleaming knife,
Or kicks the prostrate body of his unoffending wife!
Such events come all too seldom, and such scenes are all too short
For the reckless, ruthless audience you meet with at the Court.

And when the play is ended, o'er a grateful cup of tea,
They discuss hot buns and Culture at the local ABC.
Then each journeys off to Balham or his Wimbledon resort,
Much refreshed in mind and spirit by his visit to the Court.

* The Royal Court Theatre (opened as Royal Court in 1871, re opened as The Court in 1888) became famous for its 'realistic' plays. Under the directorship of Harley Granville-Barker (1877–1946), the early plays of Bernard Shaw presented here were in sharp contrast to the musical comedies and melodramas that filled the other London theatres of the time.

† G. P. Huntley (1868–1927) and Edmund Payne (1865–1914) were the mainstays of the famous Gaiety musical comedies. Huntley specialized in playing 'dude' parts while Payne used his lisp and pop-eyes to great effect in comic parts.

Mr Beerbohm Tree*

He is the very model of the actor (managerial):
He uses Shakespeare's lines to form a sort of ground-material.
The bard, in fact, provides the major portion of the letter-press:
But the scenery's his own idea. ('Superb! Could not be better!' – *Press.*)
And no maiden at a matinée without a thrill can see
The strange exotic beauty of our only Beerbohm Tree.

Tree, Tree, Beautiful Tree,
What a wonderful actor you are!
You stand all the time,
In the light of the lime:
You're a bright and particular star.
We'd come miles for a sight
Of that picturesque bend in your knee.
Our Waller – we love him,
But rank you above him,
Our one and our only Tree!

If I'm asked to tell the reasons of his well-earned popularity,
His acting's always funny, while avoiding all vulgarity:
As Hamlet, when he had his conversation with the phantom, I'm
Not certain that he didn't beat the leading lights of pantomime.
You will burst your waistcoat-buttons, though sewn tightly on they be,
If you chance to see the Hamlet of our only Beerbohm Tree.

Tree, Tree, Beautiful Tree.
May you go from success to success.
May the crowds block the streets,
When they're fighting for seats;
May you never fall out with the Press.
Though your Antony might
Be different without vexing me,
Still, the actor who's funny
Is the man for my money,
So I'll stick to my Beerbohm Tree.

* Sir Herbert Beerbohm Tree (1853–1917) was the most famous actor-manager of his generation. His playing of Hamlet at the Haymarket was particularly renowned. He was a founder of the Academy of Dramatic Art and was knighted in 1909.

Ubique*

Phyllis Dare, Phyllis Dare, though, of course, I'm aware
That your figure's divine and your beauty is rare;
At your photograph though I am willing to stare
For hours (in fact, all the time I can spare);
Though the world's admiration I own that I share
For the size of your eyes and the shade of your hair; –
Yet somehow I feel (you won't think me a bear?)
That just now you're a trifle too much in the air.

When I travel by train (having first paid my fare),
I open my paper, and lo! you are there.
' "Some Recent Events in my Life" by Miss Dare,'
' "How I Feel when I'm Singing a Song" by Miss Dare,'
' "How I Study a Part in a Play" by Miss Dare,'
Stop Press News, ' "What I Use for my Teeth" by Miss Dare,'
' "Should Peers Marry Gibson Girls?" – Chat with Miss Dare,'
' "Shall I ever play Lady Macbeth?" by Miss Dare,'
' "Should Soulful Expressions be taxed?" by Miss Dare.'
Miss Dare,
Take care!
Would you drive a respectable man to despair?
Would you have him gesticulate wildly, and swear?
His diminishing locks would you lead him to tear,
Phyllis Dare?
I repeat, you are sweet. But, oh! list to my prayer –
Take a rest for a space, and recede from the glare
Of the popular search-light; and let the fierce blare
Of the trumpet die down for a little, Miss Dare.
Your doings crowd out the last popular scare.
The Springboks, the Kaiser, C.-B., the Lord Mayor,
Can't get themselves noticed while you're in the air.
Is it fair,
Phyllis Dare?

* Phyllis Dare (1890–1975) was an enormously popular singer and comedy actress who appeared in pantomime and variety as well as in such successes as *The Belle of Mayfair* and *The Arcadians*. She continued to appear on the stage until after the Second World War. Both she and her equally famous sister Zena appeared in shows for which Wodehouse wrote the book or lyrics. Phyllis was in *Kissing Time* (1919) and Zena Dare appeared in *Sergeant Brue* (1904), *The Beauty of Bath* (1906) and *The Gay Gordons* (1907).

SHORT STORIES

Bill the Bloodhound

THERE'S a divinity that shapes our ends. Consider the case of Henry Pifield Rice, detective. I must explain Henry early, to avoid disappointment. If I simply said he was a detective, and let it go at that, I should be obtaining the reader's interest under false pretences. He was really only a sort of detective, a species of sleuth. At Stafford's International Investigation Bureau, in the Strand, where he was employed, they did not require him to solve mysteries which had baffled the police. He had never measured a footprint in his life, and what he did not know about bloodstains would have filled a library. The sort of job they gave Henry was to stand outside a restaurant in the rain, and note what time someone inside left it. In short, it is not 'Pifield Rice, Investigator. No. 1 – The Adventures of the Maharajah's Ruby' that I submit to your notice, but the unsensational doings of a quite commonplace young man variously known to his comrades at the Bureau as 'Fathead', 'That blighter what's-his-name', and 'Here, you!'.

Henry lived in a boarding-house in Guildford Street. One day a new girl came to the boarding-house, and sat next to Henry at meals. Her name was Alice Weston. She was small and quiet, and rather pretty. They got on splendidly. Their conversation, at first confined to the weather and the moving-pictures, rapidly became more intimate. Henry was surprised to find that she was on the stage, in the chorus. Previous chorus-girls at the boarding-house had been of a more pronounced type – good girls, but noisy, and apt to wear beauty-spots. Alice Weston was different.

'I'm rehearsing at present,' she said. 'I'm going out on tour next month in *The Girl From Brighton*. What do you do, Mr Rice?'

Henry paused for a moment before replying. He knew how sensational he was going to be.

'I'm a detective.'

Usually, when he told girls his profession, squeaks of amazed admiration greeted him. Now, he was chagrined to perceive in the brown eyes that met his, distinct disapproval.

'What's the matter?' he said, a little anxiously, for even at this early stage in their acquaintance he was conscious of a strong desire to win her approval. 'Don't you like detectives?'

'I don't know. Somehow I shouldn't have thought you were one.'

This restored Henry's equanimity somewhat. Naturally a detective does not want to look like a detective, and give the whole thing away right at the start.

'I think – you won't be offended?'

'Go on.'

'I've always looked on it as rather a *sneaky* job.'

'Sneaky!' moaned Henry.

'Well, creeping about, spying on people.'

Henry was appalled. She had defined his own trade to a nicety. There might be detectives whose work was above this reproach, but he was a confirmed creeper, and he knew it. It wasn't his fault. The boss told him to creep, and he crept. If he declined to creep, he would be sacked instanter. It was hard, and yet he felt the sting of her words, and in his bosom the first seeds of dissatisfaction with his occupation took root.

You might have thought that this frankness on the girl's part would have kept Henry from falling in love with her. Certainly the dignified thing would have been to change his seat at table, and take his meals next to someone who appreciated the romance of detective work a little more. But no, he remained where he was, and presently Cupid, who never shoots with a surer aim than through the steam of boarding-house hash, sniped him where he sat.

He proposed to Alice Weston. She refused him.

'It's not because I'm not fond of you. I think you're the nicest man I ever met.' A good deal of assiduous attention had enabled Henry to win this place in her affections. He had worked patiently and well before actually putting his fortune to the test. 'I'd marry you tomorrow if things were different. But I'm on the stage, and I mean to stick there. Most of the girls want to get off it, but not me. And one thing I'll never do is marry someone who isn't in the profession. My sister Genevieve did, and look what happened to her. She married a commercial traveller, and take it from me he travelled. She never saw him for more than five minutes in the year, except when he was selling gent's hosiery in the same town where she was doing her refined speciality, and then he'd just wave his hand and whiz by, and start travelling again. My husband has got to be close by, where I can see him. I'm sorry, Henry, but I know I'm right.'

It seemed final, but Henry did not wholly despair. He was a resolute young man. You have to be to wait outside restaurants in the rain for any length of time.

He had an inspiration. He sought out a dramatic agent.

'I want to go on the stage, in musical comedy.'

'Let's see you dance.'

'I can't dance.'

'Sing,' said the agent. 'Stop singing,' added the agent, hastily.

'You go away and have a nice cup of hot tea,' said the agent, soothingly, 'and you'll be as right as anything in the morning.'

Henry went away.

A few days later, at the Bureau, his fellow-detective Simmonds hailed him.

'Here, you! The boss wants you. Buck up!'

Mr Stafford was talking into the telephone. He replaced the receiver as Henry entered.

'Oh, Rice, here's a woman wants her husband shadowed while he's on the road. He's an actor. I'm sending you. Go to this address, and get photographs and all particulars. You'll have to catch the eleven o'clock train on Friday.'

'Yes, sir.'

'He's in the *Girl From Brighton* company. They open at Bristol.'

It sometimes seemed to Henry as if Fate did it on purpose. If the commission had had to do with any other company, it would have been well enough, for, professionally speaking, it was the most important with which he had ever been entrusted. If he had never met Alice Weston, and heard her views upon detective work, he would have been pleased and flattered. Things being as they were, it was Henry's considered opinion that Fate had slipped one over on him.

In the first place, what torture to be always near her, unable to reveal himself; to watch while she disported herself in the company of other men. He would be disguised, and she would not recognize him; but he would recognize her, and his sufferings would be dreadful.

In the second place, to have to do his creeping about and spying practically in her presence –

Still, business was business.

At five minutes to eleven on the morning named he was at the station, a false beard and spectacles shielding his identity from the public eye. If you had asked him, he would have said that he was a Scotch businessman. As a matter of fact, he looked far more like a motor-car coming through a haystack.

The platform was crowded. Friends of the company had come to see the company off. Henry looked on discreetly from behind a stout porter, whose bulk formed a capital screen. In spite of himself, he was impressed. The stage at close quarters always thrilled him. He recognized celebrities. The fat man in the brown suit was Walter Jelliffe, the comedian and star of the company. He stared keenly at him through the spectacles. Others of the famous were scattered about. He saw Alice. She was talking to a man with a face like a hatchet, and smiling, too, as if she enjoyed it. Behind the matted foliage which he had inflicted on his face, Henry's teeth came together with a snap.

In the weeks that followed, as he dogged the *Girl From Brighton* company from town to town, it would be difficult to say whether Henry was happy or unhappy. On the one hand, to realize that Alice was so near and yet so inaccessible was a constant source of misery; yet, on the other, he could not but admit that he was having the very dickens of a time, loafing round the country like this.

He was made for this sort of life, he considered. Fate had placed him in a London office, but what he really enjoyed was this unfettered travel. Some gypsy strain in him rendered even the obvious discomforts of theatrical touring agreeable. He liked catching trains; he liked invading strange hotels; above all, he revelled in the artistic pleasure of watching unsuspected fellowmen as if they were so many ants.

That was really the best part of the whole thing. It was all very well for Alice to talk about creeping and spying, but, if you considered it without bias, there was nothing degrading about it at all. It was an art. It took brains and a genius for disguise to make a man a successful creeper and spyer. You couldn't simply say to yourself, 'I will creep.' If you attempted to do it in your own person, you would be detected instantly. You had to be an adept at masking your personality. You had to be one man at Bristol and another quite different man at Hull – especially if, like Henry, you were of a gregarious disposition, and liked the society of actors.

The stage had always fascinated Henry. To meet even minor members of the profession off the boards gave him a thrill. There was a resting juvenile, of fit-up calibre, at his boarding-house who could always get a shilling out of him simply by talking about how he had jumped in and saved the show at the hamlets which he had visited in the course of his wanderings. And on this *Girl From Brighton* tour he was in constant touch with men who really amounted to something. Walter Jelliffe had been a celebrity when Henry was going to school; and Sidney Crane, the baritone, and others of the lengthy cast, were all players not unknown in London. Henry courted them assiduously.

It had not been hard to scrape acquaintance with them. The principals of the company always put up at the best hotel, and – his expenses being paid by his employer – so did Henry. It was the easiest thing possible to bridge with a well-timed whisky-and-soda the gulf between non-acquaintance and warm friendship. Walter Jelliffe, in particular, was peculiarly accessible. Every time Henry accosted him – as a different individual, of course – and renewed in a fresh disguise the friendship which he had enjoyed at the last town, Walter Jeliffe met him more than half-way.

It was in the sixth week of the tour that the comedian, promoting him from mere casual acquaintanceship, invited him to come up to his room and smoke a cigar.

Henry was pleased and flattered. Jelliffe was a personage, always surrounded by admirers, and the compliment was consequently of a high order.

He lit his cigar. Among his friends at the Green-Room Club it was unanimously held that Walter Jeliffe's cigars brought him within the scope of the law forbidding the carrying of concealed weapons; but Henry would have smoked the gift of such a man if it had been a cabbage-leaf. He puffed away contentedly. He was made up as an old Indian colonel that week, and he complimented his host on the aroma with a fine old-world courtesy.

Walter Jeliffe seemed gratified.

'Quite comfortable?' he asked.

'Quite, I thank you,' said Henry, fondling his silver moustache.

'That's right. And now tell me old man, which of us is it you're trailing?'

Henry nearly swallowed his cigar.

'What do you mean?'

'Oh, come,' protested Jelliffe; 'there's no need to keep it up with me. I know you're a detective. The question is, Who's the man you're after? That's what we've all been wondering all this time.'

All! They had all been wondering! It was worse than Henry could have imagined. Till now he had pictured his position with regard to the *Girl From Brighton* company rather as that of some scientist who, seeing but unseen, keeps a watchful eye on the denizens of a drop of water under his microscope. And they had all detected him – every one of them.

It was a stunning blow. If there was one thing on which Henry prided himself it was the impenetrability of his disguises. He might be slow; he might be on the stupid side; but he could disguise himself. He had a variety of disguises, each designed to befog the public more hopelessly than the last.

Going down the street, you would meet a typical commercial traveller, dapper and alert. Anon, you encountered a heavily bearded Australian. Later, maybe, it was a courteous old retired colonel who stopped you and inquired the way to Trafalgar Square. Still later, a rather flashy individual of the sporting type asked you for a match for his cigar. Would you have suspected for one instant that each of these widely differing personalities was in reality one man?

Certainly you would.

Henry did not know it, but he had achieved in the eyes of the small servant who answered the front-door bell at his boarding-house a well-established reputation as a humorist of the more practical kind. It was his habit to try his disguises on her. He would ring the bell, inquire for the landlady, and when Bella had gone, leap up the stairs to his room. Here he would remove the disguise, resume his normal appearance, and come downstairs again, humming a careless air. Bella, meanwhile, in the kitchen, would be confiding to her ally the cook that 'Mr Rice had jest come in, lookin' sort o' funny again'.

He sat and gaped at Walter Jeliffe. The comedian regarded him curiously.

'You look at least a hundred years old,' he said. 'What are you made up as? A piece of Gorgonzola?'

Henry glanced hastily at the mirror. Yes, he did look rather old. He must have overdone some of the lines on his forehead. He looked something between a youngish centenarian and a nonagenarian who had seen a good deal of trouble.

'If you knew how you were demoralizing the company,' Jelliffe went on, 'you would drop it. As steady and quiet a lot of boys as ever you met till you came along. Now they do nothing but bet on what disguise you're going to choose for the next town. I don't see why you need to change so often. You were all right as the Scotchman at Bristol. We were all saying how nice you looked. You should have stuck to that. But what do you do at Hull but roll in in a scrubby moustache and a tweed suit, looking rotten. However, all that is beside the point. It's a free country. If you like to spoil your beauty, I suppose there's no law against it. What I want to know is, who's the man? Whose tracks are you sniffing on, Bill? You'll pardon my calling you Bill. You're known as Bill the Bloodhound in the company. Who's the man?'

'Never mind,' said Henry.

He was aware, as he made it, that it was not a very able retort, but he was feeling too limp for satisfactory repartee. Criticisms in the Bureau, dealing with his alleged solidity of skull, he did not resent. He attributed them to man's natural desire to chaff his fellow-man. But to be unmasked by the general public in this way was another matter. It struck at the root of all things.

'But I do mind,' objected Jelliffe. 'It's most important. A lot of money hangs on it. We've got a sweepstake on in the company, the holder of the winning name to take the entire receipts. Come on. Who is he?'

Henry rose and made for the door. His feelings were too deep for words. Even a minor detective has his professional pride; and the knowledge that his espionage is being made the basis of sweepstakes by his quarry cuts this to the quick.

'Here, don't go! Where are you going?'

'Back to London,' said Henry, bitterly. 'It's a lot of good my staying here now, isn't it?'

'I should say it was – to me. Don't be in a hurry. You're – thinking that, now we know all about you, your utility as a sleuth has waned to some extent. Is that it?'

'Well?'

'Well, why worry? What does it matter to you? You don't get paid by results, do you? Your boss said, "Trail along." Well, do it, then. I should hate to lose you. I don't suppose you know it, but you've been the best mascot this tour that I've ever come across. Right from the start we've been playing to enormous business. I'd rather kill a black cat than lose you. Drop the disguises, and stay with us. Come behind all you want, and be sociable.'

A detective is only human. The less of a detective, the more human he is. Henry was not much of a detective, and his human traits were consequently highly developed. From a boy, he had never been able to resist curiosity. If a crowd collected in the street he always added himself to it, and he would have stopped to gape at a window with 'Watch this window' written on it, if he had been running for his life from wild bulls. He was, and always had been, intensely desirous of some day penetrating behind the scenes of a theatre.

And there was another thing. At least, if he accepted this invitation, he would be able to see and speak to Alice Weston, and interfere with the manoeuvres of the hatchet-faced man, on whom he had brooded with suspicion and jealousy since that first morning at the station. To see Alice! Perhaps, with eloquence, to talk her out of that ridiculous resolve of hers!

'Why, there's something in that,' he said.

'Rather! Well, that's settled. And now, touching that sweep, who *is* it?'

'I can't tell you that. You see, so far as that goes, I'm just where I was before. I can still watch – whoever it is I'm watching.'

'Dash it, so you can. I didn't think of that,' said Jelliffe, who possessed a sensitive conscience. 'Purely between ourselves, it isn't *me*, is it?'

Henry eyed him inscrutably. He could look inscrutable at times.

'Ah!' he said, and left quickly, with the feeling that, however poorly he had shown up during the actual interview, his exit had been good. He might have been a failure in the matter of disguise, but nobody could have put more quiet sinisterness into that 'Ah!'. It did so much to soothe him and ensure a peaceful night's rest.

On the following night, for the first time in his life, Henry found himself behind the scenes of a theatre, and instantly began to experience all the complex emotions which come to the layman in that situation. That is to say, he felt like a cat which has strayed into a strange hostile back-yard. He was in a new world, inhabited by weird creatures, who flitted about in an eerie semi-darkness, like brightly coloured animals in a cavern.

The Girl From Brighton was one of those exotic productions specially designed for the Tired Businessman. It relied for a large measure of its success on the size and appearance of its chorus, and on their constant change of costume. Henry, as a consequence, was the centre of a kaleidoscopic whirl of feminine loveliness, dressed to represent such varying flora and fauna as rabbits, Parisian students, colleens, Dutch peasants, and daffodils. Musical comedy is the Irish stew of the drama. Anything may be put into it, with the certainty that it will improve the general effect.

He scanned the throng for a sight of Alice. Often as he had seen the piece in the course of its six weeks' wandering in the wilderness he had never succeeded in recognizing her from the front of the house. Quite possibly, he thought, she might be on the stage already, hidden in a rose-tree or some other shrub, ready at the signal to burst forth upon the audience in short skirts; for in *The Girl From Brighton* almost anything could turn suddenly into a chorus-girl.

Then he saw her, among the daffodils. She was not a particularly convincing daffodil, but she looked good to Henry. With wobbling knees he butted his way through the crowd and seized her hand enthusiastically.

'Why, Henry! Where did you come from?'

'I *am* glad to see you!'

'How did you get here?'

'I *am* glad to see you!'

At this point the stage-manager, bellowing from the prompt-box, urged Henry to desist. It is one of the mysteries of behind-the-scenes acoustics that a whisper from any minor member of the company can be heard all over the house, while the stage-manager can burst himself without annoying the audience.

Henry, awed by authority, relapsed into silence. From the unseen stage came the sound of someone singing a song about the moon. June was also mentioned. He recognized the song as one that had always bored him. He disliked the woman who was singing it – a Miss Clarice Weaver, who played the heroine of the piece to Sidney Crane's hero.

In his opinion he was not alone. Miss Weaver was not popular in the company. She had secured the role rather as a testimony of personal esteem from the management than because of any innate ability. She sang badly, acted indifferently, and was uncertain what to do with her hands. All these things might have been forgiven her, but she supplemented them by the crime known in stage circles as 'throwing her weight about'. That is to say, she was hard to please, and, when not pleased, apt to say so in no uncertain voice. To his personal friends Walter Jelliffe had frequently confided that, though not a rich man, he was in the market with a substantial reward for anyone who was man enough to drop a ton of iron on Miss Weaver.

Tonight the song annoyed Henry more than usual, for he knew that very soon the daffodils were due on the stage to clinch the verisimilitude of the scene by dancing the tango with the rabbits. He endeavoured to make the most of the time at his disposal.

'I *am* glad to see you!' he said.

'Sh – h!' said the stage-manager.

Henry was discouraged. Romeo could not have made love under these conditions. And then, just when he was pulling himself together to begin again, she was torn from him by the exigencies of the play.

He wandered moodily off into the dusty semi-darkness. He avoided the prompt-box, whence he could have caught a glimpse of her, being loath to meet the stage-manager just at present.

Walter Jelliffe came up to him, as he sat on a box and brooded on life.

'A little less of the double forte, old man,' he said. 'Miss Weaver has been kicking about the noise on the side. She wanted you thrown out, but I said you were my mascot, and I would die sooner than part with you. But I should go easy on the chest-notes, I think, all the same.'

Henry nodded moodily. He was depressed. He had the feeling, which comes so easily to the intruder behind the scenes, that nobody loved him.

The piece proceeded. From the front of the house roars of laughter indicated the presence on the stage of Walter Jelliffe, while now and then a lethargic silence suggested that Miss Clarice Weaver was in action. From time to time the empty space about him filled with girls dressed in accordance with the exuberant fancy of the producer of the piece. When this happened, Henry would leap from his seat and endeavour to locate Alice; but always, just as he thought he had done so, the hidden orchestra would burst into melody and the chorus would be called to the front.

It was not till late in the second act that he found an opportunity for further speech.

The plot of *The Girl From Brighton* had by then reached a critical stage. The situation was as follows: The hero, having been disinherited by his wealthy and titled father for falling in love with the heroine, a poor shop-girl, has disguised himself (by wearing a different coloured necktie) and has come in pursuit of her to a well-known seaside resort, where, having disguised herself by changing her dress, she is serving as a waitress in the Rotunda, on the Esplanade. The family butler, disguised as a bath-chair man, has followed the hero, and the wealthy and titled father, disguised as an Italian opera-singer, has come to the place for a reason which, though extremely sound, for the moment eludes the memory. Anyhow, he is there, and they all meet on the Esplanade. Each recognizes the other, but thinks he himself is unrecognized. *Exeunt* all, hurriedly, leaving the heroine alone on the stage.

It is a crisis in the heroine's life. She meets it bravely. She sings a song entitled 'My Honolulu Queen', with chorus of Japanese girls and Bulgarian officers.

Alice was one of the Japanese girls.

She was standing a little apart from the other Japanese girls. Henry was on her with a bound. Now was his time. He felt keyed up, full of persuasive words. In the interval which had elapsed since their last conversation yeasty emotions had been playing the dickens with his self-control. It is practically impossible for a novice, suddenly introduced behind the scenes of a musical comedy, not to fall in love with somebody; and, if he is already in love, his fervour is increased to a dangerous point.

Henry felt that it was now or never. He forgot that it was perfectly possible – indeed, the reasonable course – to wait till the performance was over, and renew his appeal to Alice to marry him on the way back to her hotel. He had the feeling that he had got just about a quarter of a minute. Quick action! That was Henry's slogan.

He seized her hand.

'Alice!'

'Sh – h!' hissed the stage-manager.

'Listen! I love you. I'm crazy about you. What does it matter whether I'm on the stage or not? I love you.'

'Stop that row there!'

'Won't you marry me?'

She looked at him. It seemed to him that she hesitated.

'Cut it out!' bellowed the stage-manager, and Henry cut it out.

And at this moment, when his whole fate hung in the balance, there came from the stage that devastating high note which is the sign that the solo is over and that the chorus are now about to mobilize. As if drawn by some magnetic power, she suddenly receded from him, and went on to the stage.

A man in Henry's position and frame of mind is not responsible for his actions. He saw nothing but her; he was blind to the fact that important manoeuvres were in progress. All he understood was that she was going from him, and that he must stop her and get this thing settled.

He clutched at her. She was out of range, and getting farther away every instant.

He sprang forward.

The advice that should be given to every young man starting life is – if you happen to be behind the scenes at a theatre, never spring forward. The whole architecture of the place is designed to undo those who so spring. Hours before, the stage-carpenters have laid their traps, and in the semi-darkness you cannot but fall into them.

The trap into which Henry fell was a raised board. It was not a very highly raised board. It was not so deep as a well, nor so wide as a church-door, but 'twas enough – it served. Stubbing it squarely with his toe, Henry shot forward, all arms and legs.

It is the instinct of Man, in such a situation, to grab at the nearest support. Henry grabbed at the Hotel Superba, the pride of the Esplanade. It was a thin wooden edifice, and it supported him for perhaps a tenth of a second. Then he staggered with it into the limelight, tripped over a Bulgarian officer who was inflating himself for a deep note, and finally fell in a complicated heap as exactly in the centre of the stage as if he had been a star of years' standing.

It went well; there was no question of that. Previous audiences had always been rather cold towards this particular song, but this one got on its feet and yelled for more. From all over the house came rapturous demands that Henry should go back and do it again.

But Henry was giving no encores. He rose to his feet, a little stunned, and automatically began to dust his clothes. The orchestra, unnerved by this unrehearsed infusion of new business, had stopped playing. Bulgarian officers and Japanese girls alike seemed unequal to the situation. They stood about, waiting for the next thing to break loose. From somewhere far away came faintly the voice of the stage-manager inventing new words, new combinations of words, and new throat noises.

And then Henry, massaging a stricken elbow, was aware of Miss Weaver at his side. Looking up, he caught Miss Weaver's eye.

A familiar stage-direction of melodrama reads, 'Exit cautious through gap in hedge.' It was Henry's first appearance on any stage, but he did it like a veteran.

'My dear fellow,' said Walter Jelliffe. The hour was midnight, and he was sitting in Henry's bedroom at the hotel. Leaving the theatre, Henry had gone to bed almost instinctively. Bed seemed the only haven for him. 'My dear fellow, don't apologize. You have put me under lasting obligations. In the first place, with your unerring sense of the stage, you saw just the spot where the piece needed livening up, and you livened it up. That was good; but far better was it that you also sent our Miss Weaver into violent hysterics, from which she emerged to hand in her notice. She leaves us tomorrow.'

Henry was appalled at the extent of the disaster for which he was responsible.

'What will you do?'

'Do! Why, it's what we have all been praying for – a miracle which should eject Miss Weaver. It needed a genius like you to come to bring it off. Sidney Crane's wife can play the part without rehearsal. She understudied it all last season in London. Crane has just been speaking to her on the phone, and she is catching the night express.'

Henry sat up in bed.

'What!'

'What's the trouble now?'

'Sidney Crane's wife?'

'What about her?'

A bleakness fell upon Henry's soul.

'She was the woman who was employing me. Now I shall be taken off the job, and have to go back to London.'

'You don't mean that it was really Crane's wife?'

Jelliffe was regarding him with a kind of awe.

'Laddie,' he said, in a hushed voice, 'you almost scare me. There seems to be no limit to your powers as a mascot. You fill the house every night, you get rid of the Weaver woman, and now you tell me this. I drew Crane in the sweep, and I would have taken twopence for my chance of winning it.'

'I shall get a telegram from my boss tomorrow recalling me.'

'Don't go. Stick with me. Join the troupe.'

Henry stared.

'What do you mean? I can't sing or act.'

Jelliffe's voice thrilled with earnestness.

'My boy, I can go down the Strand and pick up a hundred fellows who can sing and act. I don't want them. I turn them away. But a seventh son of a seventh son like you, a human horse-shoe like you, a king of mascots like you – they don't make them nowadays. They've lost the pattern. If you like to come with me I'll give you a contract for any number of years you suggest. I need you in my business.' He rose. 'Think it over, laddie, and let me know tomorrow. Look here upon this picture, and on that. As a sleuth you are poor. You couldn't detect a bass-drum in a telephone-booth. You have no future. You are merely among those present. But as a mascot – my boy, you're the only thing in sight. You can't help succeeding on the stage. You don't have to know how to act. Look at the dozens of good actors who are out of jobs. Why? Unlucky. No other reason. With your luck and a little experience you'll be a star before you know you've begun. Think it over, and let me know in the morning.'

Before Henry's eyes there rose a sudden vision of Alice: Alice no longer unattainable; Alice walking on his arm down the aisle; Alice mending his socks; Alice with her heavenly hands fingering his salary envelope.

'Don't go,' he said. 'Don't go. I'll let you know now.'

The scene is the Strand, hard by Bedford Street; the time, that restful hour of the afternoon when they of the gnarled faces and the bright clothing gather together in groups to tell each other how good they are.

Hark! A voice.

'Rather! Courtneidge and the Guv'nor keep on trying to get me, but I turn them down every time. "No" I said to Malone only yesterday, "not for me! I'm going with old Walter Jelliffe, the same as usual, and there isn't the money in the Mint that'll get me away." Malone got all worked up. He—'

It is the voice of Pifield Rice, actor.

In Alcala

1

IN Alcala, as in most of New York's apartment houses, the schedule of prices is like a badly rolled cigarette – thick in the middle and thin at both ends. The rooms half-way up are expensive; some of them almost as expensive as if Fashion, instead of being gone for ever, were still lingering. The top rooms are cheap, the ground-floor rooms cheaper still.

Cheapest of all was the hall-bedroom. Its furniture was of the simplest. It consisted of a chair, another chair, a worn carpet, and a folding-bed. The folding-bed had an air of depression and baffled hopes. For years it had been trying to look like a bookcase in the daytime, and now it looked more like a folding-bed than ever. There was also a plain deal table, much stained with ink. At this, night after night, sometimes far into the morning, Rutherford Maxwell would sit and write stories. Now and then it happened that one would be a good story and find a market.

Rutherford Maxwell was an Englishman, and the younger son of an Englishman; and his lot was the lot of the younger sons all the world over. He was by profession one of the numerous employees of the New Asiatic Bank, which has its branches all over the world. It is a sound, trustworthy institution, and steady-going relatives would assure Rutherford that he was lucky to have got a berth in it. Rutherford did not agree with them. However sound and trustworthy, it was not exactly romantic. Nor did it err on the side of over-lavishness to those who served it. Rutherford's salary was small. So were his prospects – if he remained in the bank. At a very early date he had registered a vow that he would not. And the road that led out of it for him was the uphill road of literature.

He was thankful for small mercies. Fate had not been over-kind up to the present, but at least she had dispatched him to New York, the centre of things, where he would have the chance to try, instead of to some spot off the map. Whether he won or lost, at any rate he was in the ring, and could fight. So every night he sat in Alcala, and wrote. Sometimes he would only try to write, and that was torture.

There is never an hour of the day or night when Alcala is wholly asleep. The middle of the house is a sort of chorus-girl belt, while in the upper rooms there are reporters and other nightbirds. Long after he had gone to bed, Rutherford would hear footsteps passing his door and the sound of voices in the passage. He grew to welcome them. They seemed to connect him with the outer world. But for them he was alone after he had left the office, utterly alone, as it is possible to be only in the heart of a great city. Some nights he would hear scraps of conversations, at rare intervals a name. He used to build up in his mind identities for the owners of the names. One in particular, Peggy, gave him much food for thought. He pictured her as bright and vivacious. This was because she sang sometimes as she passed his door. She had been singing when he first heard her name. 'Oh, cut it out, Peggy,' a girl's voice had said. 'Don't you get enough of that tune at the theatre?' He felt that he would like to meet Peggy.

June came, and July, making an oven of New York, bringing close, scorching days and nights when the pen seemed made of lead; and still Rutherford worked on, sipping ice-water in his shirt-sleeves, and filling the sheets of paper slowly, but with a dogged persistence which the weather could not kill. Despite the heat, he was cheerful. Things were beginning to run his way a little now. A novelette, an airy trifle, conceived in days when the thermometer was lower and it was possible to think, and worked out almost mechanically, had been accepted by a magazine of a higher standing than those which hitherto had shown him hospitality. He began to dream of a holiday in the woods. The holiday spirit was abroad. Alcala was emptying itself. It would not be long before he too would be able to get away.

He was so deep in his thoughts that at first he did not hear the knocking at the door. But it was a sharp, insistent knocking, and forced itself upon his attention. He got up and turned the handle.

Outside in the passage was standing a girl, tall and sleepy-eyed. She wore a picture-hat and a costume the keynote of which was a certain aggressive attractiveness. There was no room for doubt as to which particular brand of scent was her favourite at the moment.

She gazed at Rutherford dully. Like Banquo's ghost, she had no speculation in her eye. Rutherford looked at her inquiringly, somewhat conscious of his shirt-sleeves.

'Did you knock?' he said, opening, as a man must do, with the inevitable foolish question.

The apparition spoke.

'Say,' she said, 'got a cigarette?'

'I'm afraid I haven't,' said Rutherford, apologetically. 'I've been smoking a pipe. I'm very sorry.'

'What?' said the apparition.

'I'm afraid I haven't.'

'Oh!' A pause. 'Say, got a cigarette?'

The intellectual pressure of the conversation was beginning to be a little too much for Rutherford. Combined with the heat of the night it made his head swim.

His visitor advanced into the room. Arriving at the table, she began fiddling with its contents. The pen seemed to fascinate her. She picked it up and inspected it closely.

'Say, what d'you call this?' she said.

'That's a pen,' said Rutherford, soothingly. 'A fountain-pen.'

'Oh!' A pause. 'Say, got a cigarette?'

Rutherford clutched a chair with one hand, and his forehead with the other. He was in sore straits.

At this moment Rescue arrived, not before it was needed. A brisk sound of footsteps in the passage, and there appeared in the doorway a second girl.

'What do you think you're doing, Gladys?' demanded the newcomer. 'You mustn't come butting into folks' rooms this way. Who's your friend?'

'My name is Maxwell,' began Rutherford eagerly.

'What say, Peggy?' said the seeker after cigarettes, dropping a sheet of manuscript to the floor.

Rutherford looked at the girl in the doorway with interest. So this was Peggy. She was little, and trim of figure. That was how he had always imagined her. Her dress was simpler than the other's. The face beneath the picture-hat was small and well-shaped, the nose delicately tip-tilted, the chin determined, the mouth a little wide and suggesting good-humour. A pair of grey eyes looked steadily into his before transferring themselves to the statuesque being at the table.

'Don't monkey with the man's inkwell, Gladys. Come along up to bed.'

'What? Say, got a cigarette?'

'There's plenty upstairs. Come along.'

The other went with perfect docility. At the door she paused, and inspected Rutherford with a grave stare.

'Good night, boy!' she said, with haughty condescension.

'Good night!' said Rutherford.

'Pleased to have met you. Good night.'

'Good night!' said Rutherford.

'Good night!'

'Come along, Gladys,' said Peggy, firmly.

Gladys went.

Rutherford sat down and dabbed his forehead with his handkerchief, feeling a little weak. He was not used to visitors.

2

He had lit his pipe, and was re-reading his night's work preparatory to turning in, when there was another knock at the door. This time there was no waiting. He was in the state of mind when one hears the smallest noise.

'Come in!' he cried.

It was Peggy.

Rutherford jumped to his feet.

'Won't you—' he began, pushing the chair forward.

She seated herself with composure on the table. She no longer wore the picture-hat, and Rutherford, looking at her, came to the conclusion that the change was an improvement.

'This'll do for me,' she said. 'Thought I'd just look in. I'm sorry about Gladys. She isn't often like that. It's the hot weather.'

'It is hot,' said Rutherford.

'You've noticed it? Bully for you! Back to the bench for Sherlock Holmes. Did Gladys try to shoot herself?'

'Good heavens, no! Why?'

'She did once. But I stole her gun, and I suppose she hasn't thought to get another. She's a good girl really, only she gets like that sometimes in the hot weather.' She looked round the room for a moment, then gazed unwinkingly at Rutherford. 'What did you say your name was?' she asked.

'Rutherford Maxwell.'

'Gee! That's going some, isn't it? Wants amputation, a name like that. I call it mean to give a poor, defenceless kid a cussword like – what's it? Rutherford? I got it – to go through the world with. Haven't you got something shorter – Tom, or Charles or something?'

'I'm afraid not.'

The round, grey eyes fixed him again.

'I shall call you George,' she decided at last.

'Thanks, I wish you would,' said Rutherford.

'George it is, then. You can call me Peggy. Peggy Norton's my name.'

'Thanks, I will.'

'Say, you're English, aren't you?' she said.

'Yes. How did you know?'

'You're so strong on the gratitude thing. It's "Thanks, thanks," all the time. Not that I mind it, George.'

'Thanks. Sorry. I should say, "Oh, you Peggy!" '

She looked at him curiously.

'How d'you like New York, George?'

'Fine – tonight.'

'Been to Coney?'

'Not yet.'

'You should. Say, what do you do, George?'

'What do I do?'

'Cut it out, George! Don't answer back as though we were a vaudeville team doing a cross-talk act. What do you do? When your boss crowds your envelope on to you Saturdays, what's it for?'

'I'm in a bank.'

'Like it?'

'Hate it!'

'Why don't you quit, then?'

'Can't afford to. There's money in being in a bank. Not much, it's true, but what there is of it is good.'

'What are you doing out of bed at this time of night? They don't work you all day, do they?'

'No; they'd like to, but they don't. I have been writing.'

'Writing what? Say, you don't mind my putting you on the witness-stand, do you? If you do, say so, and I'll cut out the District Attorney act and talk about the weather.'

'Not a bit, really, I assure you. Please ask as many questions as you like.'

'Guess there's no doubt about your being English, George. We don't have time over here to shoot it off like that. If you'd have just said "Sure!" I'd have got a line on your meaning. You don't mind me doing school-marm, George, do you? It's all for your good.'

'Sure,' said Rutherford, with a grin.

She smiled approvingly.

'That's better! You're Little Willie, the Apt Pupil, all right. What were we talking about before we switched off on to the educational rail? I know – about your writing. What were you writing?'

'A story.'

'For a paper?'

'For a magazine.'

'What! One of the fiction stories about the Gibson hero and the girl whose life he saved, like you read?'

'That's the idea.'

She looked at him with a new interest.

'Gee, George, who'd have thought it! Fancy you being one of the high-brows! You ought to hang out a sign. You look just ordinary.'

'Thanks!'

'I mean as far as the grey matter goes. I didn't mean you were a bad looker. You're not. You've got nice eyes, George.'

'Thanks.'

'I like the shape of your nose, too.'

'I say, thanks!'

'And your hair's just lovely!'

'I say, really. Thanks awfully!'

She eyed him in silence for a moment. Then she burst out:

'You say you don't like the bank?'

'I certainly don't.'

'And you'd like to strike some paying line of business?'

'Sure.'

'Then why don't you make your fortune by hiring yourself out to a museum as the biggest human clam in captivity? That's what you are. You sit there just saying "Thanks," and "Bai Jawve, thanks awf'lly," while a girl's telling you nice things about your eyes and hair, and you don't do a thing!'

Rutherford threw back his head and roared with laughter.

'I'm sorry!' he said. 'Slowness is our national failing, you know.'

'I believe you.'

'Tell me about yourself. You know all about me, by now. What do you do beside brightening up the dull evenings of poor devils of bank-clerks?'

'Give you three guesses.'

'Stage?'

'Gee! You're the human sleuth all right, all right! It's a home-run every time when you get your deductive theories unlimbered. Yes, George; the stage it is. I'm an actorine – one of the pony ballet in *The Island of Girls* at the Melody. Seen our show?'

'Not yet. I'll go tomorrow.'

'Great! I'll let them know, so that they can have the awning out and the red carpet down. It's a cute little piece.'

'So I've heard.'

'Well, if I see you in front tomorrow, I'll give you half a smile, so that you shan't feel you haven't got your money's worth. Good night, George!'

'Good night, Peggy!'

She jumped down from the table. Her eye was caught by the photographs on the mantelpiece. She began to examine them.

'Who are these Willies?' she said, picking up a group.

'That is the football team of my old school. The lout with the sheepish smirk, holding the ball, is myself as I was before the cares of the world soured me.'

Her eye wandered along the mantelpiece, and she swooped down on a cabinet photograph of a girl.

'And who's *this*, George?' she cried.

He took the photograph from her, and replaced it, with a curious blend of shyness and defiance, in the very centre of the mantelpiece.

For a moment he stood looking intently at it, his elbows resting on the imitation marble.

'Who is it?' asked Peggy. 'Wake up, George. Who's this?'

Rutherford started.

'Sorry,' he said. 'I was thinking about something.'

'I bet you were. You looked like it. Well, who is she?'

'Eh! Oh, that's a girl.'

Peggy laughed satirically.

'Thanks awf'lly, as you would say. I've got eyes, George.'

'I noticed that,' said Rutherford, smiling. 'Charming ones, too.'

'Gee! What would she say if she heard you talking like that!'

She came a step nearer, looking up at him. Their eyes met.

'She would say,' said Rutherford, slowly: ' "I know you love me, and I know I can trust you, and I haven't the slightest objection to your telling Miss Norton the truth about her eyes. Miss Norton is a dear, good little sort, one of the best, in fact, and I hope you'll be great pals!" '

There was a silence.

'She'd say that, would she?' said Peggy, at last.

'She would.'

Peggy looked at the photograph, and back again at Rutherford.

'You're pretty fond of her, George, I guess, aren't you?'

'I am,' said Rutherford, quietly.

'George.'

'Yes?'

'George, she's a pretty good long way away, isn't she?'

She looked up at him with a curious light in her grey eyes. Rutherford met her glance steadily.

'Not to me,' he said. 'She's here now, and all the time.'

He stepped away and picked up the sheaf of papers which he had dropped at Peggy's entrance. Peggy laughed.

'Good night, Georgie boy,' she said. 'I mustn't keep you up any more, or you'll be late in the morning. And what would the bank do then? Smash or something, I guess. Good night, Georgie! See you again one of these old evenings.'

'Good night, Peggy!'

The door closed behind her. He heard her footsteps hesitate, stop, and then move quickly on once more.

3

He saw much of her after this first visit. Gradually it became an understood thing between them that she should look in on her return from the theatre. He grew to expect her, and to feel restless when she was late. Once she brought the cigarette-loving Gladys with her, but the experiment was not a success. Gladys was languid and rather overpoweringly refined, and conversation became forced. After that, Peggy came alone.

Generally she found him working. His industry amazed her.

'Gee, George,' she said one night, sitting in her favourite place on the table, from which he had moved a little pile of manuscripts to make room for her. 'Don't you ever let up for a second? Seems to me you write all the time.'

Rutherford laughed.

'I'll take a rest,' he said, 'when there's a bit more demand for my stuff than there is at present. When I'm in the twenty-cents-a-word class I'll write once a month, and spend the rest of my time travelling.'

Peggy shook her head.

'No travelling for mine,' she said. 'Seems to me it's just cussedness that makes people go away from Broadway when they've got plunks enough to stay there and enjoy themselves.'

'Do you like Broadway, Peggy?'

'Do I like Broadway? Does a kid like candy? Why, don't you?'

'It's all right for the time. It's not my ideal.'

'Oh, and what particular sort of little old Paradise do *you* hanker after?'

He puffed at his pipe, and looked dreamily at her through the smoke.

'Way over in England, Peggy, there's a county called Worcestershire. And somewhere near the edge of that there's a grey house with gables, and there's a lawn and a meadow and a shrubbery, and an orchard and rose-garden, and a big cedar on the terrace before you get to the rose-garden. And if you climb to the top of that cedar, you can see the river through the apple trees in the orchard. And in the distance there are hills. And—'

'Of all the rube joints!' exclaimed Peggy, in deep disgust. 'Why, a day of that would be about twenty-three hours and a bit too long for me. Broadway for mine! Put me where I can touch Forty-Second Street without over-balancing, and then you can leave me. I never thought you were such a hayseed, George.'

'Don't worry, Peggy. It'll be a long time, I expect, before I go there. I've got to make my fortune first.'

'Getting anywhere near the John D. class yet?'

'I've still some way to go. But things are moving, I think. Do you know, Peggy, you remind me of a little Billiken, sitting on that table?'

'Thank *you*, George, I always knew my mouth was rather wide but I did think I had Billiken to the bad. Do you do that sort of Candid Friend stunt with *her*?' She pointed to the photograph on the mantelpiece. It was the first time since the night when they had met that she had made any allusion to it. By silent agreement the subject had been ruled out between them. 'By the way, you never told me her name.'

'Halliday,' said Rutherford, shortly.

'What else?'

'Alice.'

'Don't bite at me, George! I'm not hurting you. Tell me about her. I'm interested. Does she live in the grey house with the pigs and chickens and all them roses, and the rest of the rube outfit?'

'No.'

'Be chummy, George. What's the matter with you?'

'I'm sorry, Peggy,' he said. 'I'm a fool. It's only that it all seems so damned hopeless! Here am I, earning about half a dollar a year, and – Still, it's no use kicking, is it? Besides, I may make a home-run with my writing one of these days. That's what I meant when I said you were a Billiken, Peggy. Do you know, you've brought me luck. Ever since I met you, I've been doing twice as well. You're my mascot.'

'Bully for me! We've all got our uses in the world, haven't we? I wonder if it would help any if I was to kiss you, George?'

'Don't you do it. One mustn't work a mascot too hard.'

She jumped down, and came across the room to where he sat, looking down at him with the round, grey eyes that always reminded him of a kitten's.

'George!'

'Yes?'

'Oh, nothing!'

She turned away to the mantelpiece, and stood gazing at the photograph, her back towards him.

'George!'

'Hullo?'

'Say, what colour eyes has she got?'

'Grey.'

'Like mine?'

'Darker than yours.'

'Nicer than mine?'

'Don't you think we might talk about something else?'

She swung round, her fists clenched, her face blazing.

'I hate you!' she cried. 'I do! I wish I'd never seen you! I wish—'

She leaned on the mantelpiece, burying her face in her arms, and burst into a passion of sobs. Rutherford leaped up, shocked and helpless. He sprang to her, and placed a hand gently on her shoulder.

'Peggy, old girl—'

She broke from him.

'Don't you touch me! Don't you do it! Gee, I wish I'd never seen you!'

She ran to the door, darted through, and banged it behind her.

Rutherford remained where he stood, motionless. Then, almost mechanically, he felt in his pocket for matches, and relit his pipe.

Half an hour passed. Then the door opened slowly. Peggy came in. She was pale, and her eyes were red. She smiled – a pathetic little smile.

'Peggy!'

He took a step towards her.

She held out her hand.

'I'm sorry, George. I feel mean.'

'Dear old girl, what rot!'

'I do. You don't know how mean I feel. You've been real nice to me, George. Thought I'd look in and say I was sorry. Good night, George!'

On the following night he waited, but she did not come. The nights went by, and still she did not come. And one morning, reading his paper, he saw that *The Island of Girls* had gone west to Chicago.

4

Things were not running well for Rutherford. He had had his vacation, a golden fortnight of fresh air and sunshine in the Catskills, and was back in Alcala, trying, with poor success, to pick up the threads of his work. But though the Indian Summer had begun, and there was energy in the air, night after night he sat idle in his room; night after night went wearily to bed, oppressed with a dull sense of failure. He could not work. He was restless. His thoughts would not concentrate themselves. Something was wrong; and he knew what it was, though he fought against admitting it to himself. It was the absence of Peggy that had brought about the change. Not till now had he realized to the full how greatly her visits had stimulated him. He had called her laughingly his mascot; but the thing was no joke. It was true. Her absence was robbing him of the power to write.

He was lonely. For the first time since he had come to New York he was really lonely. Solitude had not hurt him till now. In his black moments it had been enough for him to look up at the photograph on the mantelpiece, and instantly he was alone no longer. But now the photograph had lost its magic. It could not hold him. Always his mind would wander back to the little, black-haired ghost that sat on the table, smiling at him, and questioning him with its grey eyes.

And the days went by, unvarying in their monotony. And always the ghost sat on the table, smiling at him.

With the Fall came the reopening of the theatres. One by one the electric signs blazed out along Broadway, spreading the message that the dull days were over, and New York was itself again. At the Melody, where ages ago *The Island of Girls* had run its light-hearted course, a new musical piece was in rehearsal. Alcala was full once more. The nightly snatches of conversation outside his door had recommenced. He listened for her voice, but he never heard it.

He sat up, waiting, into the small hours, but she did not come. Once he had been trying to write, and had fallen, as usual, to brooding – there was a soft knock at the door. In an instant he had bounded from his chair, and turned the handle. It was one of the reporters from upstairs, who had run out of matches. Rutherford gave him a handful. The reporter went out, wondering what the man had laughed at.

There is balm in Broadway, especially by night. Depression vanishes before the cheerfulness of the great white way when the lights are lit and the human tide is in full flood. Rutherford had developed of late a habit of patrolling the neighbourhood of 42nd Street at theatre-time. He found it did him good. There is a gaiety, a bonhomie, in the atmosphere of the New York streets. Rutherford loved to stand on the sidewalk and watch the passers-by, weaving stories round them.

One night his wanderings had brought him to Herald Square. The theatres were just emptying themselves. This was the time he liked best. He drew to one side to watch, and as he moved he saw Peggy.

She was standing at the corner, buttoning a glove. He was by her side in an instant.

'Peggy!' he cried.

She was looking pale and tired, but the colour came back to her cheeks as she held out her hand. There was no trace of embarrassment in her manner; only a frank pleasure at seeing him again.

'Where have you been?' he said. 'I couldn't think what had become of you.'

She looked at him curiously.

'Did you miss me, George?'

'Miss you? Of course I did. My work's been going all to pieces since you went away.'

'I only came back last night. I'm in the new piece at the Madison. Gee, I'm tired, George! We've been rehearsing all day.'

He took her by the arm.

'Come along and have some supper. You look worn out. By Jove, Peggy, it's good seeing you again! Can you walk as far as Rector's, or shall I carry you?'

'Guess I can walk that far. But Rector's? Has your rich uncle died and left you a fortune, George?'

'Don't you worry, Peggy. This is an occasion. I thought I was never going to see you again. I'll buy you the whole hotel, if you like.'

'Just supper'll do, I guess. You're getting quite the rounder, George.'

'You bet I am. There are all sorts of sides to my character you've never so much as dreamed of.'

They seemed to know Peggy at Rector's. Paul, the head waiter, beamed upon her paternally. One or two men turned and looked after her as she passed. The waiters smiled slight but friendly smiles. Rutherford, intent on her, noticed none of these things.

Despite her protests, he ordered an elaborate and expensive supper. He was particular about the wine. The waiter, who had been doubtful about him, was won over, and went off to execute the order, reflecting that it was never safe to judge a man by his clothes, and that Rutherford was probably one of these eccentric young millionaires who didn't care how they dressed.

'Well?' said Peggy, when he had finished.

'Well?' said Rutherford.

'You're looking brown, George.'

'I've been away in the Catskills.'

'Still as strong on the rube proposition as ever?'

'Yes. But Broadway has its points, too.'

'Oh, you're beginning to see that? Gee, I'm glad to be back. I've had enough of the Wild West. If anybody ever tries to steer you west of Eleventh Avenue, George, don't you go. There's nothing doing. How have you been making out at your writing stunt?'

'Pretty well. But I wanted you. I was lost without my mascot. I've got a story in this month's *Wilson's*. A long story and paid accordingly. That's why I'm able to go about giving suppers to great actresses.'

'I read it on the train,' said Peggy. 'It's dandy. Do you know what you ought to do, George? You ought to turn it into a play. There's a heap of money in plays.'

'I know. But who wants a play by an unknown man?'

'I know who would want *Willie in the Wilderness*, if you made it into a play, and that's Winfield Knight. Ever seen him?'

'I saw him in *The Outsider*. He's clever.'

'He's It, if he gets a part to suit him. If he doesn't, he don't amount to a row of beans. It's just a gamble. This thing he's in now is no good. The part doesn't begin to fit him. In a month he'll be squealing for another play, so's you can hear him in Connecticut.'

'He shall not squeal in vain,' said Rutherford. 'If he wants my work, who am I that I should stand in the way of his simple pleasures? I'll start on the thing tomorrow.'

'I can help you some too, I guess. I used to know Winfield Knight. I can put you wise on lots of things about him that'll help you work up Willie's character so's it'll fit him like a glove.'

Rutherford raised his glass.

'Peggy,' he said, 'you're more than a mascot. You ought to be drawing a big commission on everything I write. It beats me how any of these other fellows ever write anything without you there to help them. I wonder what's the most expensive cigar they keep here? I must have it, whatever it is. *Noblesse oblige*. We popular playwrights mustn't be seen in public smoking any cheap stuff.'

It was Rutherford's artistic temperament which, when they left the restaurant, made him hail a taxi-cab. Taxi-cabs are not for young men drawing infinitesimal salaries in banks, even if those salaries are supplemented at rare intervals by a short story in a magazine. Peggy was for returning to Alcala by car, but Rutherford refused to countenance such an anti-climax.

Peggy nestled into the corner of the cab, with a tired sigh, and there was silence as they moved smoothly up Broadway.

He peered at her in the dim light. She looked very small and wistful and fragile. Suddenly an intense desire surged over him to pick her up and crush her to him. He fought against it. He tried to fix his thoughts on the girl at home, to tell himself that he was a man of honour. His fingers, gripping the edge of the seat, tightened till every muscle of his arm was rigid.

The cab, crossing a rough piece of road, jolted Peggy from her corner. Her hand fell on his.

'Peggy!' he cried, hoarsely.

Her grey eyes were wet. He could see them glisten. And then his arms were round her, and he was covering her upturned face with kisses.

The cab drew up at the entrance to Alcala. They alighted in silence, and without a word made their way through into the hall. From force of habit, Rutherford glanced at the letter-rack on the wall at the foot of the stairs. There was one letter in his pigeon-hole.

Mechanically he drew it out; and, as his eyes fell on the handwriting, something seemed to snap inside him.

He looked at Peggy, standing on the bottom stair, and back again at the envelope in his hand. His mood was changing with a violence that left him physically weak. He felt dazed, as if he had wakened out of a trance.

With a strong effort he mastered himself. Peggy had mounted a few steps, and was looking back at him over her shoulder. He could read the meaning now in the grey eyes.

'Good night, Peggy,' he said in a low voice. She turned, facing him, and for a moment neither moved.

'Good night!' said Rutherford again.

Her lips parted, as if she were about to speak, but she said nothing.

Then she turned again, and began to walk slowly upstairs.

He stood watching her till she had reached the top of the long flight. She did not look back.

5

Peggy's nightly visits began afresh after this, and the ghost on the table troubled Rutherford no more. His restlessness left him. He began to write with a new vigour and success. In after years he wrote many plays, most of them good, clear-cut pieces of work, but none that came from him with the utter absence of labour which made the writing of *Willie in the Wilderness* a joy. He wrote easily, without effort. And always Peggy was there, helping, stimulating, encouraging.

Sometimes, when he came in after dinner to settle down to work, he would find a piece of paper on his table covered with her schoolgirl scrawl. It would run somewhat as follows:

'He is proud of his arms. They are skinny, but he thinks them the limit. Better put in a shirt-sleeve scene for Willie somewhere.

'He thinks he has a beautiful profile. Couldn't you make one of the girls say something about Willie having the goods in that line?

'He is crazy about golf.

'He is proud of his French accent. Couldn't you make Willie speak a little piece in French?'

'He' being Winfield Knight.

And so, little by little, the character of Willie grew, till it ceased to be the Willie of the magazine story, and became Winfield Knight himself, with improvements. The task began to fascinate Rutherford. It was like planning a pleasant surprise for a child. 'He'll like that,' he would say to himself, as he wrote in some speech enabling Willie to display one of the accomplishments, real or imagined, of the absent actor. Peggy read it, and approved. It was she who suggested the big speech in the second act where Willie described the progress of his love affair in terms of the golf-links. From her, too, came information as to little traits in the man's character which the stranger would not have suspected.

As the play progressed Rutherford was amazed at the completeness of the character he had built. It lived. Willie in the magazine story might have been anyone. He fitted into the story, but you could not see him. He had no real individuality. But Willie in the play! He felt that he would recognize him in the street. There was all the difference between the two that there is between a nameless figure in some cheap picture and a portrait by Sargent. There were times when the story of the play seemed thin to him, and the other characters wooden, but in his blackest moods he was sure of Willie. All the contradictions in the character rang true: the humour, the pathos, the surface vanity covering a real diffidence, the strength and weakness fighting one another.

'You're alive, my son,' said Rutherford, admiringly, as he read the sheets. 'But you don't belong to me.'

At last there came the day when the play was finished, when the last line was written, and the last possible alteration made; and later, the day when Rutherford, bearing the brown-paper-covered package under his arm, called at the Players' Club to keep an appointment with Winfield Knight.

Almost from the first Rutherford had a feeling that he had met the man before, that he knew him. As their acquaintance progressed – the actor was in an expansive mood, and talked much before coming to business – the feeling grew. Then he understood. This was Willie, and no other. The likeness was extraordinary. Little turns of thought, little expressions – they were all in the play.

The actor paused in a description of how he had almost beaten a champion at golf, and looked at the parcel.

'Is that the play?' he said.

'Yes,' said Rutherford. 'Shall I read it?'

'Guess I'll just look through it myself. Where's Act I? Here we are! Have a cigar while you're waiting?'

Rutherford settled himself in his chair, and watched the other's face. For the first few pages, which contained some tame dialogue between minor characters, it was blank.

' "Enter Willie," ' he said. 'Am I Willie?'

'I hope so,' said Rutherford, with a smile. 'It's the star part.'

'H'm.'

He went on reading. Rutherford watched him with furtive keenness. There was a line coming at the bottom of the page which he was then reading which ought to hit him, an epigram on golf, a whimsical thought put almost exactly as he had put it himself five minutes back when telling his golf story.

The shot did not misfire. The chuckle from the actor and the sigh of relief from Rutherford were almost simultaneous. Winfield Knight turned to him.

'That's a dandy line about golf,' said he.

Rutherford puffed complacently at his cigar.

'There's lots more of them in the piece,' he said.

'Bully for you,' said the actor. And went on reading.

Three-quarters of an hour passed before he spoke again. Then he looked up.

'It's me,' he said; 'it's me all the time. I wish I'd seen this before I put on the punk I'm doing now. This is me from the drive off the tee. It's great! Say, what'll you have?'

Rutherford leaned back in his chair, his mind in a whirl. He had arrived at last. His struggles were over. He would not admit of the possibility of the play being a failure. He was a made man. He could go where he pleased, and do as he pleased.

It gave him something of a shock to find how persistently his thoughts refused to remain in England. Try as he might to keep them there, they kept flitting back to Alcala.

6

Willie in the Wilderness was not a failure. It was a triumph. Principally, it is true, a personal triumph for Winfield Knight. Everyone was agreed that he had never had a part that suited him so well. Critics forgave the blunders of the piece for the sake of its principal character. The play was a curiously amateurish thing. It was only later that Rutherford learned craft and caution. When he wrote *Willie* he was a colt, rambling unchecked through the field of play-writing, ignorant of its pitfalls. But, with all its faults, *Willie in the Wilderness* was a success. It might, as one critic pointed out, be more of a monologue act for Winfield Knight than a play, but that did not affect Rutherford.

It was late on the opening night when he returned to Alcala. He had tried to get away earlier. He wanted to see Peggy. But Winfield Knight, flushed with success, was in his most expansive mood. He seized upon Rutherford and would not let him go. There was supper, a gay, uproarious supper, at which everybody seemed to be congratulating everybody else. Men he had never met before shook him warmly by the hand. Somebody made a speech, despite the efforts of the rest of the company to prevent him. Rutherford sat there, dazed, out of touch with the mood of the party. He wanted Peggy. He was tired of all this excitement and noise. He had had enough of it. All he asked was to be allowed to slip away quietly and go home. He wanted to think, to try and realize what all this meant to him.

At length the party broke up in one last explosion of handshaking and congratulations; and, eluding Winfield Knight, who proposed to take him off to his club, he started to walk up Broadway.

It was late when he reached Alcala. There was a light in his room. Peggy had waited up to hear the news.

She jumped off the table as he came in.

'Well?' she cried.

Rutherford sat down and stretched out his legs.

'It's a success,' he said. 'A tremendous success!'

Peggy clapped her hands.

'Bully for you, George! I knew it would be. Tell me all about it. Was Winfield good?'

'He was the whole piece. There was nothing in it but him.' He rose and placed his hands on her shoulders. 'Peggy, old girl, I don't know what to say. You know as well as I do that it's all owing to you that the piece has been a success. If I hadn't had your help—'

Peggy laughed.

'Oh, beat it, George!' she said. 'Don't you come jollying me. I look like a high-brow playwright, don't I! No; I'm real glad you've made a hit, George, but don't start handing out any story about it's not being your own. I didn't do a thing.'

'You did. You did everything.'

'I didn't. But, say, don't let's start quarrelling. Tell me more about it. How many calls did you take?'

He told her all that had happened. When he had finished, there was a silence.

'I guess you'll be quitting soon, George?' said Peggy, at last. 'Now that you've made a home-run. You'll be going back to that rube joint, with the cows and hens – isn't that it?'

Rutherford did not reply. He was starting thoughtfully at the floor. He did not seem to have heard.

'I guess that girl'll be glad to see you,' she went on. 'Shall you cable tomorrow, George? And then you'll get married and go and live in the rube house, and become a regular hayseed and—' She broke off suddenly, with a catch in her voice. 'Gee,' she whispered, half to herself, 'I'll be sorry when you go, George.'

He sprang up.

'Peggy!'

He seized her by the arm. He heard the quick intake of her breath.

'Peggy, listen!' He gripped her till she winced with pain. 'I'm not going back. I'm never going back. I'm a cad, I'm a hound! I know I am. But I'm not going back. I'm going to stay here with you. I want you, Peggy. Do you hear? I want you!'

She tried to draw herself away, but he held her.

'I love you, Peggy! Peggy, will you be my wife?'

There was utter astonishment in her grey eyes. Her face was very white.

'Will you, Peggy?'

He dropped her arm.

'Will you, Peggy?'

'No!' she cried.

He drew back.

'No!' she cried sharply, as if it hurt her to speak. 'I wouldn't play you such a mean trick. I'm too fond of you, George. There's never been anybody just like you. You've been mighty good to me. I've never met a man who treated me like you. You're the only real white man that's ever happened to me, and I guess I'm not going to play you a low-down trick like spoiling your life. George, I thought you knew. Honest, I thought you knew. How did you think I lived in a swell place like this, if you didn't know? How did you suppose everyone knew me at Rector's? How did you think I'd managed to find out so much about Winfield Knight? Can't you guess?'

She drew a long breath.

'I—'

He interrupted her hoarsely.

'Is there anyone now, Peggy?'

'Yes,' she said, 'there is.'

'You don't love him, Peggy, do you?'

'Love him?' She laughed bitterly. 'No; I don't love him.'

'Then come to me, dear,' he said.

She shook her head in silence. Rutherford sat down, his chin resting in his hands. She came across to him, and smoothed his hair.

'It wouldn't do, George,' she said. 'Honest, it wouldn't do. Listen. When we first met, I – I rather liked you, George, and I was mad at you for being so fond of the other girl and taking no notice of me – not in the way I wanted, and I tried – Gee, I feel mean. It was all my fault. I didn't think it would matter. There didn't seem no chance then of your being able to go back and have the sort of good time you wanted; and I thought you'd just stay here and we'd be pals and – but now you can go back, it's all different. I couldn't keep you. It would be too mean. You see, you don't really want to stop. You think you do, but you don't!'

'I love you,' he muttered.

'You'll forget me. It's all just a Broadway dream, George. Think of it like that. Broadway's got you now, but you don't really belong. You're not like me. It's not in your blood, so's you can't get it out. It's the chickens and roses you want really. Just a Broadway dream. That's what it is. George, when I was a kid, I remember crying and crying for a lump of candy in the window of a store till one of my brothers up and bought it for me just to stop the racket. Gee! For about a minute I was the busiest thing that ever happened, eating away. And then it didn't seem to interest me no more. Broadway's like that for you, George. You go back to the girl and the cows and all of it. It'll hurt some, I guess, but I reckon you'll be glad you did.'

She stooped swiftly, and kissed him on the forehead.

'I'll miss you, dear,' she said, softly, and was gone.

Rutherford sat on, motionless. Outside, the blackness changed to grey, and the grey to white. He got up. He felt very stiff and cold.

'A Broadway dream!' he muttered.

He went to the mantelpiece and took up the photograph. He carried it to the window where he could see it better.

A shaft of sunlight pierced the curtains and fell upon it.

Extricating Young Gussie

SHE sprang it on me before breakfast. There in seven words you have a complete character sketch of my Aunt Agatha. I could go on indefinitely about brutality and lack of consideration. I merely say that she routed me out of bed to listen to her painful story somewhere in the small hours. It can't have been half-past eleven when Jeeves, my man, woke me out of the dreamless and broke the news:

'Mrs Gregson to see you, sir.'

I thought she must be walking in her sleep, but I crawled out of bed and got into a dressing-gown. I knew Aunt Agatha well enough to know that, if she had come to see me, she was going to see me. That's the sort of woman she is.

She was sitting bolt upright in a chair, staring into space. When I came in she looked at me in that darn critical way that always makes me feel as if I had gelatine where my spine ought to be. Aunt Agatha is one of those strong-minded women. I should think Queen Elizabeth must have been something like her. She bosses her husband, Spencer Gregson, a battered little chappie on the Stock Exchange. She bosses my cousin, Gussie Mannering-Phipps. She bosses her sister-in-law, Gussie's mother. And, worst of all, she bosses me. She has an eye like a man-eating fish, and she has got moral suasion down to a fine point.

I dare say there are fellows in the world – men of blood and iron, don't you know, and all that sort of thing – whom she couldn't intimidate; but if you're a chappie like me, fond of a quiet life, you simply curl into a ball when you see her coming, and hope for the best. My experience is that when Aunt Agatha wants you to do a thing you do it, or else you find yourself wondering why those fellows in the olden days made such a fuss when they had trouble with the Spanish Inquisition.

'Halloa, Aunt Agatha!' I said.

'Bertie,' she said, 'you look a sight. You look perfectly dissipated.'

I was feeling like a badly wrapped brown-paper parcel. I'm never at my best in the early morning. I said so.

'Early morning! I had breakfast three hours ago, and have been walking in the park ever since, trying to compose my thoughts.'

If I ever breakfasted at half-past eight I should walk on the Embankment, trying to end it all in a watery grave.

'I am extremely worried, Bertie. That is why I have come to you.'

And then I saw she was going to start something, and I bleated weakly to Jeeves to bring me tea. But she had begun before I could get it.

'What are your immediate plans, Bertie?'

'Well, I rather thought of tottering out for a bite of lunch later on, and then possibly staggering round to the club, and after that, if I felt strong enough, I might trickle off to Walton Heath for a round of golf.'

'I am not interested in your totterings and tricklings. I mean, have you got any important engagements in the next week or so?'

I scented danger.

'Rather,' I said. 'Heaps! Millions! Booked solid!'

'What are they?'

'I – er – well, I don't quite know.'

'I thought as much. You have no engagements. Very well, then, I want you to start immediately for America.'

'America!'

Do not lose sight of the fact that all this was taking place on an empty stomach, shortly after the rising of the lark.

'Yes, America. I suppose even you have heard of America?'

'But why America?'

'Because that is where your Cousin Gussie is. He is in New York, and I can't get at him.'

'What's Gussie been doing?'

'Gussie is making a perfect idiot of himself.'

To one who knew young Gussie as well as I did, the words opened up a wide field for speculation.

'In what way?'

'He has lost his head over a creature.'

On past performances this rang true. Ever since he arrived at man's estate Gussie had been losing his head over creatures. He's that sort of chap. But, as the creatures never seemed to lose their heads over him, it had never amounted to very much.

'I imagine you know perfectly well why Gussie went to America, Bertie. You know how wickedly extravagant your Uncle Cuthbert was.'

She alluded to Gussie's governor, the late head of the family, and I am bound to say she spoke the truth. Nobody was fonder of old Uncle Cuthbert than I was, but everybody knows that, where money was concerned, he was the most complete chump in the annals of the nation. He had an expensive thirst. He never backed a horse that didn't get housemaid's knee in the middle of the race. He had a system of beating the bank at Monte Carlo which used to make the administration hang out the bunting and ring the joy-bells when he was sighted in the offing. Take him for all in all, dear old Uncle Cuthbert was as willing a spender as ever called the family lawyer a bloodsucking vampire because he wouldn't let Uncle Cuthbert cut down the timber to raise another thousand.

'He left your Aunt Julia very little money for a woman in her position. Beechwood requires a great deal of keeping up, and poor dear Spencer, though he does his best to help, has not unlimited resources. It was clearly understood why Gussie went to America. He is not clever, but he is very good-looking, and, though he has no title, the Mannering-Phippses are one of the best and oldest families in England. He had some excellent letters of introduction, and when he wrote home to say that he had met the most charming and beautiful girl in the world, I felt quite happy. He continued to rave about her for several mails, and then this morning a letter has come from him in which he says, quite casually as a sort of afterthought, that he knows we are broad-minded enough not to think any the worse of her because she is on the vaudeville stage.'

'Oh, I say!'

'It was like a thunderbolt. The girl's name, it seems, is Ray Denison, and according to Gussie she does something which he describes as a single on the big time. What this degraded performance may be I have not the least notion. As a further recommendation he states that she lifted them out of their seats at Mosenstein's last week. Who she may be, and how or why, and who or what Mr Mosenstein may be, I cannot tell you.'

'By Jove,' I said, 'it's like a sort of thingummybob, isn't it? A sort of fate, what?'

'I fail to understand you.'

'Well, Aunt Julia, you know, don't you know? Heredity, and so forth. What's bred in the bone will come out in the wash, and all that kind of thing, you know.'

'Don't be absurd, Bertie.'

That was all very well, but it was a coincidence for all that. Nobody ever mentions it, and the family have been trying to forget it for twenty-five years, but it's a known fact that my Aunt Julia, Gussie's mother, was a vaudeville artist once, and a very good one, too, I'm told. She was playing in pantomime at Drury Lane when Uncle Cuthbert saw her first. It was before my time, of course, and long before I was old enough to take notice the family had made the best of it, and Aunt Agatha had pulled up her socks and put in a lot of educative work, and with a microscope you couldn't tell Aunt Julia from a genuine dyed-in-the-wool aristocrat. Women adapt themselves so quickly!

I have a pal who married Daisy Trimble of the Gaiety, and when

I meet her now I feel like walking out of her presence backwards. But there the thing was, and you couldn't get away from it. Gussie had vaudeville blood in him, and it looked as if he were reverting to type, or whatever they call it.

'By Jove,' I said, for I am interested in this heredity stuff, 'perhaps the thing is going to be a regular family tradition, like you read about in books – a sort of Curse of the Mannering-Phippses, as it were. Perhaps each head of the family's going to marry into vaudeville for ever and ever. Unto the what-d'you-call-it generation, don't you know?'

'Please do not be quite idiotic, Bertie. There is one head of the family who is certainly not going to do it, and that is Gussie. And you are going to America to stop him.'

'Yes, but why me?'

'Why you? You are too vexing, Bertie. Have you no sort of feeling for the family? You are too lazy to try to be a credit to yourself, but at least you can exert yourself to prevent Gussie's disgracing us. You are going to America because you are Gussie's cousin, because you have always been his closest friend, because you are the only one of the family who has absolutely nothing to occupy his time except golf and night clubs.'

'I play a lot of auction.'

'And, as you say, idiotic gambling in low dens. If you require another reason, you are going because I ask you as a personal favour.'

What she meant was that, if I refused, she would exert the full bent of her natural genius to make life a Hades for me. She held me with her glittering eye. I have never met anyone who can give a better imitation of the Ancient Mariner.

'So you will start at once, won't you, Bertie?'

I didn't hesitate.

'Rather!' I said. 'Of course I will.'

Jeeves came in with the tea.

'Jeeves,' I said, 'we start for America on Saturday.'

'Very good, sir,' he said; 'which suit will you wear?'

New York is a large city conveniently situated on the edge of America, so that you step off the liner right on to it without an effort. You can't lose your way. You go out of a barn and down some stairs, and there you are, right in among it. The only possible objection any reasonable chappie could find to the place is that they loose you into it from the boat at such an ungodly hour.

I left Jeeves to get my baggage safely past an aggregation of suspicious-minded pirates who were digging for buried treasures among my shirts, and drove to Gussie's hotel, where I requested the squad of gentlemanly clerks behind the desk to produce him.

That's where I got my first shock. He wasn't there. I pleaded with them to think again, and they thought again, but it was no good. No Augustus Mannering-Phipps on the premises.

I admit I was hard hit. There I was alone in a strange city and no signs of Gussie. What was the next step? I am never one of the master minds in the early morning; the old bean doesn't somehow seem to get into its stride till pretty late in the p.m.'s, and I couldn't think what to do. However, some instinct took me through a door at the back of the lobby, and I found myself in a large room with an enormous picture stretching across the whole of one wall, and under the picture a counter, and behind the counter divers chappies in white, serving drinks. They have barmen, don't you know, in New York, not barmaids. Rum idea!

I put myself unreservedly into the hands of one of the white chappies. He was a friendly soul, and I told him the whole state of affairs. I asked him what he thought would meet the case.

He said that in a situation of that sort he usually prescribed a 'lightning whizzer', an invention of his own. He said this was what rabbits trained on when they were matched against grizzly bears, and there was only one instance on record of the bear having lasted three rounds. So I tried a couple, and, by Jove! the man was perfectly right. As I drained the second a great load seemed to fall from my heart, and I went out in quite a braced way to have a look at the city.

I was surprised to find the streets quite full. People were bustling along as if it were some reasonable hour and not the grey dawn. In the tramcars they were absolutely standing on each other's necks. Going to business or something, I take it. Wonderful johnnies!

The odd part of it was that after the first shock of seeing all this frightful energy the thing didn't seem so strange. I've spoken to fellows since who have been in New York, and they tell me they found it just the same. Apparently there's something in the air, either the ozone or the phosphates or something, which makes you sit up and take notice. A kind of zip, as it were. A sort of bally freedom if you know what I mean, that gets into your blood and bucks you up, and makes you feel that –

God's in His Heaven:
All's right with the world,

and you don't care if you've got odd socks on. I can't express it better than by saying that the thought uppermost in my mind, as I walked about the place they call Times Square, was that there were three thousand miles of deep water between me and my Aunt Agatha.

It's a funny thing about looking for things. If you hunt for a needle in a haystack you don't find it. If you don't give a darn whether you ever see the needle or not it runs into you the first time you lean against the stack. By the time I had strolled up and down once or twice, seeing the sights and letting the white chappie's corrective permeate my system, I was feeling that I wouldn't care if Gussie and I never met again, and I'm dashed if I didn't suddenly catch sight of the old lad, as large as life, just turning in at a doorway down the street.

I called after him, but he didn't hear me, so I legged it in pursuit and caught him going into an office on the first floor. The name on the door was Abe Riesbitter, Vaudeville Agent, and from the other side of the door came the sound of many voices.

He turned and stared at me.

'Bertie! What on earth are you doing? Where have you sprung from? When did you arrive?'

'Landed this morning. I went round to your hotel, but they said you weren't there. They had never heard of you.'

'I've changed my name. I call myself George Wilson.'

'Why on earth?'

'Well, you try calling yourself Augustus Mannering-Phipps over here, and see how it strikes you. You feel a perfect ass. I don't know what it is about America, but the broad fact is that it's not a place where you can call yourself Augustus Mannering-Phipps. And there's another reason. I'll tell you later. Bertie, I've fallen in love with the dearest girl in the world.'

The poor old nut looked at me in such a deuced cat-like way, standing with his mouth open, waiting to be congratulated, that I simply hadn't the heart to tell him that I knew all about that already, and had come over to the country for the express purpose of laying him a stymie.

So I congratulated him.

'Thanks awfully, old man,' he said. 'It's a bit premature, but I fancy it's going to be all right. Come along in here, and I'll tell you about it.'

'What do you want in this place? It looks a rummy spot?'

'Oh, that's part of the story. I'll tell you the whole thing.'

We opened the door marked 'Waiting Room'. I never saw such a crowded place in my life. The room was packed till the walls bulged.

Gussie explained.

'Pros,' he said, 'music-hall artistes, you know, waiting to see old Abe Riesbitter. This is September the first, vaudeville's opening day. The early fall,' said Gussie, who is a bit of a poet in his way, 'is vaudeville's springtime. All over the country, as August wanes, sparkling comediennes burst into bloom, the sap stirs in the veins of tramp cyclists, and last year's contortionists, waking from their summer sleep, tie themselves tentatively into knots. What I mean is, this is the beginning of the new season, and everybody's out hunting for bookings.'

'But what do you want here?'

'Oh, I've just got to see Abe about something. If you see a fat man with about fifty-seven chins come out of that door grab him, for that'll be Abe. He's one of those fellows who advertise each step up they take in the world by growing another chin. I'm told that way back in the nineties he only had two. If you do grab Abe, remember that he knows me as George Wilson.'

'You said that you were going to explain that George Wilson business to me, Gussie, old man.'

'Well, it's this way—'

At this juncture dear old Gussie broke off short, rose from his seat, and sprang with indescribable vim at an extraordinarily stout chappie who had suddenly appeared. There was the deuce of a rush for him, but Gussie had got away to a good start, and the rest of the singers, dancers, jugglers, acrobats, and refined sketch teams seemed to recognize that he had won the trick, for they ebbed back into their places again, and Gussie and I went into the inner room.

Mr Riesbitter lit a cigar, and looked at us solemnly over his zareba of chins.

'Now, let me tell ya something,' he said to Gussie. 'You lizzun t' me.'

Gussie registered respectful attention. Mr Riesbitter mused for a moment and shelled the cuspidor with indirect fire over the edge of the desk.

'Lizzun t' me,' he said again, 'I seen you rehearse, as I promised Miss Denison I would. You ain't bad for an amateur. You gotta lot to learn, but it's in you. What it comes to is that I can fix you up in the four-a-day, if you'll take thirty-five per. I can't do better than that, and I wouldn't have done that if the little lady hadn't of kep' after me. Take it or leave it. What do you say?'

'I'll take it,' said Gussie, huskily. 'Thank you.'

In the passage outside, Gussie gurgled with joy and slapped me on the back. 'Bertie, old man, it's all right. I'm the happiest man in New York.'

'Now what?'

'Well, you see, as I was telling you when Abe came in, Ray's father used to be in the profession. He was before our time, but I remember hearing about him – Joe Danby. He used to be well known in London before he came over to America. Well, he's a fine old boy, but as obstinate as a mule, and he didn't like the idea of Ray marrying me because I wasn't in the profession. Wouldn't hear of it. Well, you remember at Oxford I could always sing a song pretty well; so Ray got hold of old Riesbitter and made him promise to come and hear me rehearse and get me bookings if he liked my work. She stands high with him. She coached me for weeks, the darling. And now, as you heard him say, he's booked me in the small time at thirty-five dollars a week.'

I steadied myself against the wall. The effects of the restoratives supplied by my pal at the hotel bar were beginning to work off, and I felt a little weak. Through a sort of mist I seemed to have a vision of Aunt Agatha hearing that the head of the Mannering-Phippses was about to appear on the vaudeville stage. Aunt Agatha's worship of the family name amounts to an obsession. The Mannering-Phippses were an old-established clan when William the Conqueror was a small boy going round with bare legs and a catapult. For centuries they have called kings by their first names and helped dukes with their weekly rent; and there's practically nothing a Mannering-Phipps can do that doesn't blot his escutcheon. So what Aunt Agatha would say – beyond saying that it was all my fault – when she learned the horrid news, it was beyond me to imagine.

'Come back to the hotel, Gussie,' I said. 'There's a sportsman there who mixes things he calls "lightning whizzers". Something tells me I need one now. And excuse me for one minute, Gussie. I want to send a cable.'

It was clear to me by now that Aunt Agatha had picked the wrong man for this job of disentangling Gussie from the clutches of the American vaudeville profession. What I needed was reinforcements. For a moment I thought of cabling Aunt Agatha to come over, but reason told me that this would be overdoing it. I wanted assistance, but not so badly as that. I hit what seemed to me the happy mean. I cabled to Gussie's mother and made it urgent.

'What were you cabling about?' asked Gussie, later.

'Oh, just to say I had arrived safely, and all that sort of tosh,' I answered.

Gussie opened his vaudeville career on the following Monday at a rummy sort of place uptown where they had moving pictures some of the time and, in between, one or two vaudeville acts. It had taken a lot of careful handling to bring him up to scratch. He seemed to take my sympathy and assistance for granted, and I couldn't let him down. My only hope, which grew as I listened to him rehearsing, was that he would be such a frightful frost at his first appearance that he would never dare to perform again; and, as that would automatically squash the marriage, it seemed best to me to let the thing go on.

He wasn't taking any chances. On the Saturday and Sunday we practically lived in a beastly little music-room at the offices of the publishers whose songs he proposed to use. A little chappie with a hooked nose sucked a cigarette and played the piano all day. Nothing could tire that lad. He seemed to take a personal interest in the thing.

Gussie would clear his throat and begin:

'There's a great big choo-choo waiting at the deepo.'

THE CHAPPIE (playing chords): 'Is that so? What's it waiting for?'

GUSSIE (rather rattled at the interruption): 'Waiting for me.'

THE CHAPPIE (surprised): 'For you?'

GUSSIE (sticking to it): 'Waiting for me – e – ee!'

THE CHAPPIE (sceptically): 'You don't say!'

GUSSIE: 'For I'm off to Tennessee.'

THE CHAPPIE (*conceding a point*): 'Now, I live at Yonkers.'

He did this all through the song. At first poor old Gussie asked him to stop, but the chappie said, No, it was always done. It helped to get pep into the thing. He appealed to me whether the thing didn't want a bit of pep, and I said it wanted all the pep it could get. And the chappie said to Gussie, 'There you are!' So Gussie had to stand it.

The other song that he intended to sing was one of those moon songs. He told me in a hushed voice that he was using it because it was one of the songs that the girl Ray sang when lifting them out of their seats at Mosenstein's and elsewhere. The fact seemed to give it sacred associations for him.

You will scarcely believe me, but the management expected Gussie to show up and start performing at one o'clock in the afternoon. I told him they couldn't be serious, as they must know that he would be rolling out for a bit of lunch at that hour, but Gussie said this was the usual thing in the four-a-day, and he didn't suppose he would ever get any lunch again until he landed on the big time. I was just condoling with him, when I found that he was taking it for granted that I should be there at one o'clock, too. My idea had been that I should look in at night, when – if he survived – he would be coming up for the fourth time; but I've never deserted a pal in distress, so I said good-bye to the little lunch I'd been planning at a rather decent tavern I'd discovered on Fifth Avenue, and trailed along. They were showing pictures when I reached my seat. It was one of those Western films, where the cowboy jumps on his horse and rides across country at a hundred and fifty miles an hour to escape the sheriff, not knowing, poor chump!, that he might just as well stay where he is, the sheriff having a horse of his own which can do three hundred miles an hour without coughing. I was just going to close my eyes and try to forget till they put Gussie's name up when I discovered that I was sitting next to a deucedly pretty girl.

No, let me be honest. When I went in I had seen that there was a deucedly pretty girl sitting in that particular seat, so I had taken the next one. What happened now was that I began, as it were, to drink her in. I wished they would turn the lights up so that I could see her better. She was rather small, with great big eyes and a ripping smile. It was a shame to let all that run to seed, so to speak, in semi-darkness.

Suddenly the lights did go up, and the orchestra began to play a tune which, though I haven't much of an ear for music, seemed somehow familiar. The next instant out pranced old Gussie from the wings in a purple frock-coat and a brown top-hat, grinned feebly at the audience, tripped over his feet, blushed, and began to sing the Tennessee song.

It was rotten. The poor nut had got stage fright so badly that it practically eliminated his voice. He sounded like some far-off echo of the past 'yodelling' through a woollen blanket.

For the first time since I heard that he was about to go into vaudeville I felt a faint hope creeping over me. I was sorry for the wretched chap, of course, but there was no denying that the thing had its bright side. No management on earth would go on paying thirty-five dollars a week for this sort of performance. This was going to be Gussie's first and only. He would have to leave the profession. The old boy would say, 'Unhand my daughter.' And, with decent luck, I saw myself leading Gussie on to the next English-bound liner and handing him over intact to Aunt Agatha.

He got through the song somehow and limped off amidst roars of silence from the audience. There was a brief respite, then out he came again.

He sang this time as if nobody loved him. As a song, it was not a very pathetic song, being all about coons spooning in June under the moon, and so on and so forth, but Gussie handled it in such a sad, crushed way that there was genuine anguish in every line. By the time he reached the refrain I was nearly in tears. It seemed such a rotten sort of world with all that kind of thing going on in it.

He started the refrain, and then the most frightful thing happened. The girl next me got up in her seat, chucked her head back, and began to sing too. I say 'too', but it wasn't really too, because her first note stopped Gussie dead, as if he had been pole-axed.

I never felt so bally conspicuous in my life. I huddled down in my seat and wished I could turn my collar up. Everybody seemed to be looking at me.

In the midst of my agony I caught sight of Gussie. A complete change had taken place in the old lad. He was looking most frightfully bucked. I must say the girl was singing most awfully well, and it seemed to act on Gussie like a tonic. When she came to the end of the refrain, he took it up, and they sang together, and the end of it was that he went off the popular hero. The audience yelled for more, and were only quieted when they turned down the lights and put on a film.

When I recovered I tottered round to see Gussie. I found him sitting on a box behind the stage, looking like one who had seen visions.

'Isn't she a wonder, Bertie?' he said, devoutly. 'I hadn't a notion she was going to be there. She's playing at the Auditorium this week, and she can only just have had time to get back to her *matinée*. She risked being late, just to come and see me through. She's my good angel, Bertie. She saved me. If she hadn't helped me out I don't know what would have happened. I was so nervous I didn't know what I was doing. Now that I've got through the first show I shall be all right.'

I was glad I had sent that cable to his mother. I was going to need her. The thing had got beyond me.

During the next week I saw a lot of old Gussie, and was introduced to the girl. I also met her father, a formidable old boy with thick eyebrows and a sort of determined expression. On the following Wednesday Aunt Julia arrived. Mrs Mannering-Phipps, my Aunt Julia, is I think, the most dignified person I know. She lacks Aunt Agatha's punch, but in a quiet way she has always contrived to make me feel, from boyhood up, that I was a poor worm. Not that she harries me like Aunt Agatha. The difference between the two is that Aunt Agatha conveys the impression that she considers me personally responsible for all the sin and sorrow in the world, while Aunt Julia's manner seems to suggest that I am more to be pitied then censured.

If it wasn't that the thing was a matter of historical fact, I should be inclined to believe that Aunt Julia had never been on the vaudeville stage. She is like a stage duchess.

She always seems to me to be in a perpetual state of being about to desire the butler to instruct the head footman to serve lunch in the blue-room overlooking the west terrace. She exudes dignity. Yet, twenty-five years ago, so I've been told by old boys who were lads about town in those days, she was knocking them cold at the Tivoli in a double act called 'Fun in a Tea-Shop', in which she wore tights and sang a song with a chorus that began 'Rumpty-tiddley-umpty-ay'.

There are some things a chappie's mind absolutely refuses to picture, and Aunt Julia singing 'Rumpty-tiddley-umpty-ay' is one of them.

She got straight to the point within five minutes of our meeting.

'What is this about Gussie? Why did you cable for me, Bertie?'

'It's rather a long story,' I said, 'and complicated. If you don't mind, I'll let you have it in a series of motion pictures. Suppose we look in at the Auditorium for a few minutes.'

The girl, Ray, had been re-engaged for a second week at the Auditorium, owing to the big success of her first week. Her act consisted of three songs. She did herself well in the matter of costume and scenery. She had a ripping voice. She looked most awfully pretty; and altogether the act was, broadly speaking, a pippin.

Aunt Julia didn't speak till we were in our seats. Then she gave a sort of sigh.

'It's twenty-five years since I was in a music-hall!'

She didn't say any more, but sat there with her eyes glued on the stage.

After about half an hour the johnnies who work the card-index system at the side of the stage put up the name of Ray Denison, and there was a good deal of applause.

'Watch this act, Aunt Julia,' I said.

She didn't seem to hear me.

'Twenty-five years! What did you say, Bertie?'

'Watch this act and tell me what you think of it.'

'Who is it? Ray. Oh!'

'Exhibit A,' I said. 'The girl Gussie's engaged to.'

The girl did her act, and the house rose at her. They didn't want to let her go. She had to come back again and again. When she had finally disappeared I turned to Aunt Julia.

'Well?' I said.

'I like her work. She's an artist.'

'We will now, if you don't mind, step a goodish way uptown.'

And we took the subway to where Gussie, the human film, was earning his thirty-five per. As luck would have it, we hadn't been in the place ten minutes when out he came.

'Exhibit B,' I said. 'Gussie.'

I don't quite know what I had expected her to do, but I certainly didn't expect her to sit there without a word. She did not move a muscle, but just stared at Gussie as he drooled on about the moon. I was sorry for the woman, for it must have been a shock to her to see her only son in a mauve frock-coat and a brown top-hat, but I thought it best to let her get a strangle-hold on the intricacies of the situation as quickly as possible. If I had tried to explain the affair without the aid of illustrations I should have talked all day and left her muddled up as to who was going to marry whom, and why.

I was astonished at the improvement in dear old Gussie. He had got back his voice and was putting the stuff over well. It reminded me of the night at Oxford when, then but a lad of eighteen, he sang 'Let's All Go Down the Strand' after a bump supper, standing the while up to his knees in the college fountain. He was putting just the same zip into things now.

When he had gone off Aunt Julia sat perfectly still for a long time, and then she turned to me. Her eyes shone queerly.

'What does this mean, Bertie?'

She spoke quite quietly, but her voice shook a bit.

'Gussie went into the business,' I said, 'because the girl's father wouldn't let him marry her unless he did. If you feel up to it perhaps you wouldn't mind tottering round to One Hundred and Thirty-Third Street and having a chat with him. He's an old boy with eyebrows, and he's Exhibit C on my list. When I've put you in touch with him I rather fancy my share of the business is concluded, and it's up to you.'

The Danbys lived in one of those big apartments uptown which look as if they cost the earth and really cost about half as much as a hall-room down in the forties. We were shown into the sitting-room, and presently old Danby came in.

'Good afternoon, Mr Danby,' I began.

I had got as far as that when there was a kind of gasping cry at my elbow.

'Joe!' cried Aunt Julia, and staggered against the sofa.

For a moment old Danby stared at her, and then his mouth fell open and his eyebrows shot up like rockets.

'Julie!'

And then they had got hold of each other's hands and were shaking them till I wondered their arms didn't come unscrewed.

I'm not equal to this sort of thing at such short notice. The change in Aunt Julia made me feel quite dizzy. She had shed her *grande-dame* manner completely, and was blushing and smiling. I don't like to say such things of any aunt of mine, or I would go further and put it on record that she was giggling. And old Danby, who usually looked like a cross between a Roman emperor and Napoleon Bonaparte in a bad temper, was behaving like a small boy.

'Joe!'

'Julie!'

'Dear old Joe! Fancy meeting you again!'

'Wherever have you come from, Julie?'

Well, I didn't know what it was all about, but I felt a bit out of it. I butted in:

'Aunt Julia wants to have a talk with you, Mr Danby.'

'I knew you in a second, Joe!'

'It's twenty-five years since I saw you, kid, and you don't look a day older.'

'Oh, Joe! I'm an old woman!'

'What are you doing over here? I suppose' – old Danby's cheerfulness waned a trifle – 'I suppose your husband is with you?'

'My husband died a long, long while ago, Joe.'

Old Danby shook his head.

'You never ought to have married out of the profession, Julie. I'm not saying a word against the late – I can't remember his name; never could – but you shouldn't have done it, an artist like you. Shall

I ever forget the way you used to knock them with "Rumpty-tiddley-umpty-ay"?'

'Ah! how wonderful you were in that act, Joe.' Aunt Julia sighed. 'Do you remember the back-fall you used to do down the steps? I always have said that you did the best back-fall in the profession.'

'I couldn't do it now!'

'Do you remember how we put it across at the Canterbury, Joe? Think of it! The Canterbury's a moving-picture house now, and the old Mogul runs French revues.'

'I'm glad I'm not there to see them.'

'Joe, tell me, why did you leave England?'

'Well, I – I wanted a change. No, I'll tell you the truth, kid. I wanted you, Julie. You went off and married that – whatever that stage-door johnny's name was – and it broke me all up.'

Aunt Julia was staring at him. She is what they call a well-preserved woman. It's easy to see that, twenty-five years ago, she must have been something quite extraordinary to look at. Even now she's almost beautiful. She has very large brown eyes, a mass of soft grey hair, and the complexion of a girl of seventeen.

'Joe, you aren't going to tell me you were fond of me yourself!'

'Of course I was fond of you. Why did I let you have all the fat in "Fun in a Tea-Shop"? Why did I hang about up-stage while you sang "Rumpty-tiddley-umpty-ay"? Do you remember my giving you a bag of buns when we were on the road at Bristol?'

'Yes, but—'

'Do you remember my giving you the ham sandwiches at Portsmouth?'

'Joe!'

'Do you remember my giving you a seed-cake at Birmingham? What did you think all that meant, if not that I loved you? Why, I was working up by degrees to telling you straight out when you suddenly went off and married that cane-sucking dude. That's why I wouldn't let my daughter marry this young chap, Wilson, unless he went into the profession. She's an artist—'

'She certainly is, Joe.'

'You've seen her? Where?'

'At the Auditorium just now. But, Joe, you mustn't stand in the way of her marrying the man she's in love with. He's an artist, too.'

'In the small time.'

'You were in the small time once, Joe. You mustn't look down on him because he's a beginner. I know you feel that your daughter is marrying beneath her, but—'

'How on earth do you know anything about young Wilson?'

'He's my son.'

'Your son?'

'Yes, Joe. And I've just been watching him work. Oh, Joe, you can't think how proud I was of him! He's got it in him. It's fate. He's my son and he's in the profession! Joe, don't you know what I've been through for his sake. They made a lady of me. I never worked so hard in my life as I did to become a real lady. They kept telling me I had got to put it across, no matter what it cost, so that he wouldn't be ashamed of me. The study was something terrible. I had to watch myself every minute for years, and I never knew when I might fluff in my lines or fall down on some bit of business. But I did it, because I didn't want him to be ashamed of me, though all the time I was just aching to be back where I belonged.'

Old Danby made a jump at her, and took her by the shoulders.

'Come back where you belong, Julie!' he cried. 'Your husband's dead, your son's a pro. Come back! It's twenty-five years ago, but I haven't changed. I want you still. I've always wanted you. You've got to come back, kid, where you belong.'

Aunt Julia gave a sort of gulp and looked at him.

'Joe!' she said in a kind of whisper.

'You're here, kid,' said Old Danby huskily. 'You've come back . . . Twenty-five years! . . . You've come back and you're going to stay!'

She pitched forward into his arms, and he caught her.

'Oh, Joe! Joe! Joe!' she said. 'Hold me. Don't let me go. Take care of me.'

And I edged for the door and slipped from the room. I felt weak. The old bean will stand a certain amount, but this was too much. I groped my way out into the street and waited for a taxi.

Gussie called on me at the hotel that night. He curveted into the room as if he had bought it and the rest of the city.

'Bertie,' he said, 'I feel as if I were dreaming.'

'I wish I could feel like that, old top,' I said, and I took another glance at a cable that had arrived half an hour ago from Aunt Agatha. I had been looking at it at intervals ever since.

'Ray and I got back to her flat this evening. Who do you think was there? The mater! She was sitting hand in hand with old Danby.'

'Yes?'

'He was sitting hand in hand with her.'

'Really?'

'They are going to be married.'

'Exactly.'

'Ray and I are going to be married.'

'I suppose so.'

'Bertie, old man, I feel immense. I look round me, and everything seems to be absolutely corking. The change in the mater is marvellous. She is twenty-five years younger. She and old Danby are talking of reviving "Fun in a Tea-Shop", and going out on the road with it.'

I got up.

'Gussie, old top,' I said, 'leave me for awhile. I would be alone. I think I've got brain fever or something.'

'Sorry, old man; perhaps New York doesn't agree with you. When do you expect to go back to England?'

I looked again at Aunt Agatha's cable.

'With luck,' I said, 'in about ten years.'

When he was gone I took up the cable and read it again.

'What is happening?' it read. 'Shall I come over?'

I sucked a pencil for a while, and then I wrote the reply.

It was not an easy cable to word, but I managed it.

'No,' I wrote, 'stay where you are. Profession overcrowded.'

The Metropolitan Touch

NOBODY is more alive than I am to the fact that young Bingo Little is in many respects a sound old egg. In one way and another he has made life pretty interesting for me at intervals ever since we were at school. As a companion for a cheery hour I think I would choose him before anybody. On the other hand, I'm bound to say that there are things about him that could be improved. His habit of falling in love with every second girl he sees is one of them; and another is his way of letting the world in on the secrets of his heart. If you want shrinking reticence, don't go to Bingo, because he's got about as much of it as a soap advertisement.

I mean to say – well, here's the telegram I got from him one evening in November, about a month after I'd got back to town from my visit to Twing Hall:

I SAY BERTIE OLD MAN I AM IN LOVE AT LAST. SHE IS THE MOST WONDERFUL GIRL BERTIE OLD MAN. THIS IS THE REAL THING AT LAST BERTIE. COME HERE AT ONCE AND BRING JEEVES. OH I SAY YOU KNOW THAT TOBACCO SHOP IN BOND STREET ON THE LEFT SIDE AS YOU GO UP. WILL YOU GET ME A HUNDRED OF THEIR SPECIAL CIGARETTES AND SEND THEM TO ME HERE. I HAVE RUN OUT. I KNOW WHEN YOU SEE HER YOU WILL THINK SHE IS THE MOST WONDERFUL GIRL. MIND YOU BRING JEEVES. DON'T FORGET THE CIGARETTES – BINGO.

It had been handed in at Twing Post Office. In other words, he had submitted that frightful rot to the goggling eye of a village post-mistress who was probably the mainspring of local gossip and would have the place ringing with the news before nightfall. He couldn't have given himself away more completely if he had hired the town crier. When I was a kid, I used to read stories about knights and vikings and that species of chappie who would get up without a blush in the middle of a crowded banquet and loose off a song about how perfectly priceless they thought their best girl. I've often felt that those days would have suited young Bingo down to the ground.

Jeeves had brought the thing in with the evening drink, and I slung it over to him.

'It's about due, of course,' I said. 'Young Bingo hasn't been in love for at least a couple of months. I wonder who it is this time?'

'Miss Mary Burgess, sir,' said Jeeves, 'the niece of the Reverend Mr Heppenstall. She is staying at Twing Vicarage.'

'Great Scott!' I knew that Jeeves knew practically everything in the world, but this sounded like second-sight. 'How do you know that?'

'When we were visiting Twing Hall in the summer, sir, I formed a somewhat close friendship with Mr Heppenstall's butler. He is good enough to keep me abreast of the local news from time to time. From his account, sir, the young lady appears to be a very estimable young lady. Of a somewhat serious nature, I understand. Mr Little is very *épris*, sir. Brookfield, my correspondent, writes that last week he observed him in the moonlight at an advanced hour gazing up at his window.'

'Whose window? Brookfield's?'

'Yes, sir. Presumably under the impression that it was the young lady's.'

'But what the deuce is he doing at Twing at all?'

'Mr Little was compelled to resume his old position as tutor to Lord Wickhammersley's son at Twing Hall, sir. Owing to having been unsuccessful in some speculations at Hurst Park at the end of October.'

'Good Lord, Jeeves! Is there anything you don't know?'

'I couldn't say, sir.'

I picked up the telegram.

'I suppose he wants us to go down and help him out a bit?'

'That would appear to be his motive in dispatching the message, sir.'

'Well, what shall we do? Go?'

'I would advocate it, sir. If I may say so, I think that Mr Little should be encouraged in this particular matter.'

'You think he's picked a winner this time?'

'I hear nothing but excellent reports of the young lady, sir. I think it is beyond question that she would be an admirable influence for Mr Little, should the affair come to a happy conclusion. Such a union would also, I fancy, go far to restore Mr Little to the good graces of his uncle, the young lady being well connected and possessing private means. In short, sir, I think that if there is anything that we can do we should do it.'

'Well, with you behind him,' I said, 'I don't see how he can fail to click.'

'You are very good, sir,' said Jeeves. 'The tribute is much appreciated.'

Bingo met us at Twing station next day, and insisted on my sending

Jeeves on in the car with the bags while he and I walked. He started in about the female the moment we had begun to hoof it.

'She is very wonderful, Bertie. She is not one of these flippant, shallow-minded modern girls. She is sweetly grave and beautifully earnest. She reminds me of – what is the name I want?'

'Marie Lloyd?'

'Saint Cecilia,' said young Bingo, eyeing me with a good deal of loathing. 'She reminds me of Saint Cecilia. She makes me yearn to be a better, nobler, deeper, broader man.'

'What beats me,' I said, following up a train of thought, 'is what principle you pick them on. The girls you fall in love with, I mean. I mean to say, what's your system? As far as I can see, no two of them are alike. First it was Mabel the waitress, then Honoria Glossop, then that fearful blister Charlotte Corday Rowbotham—'

I own that Bingo had the decency to shudder. Thinking of Charlotte always made me shudder, too.

'You don't seriously mean, Bertie, that you are intending to compare the feeling I have for Mary Burgess, the holy devotion, the spiritual—'

'Oh, all right, let it go,' I said. 'I say, old lad, aren't we going rather a long way round?'

Considering that we were supposed to be heading for Twing Hall, it seemed to me that we were making a longish job of it. The Hall is about two miles from the station by the main road, and we had cut off down a lane, gone across country for a bit, climbed a stile or two, and were now working our way across a field that ended in another lane.

'She sometimes takes her little brother for a walk round this way,' explained Bingo. 'I thought we would meet her and bow, and you could see her, you know, and then we would walk on.'

'Of course,' I said, 'that's enough excitement for anyone, and undoubtedly a corking reward for tramping three miles out of one's way over ploughed fields with tight boots, but don't we do anything else? Don't we tack on to the girl and buzz along with her?'

'Good Lord!' said Bingo, honestly amazed. 'You don't suppose I've got nerve enough for that, do you? I just look at her from afar off and all that sort of thing. Quick! Here she comes! No, I'm wrong!'

It was like that song of Harry Lauder's where he's waiting for the girl and says 'This is her-r-r. No, it's a rabbut.' Young Bingo made me stand there in the teeth of a nor'-east half-gale for ten minutes, keeping me on my toes with a series of false alarms, and I was just thinking of suggesting that we should lay off and give the rest of the proceedings a miss, when round the corner there came a fox-terrier, and Bingo quivered like an aspen. Then there hove in sight a small boy, and he shook like a jelly. Finally, like a star whose entrance has been worked up by the *personnel* of the *ensemble*, a girl appeared, and his emotion was painful to witness. His face got so red that, what with his white collar and the fact that the wind had turned his nose blue, he looked more like a French flag than anything else. He sagged from the waist upwards, as if he had been filleted.

He was just raising his fingers limply to his cap when he suddenly saw that the girl wasn't alone. A chappie in clerical costume was also among those present, and the sight of him didn't seem to do Bingo a bit of good. His face got redder and his nose bluer, and it wasn't till they had nearly passed that he managed to get hold of his cap.

The girl bowed, the curate said, 'Ah, Little. Rough weather,' the dog barked, and they toddled on and the entertainment was over.

The curate was a new factor in the situation to me. I reported his movements to Jeeves when I got to the Hall. Of course, Jeeves knew all about it already.

'That is the Reverend Mr Wingham, Mr Heppenstall's new curate, sir. I gathered from Brookfield that he is Mr Little's rival, and at the moment the young lady appears to favour him. Mr Wingham has the advantage of being on the premises. He and the young lady play duets after dinner, which acts as a bond. Mr Little on these occasions, I understand, prowls about in the road, chafing visibly.'

'That seems to be all the poor fish is able to do, dash it. He can chafe all right, but there he stops. He's lost his pep. He's got no dash. Why, when we met her just now, he hadn't even the common manly courage to say "Good evening"!'

'I gather that Mr Little's affection is not unmingled with awe, sir.'

'Well, how are we to help a man when he's such a rabbit as that? Have you anything to suggest? I shall be seeing him after dinner and he's sure to ask first thing what you advise.'

'In my opinion, sir, the most judicious course for Mr Little to pursue would be to concentrate on the young gentleman.'

'The small brother? How do you mean?'

'Make a friend of him, sir – take him for walks and so forth.'

'It doesn't sound one of your red-hottest ideas. I must say I expected something fruitier than that.'

'It would be a beginning, sir, and might lead to better things.'

'Well, I'll tell him. I liked the look of her, Jeeves.'

'A thoroughly estimable young lady, sir.'

I slipped Bingo the tip from the stable that night, and was glad to observe that it seemed to cheer him up.

'Jeeves is always right,' he said. 'I ought to have thought of it myself. I'll start it tomorrow.'

It was amazing how the chappie bucked up. Long before I left for town it had become a mere commonplace for him to speak to the girl.

I mean he didn't simply look stuffed when they met. The brother was forming a bond that was a dashed sight stronger than the curate's duets. She and Bingo used to take him for walks together. I asked Bingo what they talked about on these occasions, and he said Wilfred's future. The girl hoped that Wilfred would one day become a curate, but Bingo said no, there was something about curates he didn't quite like.

The day we left, Bingo came to see us off with Wilfred frisking about him like an old college chum. The last I saw of them, Bingo was standing him chocolates out of the slot-machine. A scene of peace and cheery good-will. Dashed promising, I thought.

Which made it all the more of a jar, about a fortnight later, when his telegram arrived. As follows:

BERTIE OLD MAN I SAY BERTIE COULD YOU POSSIBLY COME DOWN HERE AT ONCE. EVERYTHING GONE WRONG HANG IT ALL. DASH IT BERTIE YOU SIMPLY MUST COME. I AM IN A STATE OF ABSOLUTE DESPAIR AND HEART-BROKEN. WOULD YOU MIND SENDING ANOTHER HUNDRED OF THOSE CIGARETTES. BRING JEEVES WHEN YOU COME BERTIE. YOU SIMPLY MUST COME BERTIE. I RELY ON YOU. DON'T FORGET TO BRING JEEVES. BINGO.

For a chap who's perpetually hard-up, I must say that young Bingo is the most wasteful telegraphist I ever struck. He's got no notion of condensing. The silly ass simply pours out his wounded soul at twopence a word, or whatever it is, without a thought.

'How about it, Jeeves?' I said. 'I'm getting a bit fed. I can't go chucking all my engagements every second week in order to biff down to Twing and rally round young Bingo. Send him a wire telling him to end it all in the village pond.'

'If you could spare me for the night, sir, I should be glad to run down and investigate.'

'Oh, dash it! Well, I suppose there's nothing else to be done. After all, you're the fellow he wants. All right, carry on.'

Jeeves got back late the next day.

'Well?' I said.

Jeeves appeared perturbed. He allowed his left eyebrow to flicker upwards in a concerned sort of manner.

'I have done what I could, sir,' he said, 'but I fear Mr Little's chances do not appear bright. Since our last visit, sir, there has been a decidedly sinister and disquieting development.'

'Oh, what's that?'

'You may remember Mr Steggles, sir – the young gentleman who was studying for an examination with Mr Heppenstall at the Vicarage?'

'What's Steggles got to do with it?' I asked.

'I gather from Brookfield, sir, who chanced to overhear a conversation, that Mr Steggles is interesting himself in the affair.'

'Good Lord! What, making a book on it?'

'I understand that he is accepting wagers from those in his immediate circle, sir. Against Mr Little, whose chances he does not seem to fancy.'

'I don't like that, Jeeves.'

'No, sir. It is sinister.'

'From what I know of Steggles there will be dirty work.'

'It has already occurred, sir.'

'Already?'

'Yes, sir. It seems that, in pursuance of the policy which he had been good enough to allow me to suggest to him, Mr Little escorted Master Burgess to the church bazaar, and there met Mr Steggles, who was in the company of young Master Heppenstall, the Reverend Mr Heppenstall's second son, who is home from Rugby just now, having recently recovered from an attack of mumps. The encounter took place in the refreshment-room, where Mr Steggles was at that moment entertaining Master Heppenstall. To cut a long story short, sir, the two gentlemen became extremely interested in the hearty manner in which the lads were fortifying themselves; and Mr Steggles offered to back his nominee in a weight-for-age eating contest against Master Burgess for a pound a side. Mr Little admitted to me that he was conscious of a certain hesitation as to what the upshot might be, should Miss Burgess get to hear of the matter, but his sporting blood was too much for him and he agreed to the contest. This was duly carried out, both lads exhibiting the utmost willingness and enthusiasm, and eventually Master Burgess justified Mr Little's confidence by winning, but only after a bitter struggle. Next day both contestants were in considerable pain; inquiries were made and confessions extorted, and Mr Little – I learn from Brookfield, who happened to be near the door of the drawing-room at the moment – had an extremely unpleasant interview with the young lady, which ended in her desiring him never to speak to her again.'

There's no getting away from the fact that, if ever a man required watching, it's Steggles. Machiavelli could have taken his correspondence course.

'It was a put-up job, Jeeves!' I said. 'I mean, Steggles worked the whole thing on purpose. It's his old nobbling game.'

'There would seem to be no doubt about that, sir.'

'Well, he seems to have dished poor old Bingo all right.'

'That is the prevalent opinion, sir. Brookfield tells me that down in the village at the Cow and Horses seven to one is being freely offered on Mr Wingham and finding no takers.'

'Good Lord! Are they betting about it down in the village, too?'

'Yes, sir. And in adjoining hamlets also. The affair has caused widespread interest. I am told that there is a certain sporting reaction in even so distant a spot as Lower Bingley.'

'Well, I don't see what there is to do. If Bingo is such a chump—'

'One is fighting a losing battle, I fear, sir, but I did venture to indicate to Mr Little a course of action which might prove of advantage. I recommended him to busy himself with good works.'

'Good works?'

'About the village, sir. Reading to the bedridden – chatting with the sick – that sort of thing, sir. We can but trust that good results will ensue.'

'Yes, I suppose so,' I said doubtfully. 'But, by gosh, if I was a sick man I'd hate to have a looney like young Bingo coming and gibbering at my bedside.'

'There *is* that aspect of the matter, sir,' said Jeeves.

I didn't hear a word from Bingo for a couple of weeks, and I took it after a while that he had found the going too hard and had chucked in the towel. And then, one night not long before Christmas, I came back to the flat pretty lateish, having been out dancing at the Embassy. I was fairly tired, having swung a practically non-stop shoe from shortly after dinner till two a.m., and bed seemed to be indicated. Judge of my chagrin and all that sort of thing, therefore, when, tottering to my room and switching on the light, I observed the foul features of young Bingo all over the pillow. The blighter had appeared from nowhere and was in my bed, sleeping like an infant with a sort of happy, dreamy smile on his map.

A bit thick I mean to say! We Woosters are all for the good old medieval hosp. and all that, but when it comes to finding chappies collaring your bed, the thing becomes a trifle too mouldy. I hove a shoe, and Bingo sat up, gurgling.

' 's matter? 's matter?' said young Bingo.

'What the deuce are you doing in my bed?' I said.

'Oh, hallo, Bertie! So there you are!'

'Yes, here I am. What are you doing in my bed?'

'I came up to town for the night on business.'

'Yes, but what are you doing in my bed?'

'Dash it all, Bertie,' said young Bingo querulously, 'don't keep harping on your beastly bed. There's another made up in the spare room. I saw Jeeves make it with my own eyes. I believe he meant it for me, but I knew what a perfect host you were, so I just turned in here. I say, Bertie, old man,' said Bingo, apparently fed up with the discussion about sleeping-quarters, 'I see daylight.'

'Well, it's getting on for three in the morning.'

'I was speaking figuratively, you ass. I meant that hope has begun to dawn. About Mary Burgess, you know. Sit down and I'll tell you all about it.'

'I won't. I'm going to sleep.'

'To begin with,' said young Bingo, settling himself comfortably against the pillows and helping himself to a cigarette from my private box, 'I must once again pay a marked tribute to good old Jeeves. A modern Solomon. I was badly up against it when I came to him for advice, but he rolled up with a tip which has put me – I use the term advisedly and in a conservative spirit – on velvet. He may have told you that he recommended me to win back the lost ground by busying myself with good works? Bertie, old man,' said young Bingo earnestly, 'for the last two weeks I've been comforting the sick to such an extent that, if I had a brother and you brought him to me on a sick-bed at this moment, by Jove, old man, I'd heave a brick at him. However, though it took it out of me like the deuce, the scheme worked splendidly. She softened visibly before I'd been at it a week. Started to bow again when we met in the street, and so forth. About a couple of days ago she distinctly smiled – in a sort of faint, saint-like kind of way, you know – when I ran into her outside the Vicarage. And yesterday – I say, you remember that curate chap Wingham? Fellow with a long nose.'

'Of course I remember him. Your rival.'

'Rival?' Bingo raised his eyebrows. 'Oh, well, I suppose you could have called him that at one time. Though it sounds a little far-fetched.'

'Does it?' I said, stung by the sickening complacency of the chump's manner. 'Well, let me tell you that the last I heard was that at the Cow and Horses in Twing village and all over the place as far as Lower Bingley they were offering seven to one on the curate and finding no takers.'

Bingo started violently and sprayed cigarette-ash all over my bed.

'Betting!' he gargled. 'Betting! You don't mean that they're betting on this holy, sacred – Oh, I say, dash it all! Haven't people any sense of decency and reverence? Is nothing safe from their beastly, sordid graspingness? I wonder,' said young Bingo thoughtfully, 'if there's a chance of my getting any of that seven-to-one money? Seven to one! What a price! Who's offering it, do you know? Oh, well, I suppose it wouldn't do. No, I suppose it wouldn't be quite the thing.'

'You seem dashed confident,' I said. 'I'd always thought that Wingham—'

'Oh, I'm not worried about him,' said Bingo. 'I was just going to tell you. Wingham's got the mumps, and won't be out and about for weeks. And, jolly as that is in itself, it's not all. You see, he was producing the Village School Christmas Entertainment, and now I've taken over the job. I went to old Heppenstall last night and clinched the contract. Well, you see what that means. It means that I shall be absolutely the centre of the village life and thought for three solid weeks, with a terrific triumph to wind up with. Everybody looking up to me and fawning on me, don't you see, and all that. It's bound to have a powerful effect on Mary's mind. It will show her that I am capable of serious effort; that there is a solid foundation of worth in me; that, mere butterfly as she may once have thought me, I am in reality—'

'Oh, all right, let it go!'

'It's a big thing, you know, this Christmas Entertainment. Old Heppenstall is very much wrapped up in it. Nibs from all over the countryside rolling up. The Squire present, with family. A big chance for me, Bertie, my boy, and I mean to make the most of it. Of course, I'm handicapped a bit by not having been in on the thing from the start. Will you credit it that that uninspired doughnut of a curate wanted to give the public some rotten little fairy play out of a book for children published about fifty years ago without one good laugh or the semblance of a gag in it? It's too late to alter the thing entirely, but at least I can jazz it up. I'm going to write them in something zippy to brighten the thing up a bit.'

'You can't write.'

'Well, when I say write, I mean pinch. That's why I've popped up to town. I've been to see that revue, *Cuddle Up!* at the Palladium, tonight. Full of good stuff. Of course, it's rather hard to get anything in the nature of a big spectacular effect in the Twing Village Hall, with no scenery to speak of and a chorus of practically imbecile kids of ages ranging from nine to fourteen, but I think I see my way. Have you seen *Cuddle Up!*'

'Yes. Twice.'

'Well, there's some good stuff in the first act, and I can lift practically all the numbers. Then there's that show at the Palace. I can see the *matinée* of that tomorrow before I leave. There's sure to be some decent bits in that. Don't you worry about my not being able to write a hit. Leave it to me, laddie, leave it to me. And now, my dear old chap,' said young Bingo, snuggling down cosily, 'you mustn't keep me up talking all night. It's all right for you fellows who have nothing to do, but I'm a busy man. Good night, old thing. Close the door quietly after you and switch out the light. Breakfast about ten tomorrow, I suppose, what? Right-o. Good night.'

For the next three weeks I didn't see Bingo. He became a sort of Voice Heard Off, developing a habit of ringing me up on long-distance and consulting me on various points arising at rehearsal, until the day when he got me out of bed at eight in the morning to ask whether I thought 'Merry Christmas!' was a good title. I told him then that this nuisance must now cease, and after that he cheesed it, and practically passed out of my life, till one afternoon when I got back to the flat to dress for dinner and found Jeeves inspecting a whacking big poster sort of thing which he had draped over the back of an armchair.

'Good Lord, Jeeves!' I said. I was feeling rather weak that day, and the thing shook me. 'What on earth's that?'

'Mr Little sent it to me, sir, and desired me to bring it to your notice.'

'Well, you've certainly done it!'

I took another look at the object. There was no doubt about it, he caught the eye. It was about seven feet long, and most of the lettering in about as bright red ink as I ever struck.

This was how it ran:

TWING VILLAGE HALL,
Friday, December 23rd,
RICHARD LITTLE
presents
A New and Original Revue
Entitled
WHAT HO, TWING!!
Book by
RICHARD LITTLE
Lyrics by
RICHARD LITTLE
Music by
RICHARD LITTLE
With the Full Twing Juvenile
Company and Chorus
Scenic Effects by
RICHARD LITTLE
Produced by
RICHARD LITTLE

'What do you make of it, Jeeves?' I said.

'I confess I am a little doubtful, sir. I think Mr Little would have done better to follow my advice and confine himself to good works about the village.'

'You think the thing will be a frost?'

'I could not hazard a conjecture, sir. But my experience has been that what pleases the London public is not always so acceptable to the rural mind. The metropolitan touch sometimes proves a trifle too exotic for the provinces.'

'I suppose I ought to go down and see the dashed thing?'

'I think Mr Little would be wounded were you not present, sir.'

The Village Hall at Twing is a smallish building, smelling of apples. It was full when I turned up on the evening of the twenty-third, for I had purposely timed myself to arrive not long before the kick-off. I had had experience of one or two of these binges, and didn't want to run any risk of coming early and finding myself shoved into a seat in one of the front rows where I wouldn't be able to excute a quiet sneak into the open air half-way through the proceedings, if the occasion seemed to demand it. I secured a nice strategic position near the door at the back of the hall.

From where I stood I had a good view of the audience. As always on these occasions, the first few rows were occupied by the Nibs – consisting of the Squire, a fairly mauve old sportsman with white whiskers, his family, a platoon of local parsons and perhaps a couple of dozen of prominent pew-holders. Then came a dense squash of what you might call the lower middle classes. And at the back, where I was, we came down with a jerk in the social scale, this end of the hall being given up almost entirely to a collection of frankly Tough Eggs, who had rolled up not so much for any love of the drama as because there was a free tea after the show. Take it for all in all, a representative gathering of Twing life and thought. The Nibs were whispering in a pleased manner to each other, the Lower Middles were sitting up very straight, as if they'd been bleached, and the Tough Eggs whiled away the time by cracking nuts and exchanging low rustic wheezes. The girl, Mary Burgess, was at the piano playing a waltz. Beside her stood the curate, Wingham, apparently recovered. The temperature, I should think, was about a hundred and twenty-seven.

Somebody jabbed me heartily in the lower ribs, and I perceived the man Steggles.

'Hallo!' he said. 'I didn't know you were coming down.'

I didn't like the chap, but we Woosters can wear the mask. I beamed a bit.

'Oh, yes,' I said. 'Bingo wanted me to roll up and see his show.'

'I hear he's giving us something pretty ambitious,' said the man Steggles. 'Big effects and all that sort of thing.'

'I believe so.'

'Of course, it means a lot to him, doesn't it? He's told you about the girl, of course?'

'Yes. And I hear you're laying seven to one against him,' I said, eyeing the blighter a trifle austerely.

He didn't even quiver.

'Just a little flutter to relieve the monotony of country life,' he said. 'But you've got the facts a bit wrong. It's down in the village that they're laying seven to one. I can do you better than that, if you feel in a speculative mood. How about a tenner at a hundred to eight?'

'Good Lord! Are you giving that?'

'Yes. Somehow,' said Steggles meditatively, 'I have a sort of feeling, a kind of premonition that something's going to go wrong tonight. You know what Little is. A bungler, if ever there was one. Something tells me that this show of his is going to be a frost. And if it is, of course, I should think it would prejudice the girl against him pretty badly. His standing always was rather shaky.'

'Are you going to try and smash up the show?' I said sternly.

'Me!' said Steggles. 'Why, what could I do? Half a minute, I want to go and speak to a man.'

He buzzed off, leaving me distinctly disturbed. I could see from the fellow's eye that he was meditating some of his customary rough stuff, and I thought Bingo ought to be warned. But there wasn't time and I couldn't get at him. Almost immediately after Steggles had left me the curtain went up.

Except as a prompter, Bingo wasn't much in evidence in the early part of the performance. The thing at the outset was merely one of those weird dramas which you dig out of books published around Christmas time and entitled *Twelve Little Plays for the Tots*, or something like that. The kids drooled on in the usual manner, the booming voice of Bingo ringing out from time to time behind the scenes when the fatheads forgot their lines; and the audience was settling down into the sort of torpor usual on these occasions, when the first of Bingo's interpolated bits occurred. It was that number which What's-her-name sings in that revue at the Palace – you would recognize the tune if I hummed it, but I can never get hold of the dashed thing. It always got three encores at the Palace, and it went well now, even with a squeaky-voiced child jumping on and off the key like a chamois of the Alps leaping from crag to crag. Even the Tough Eggs liked it. At the end of the second refrain the entire house was shouting for an encore, and the kid with the voice like a slate-pencil took a deep breath and started to let it go once more.

At this point all the lights went out.

I don't know when I've had anything so sudden and devastating happen to me before. They didn't flicker. They just went out. The hall was in complete darkness.

Well, of course, that sort of broke the spell, as you might put it. People started to shout directions, and the Tough Eggs stamped their feet and settled down for a pleasant time. And, of course, young Bingo had to make an ass of himself. His voice suddenly shot at us out of the darkness.

'Ladies and gentlemen, something has gone wrong with the lights—'

The Tough Eggs were tickled by this bit of information straight from the stable. They took it up as a sort of battle-cry. Then, after about five minutes, the lights went up again, and the show was resumed.

It took ten minutes after that to get the audience back into its state of coma, but eventually they began to settle down, and everything was going nicely when a small boy with a face like a turbot edged out in front of the curtain, which had been lowered after a pretty painful scene about a wishing-ring or a fairy's curse or something of that sort, and started to sing that song of George Thingummy's out of *Cuddle Up!* You know the one I mean. 'Always Listen to Mother, Girls!' it's called, and he gets the audience to join in and sing the refrain. Quite a ripeish ballad, and one which I myself have frequently sung in my bath with not a little vim; but by no means – as anyone but a perfect sapheaded prune like young Bingo would have known – by no means the sort of thing for a children's Christmas entertainment in the old village hall. Right from the start of the first refrain the bulk of the audience had begun to stiffen in their seats and fan themselves, and the Burgess girl at the piano was accompanying in a stunned, mechanical sort of way, while the curate at her side averted his gaze in a pained manner. The Tough Eggs, however, were all for it.

At the end of the second refrain the kid stopped and began to sidle towards the wings. Upon which the following brief duologue took place:

YOUNG BINGO (*Voice heard off, ringing against the rafters*): 'Go on!'

THE KID (*coyly*): 'I don't like to.'

YOUNG BINGO (*Still louder*): 'Go on, you little blighter, or I'll slay you!'

I suppose the kid thought it over swiftly and realized that Bingo, being in a position to get at him, had better be conciliated, whatever the harvest might be; for he shuffled down to the front and, having shut his eyes and giggled hysterically, said: 'Ladies and gentlemen, I will now call upon Squire Tressidder to oblige by singing the refrain!'

You know, with the most charitable feelings towards him, there are moments when you can't help thinking that young Bingo ought to be in some sort of a home. I suppose, poor fish, he had pictured this as the big punch of the evening. He had imagined, I take it, that the Squire would spring jovially to his feet, rip the song off his chest, and all would be gaiety and mirth. Well, what happened was simply that old Tressidder – and, mark you, I'm not blaming him – just sat where he was, swelling and turning a brighter purple every second. The lower middle classes remained in frozen silence, waiting for the roof to fall. The only section of the audience that really seemed to enjoy the idea was the Tough Eggs, who yelled with enthusiasm. It was jam for the Tough Eggs.

And then the lights went out again.

When they went up, some minutes later, they disclosed the Squire marching stiffly out at the head of his family, fed up to the eyebrows; the Burgess girl at the piano with a pale, set look; and the curate gazing at her with something in his expression that seemed to suggest that, although all this was no doubt deplorable, he had spotted the silver lining.

The show went on once more. There were great chunks of Plays-for-the-Tots dialogue, and then the girl at the piano struck up the prelude to that Orange-Girl number that's the big hit of the Palace revue. I took it that this was to be Bingo's smashing act one finale. The entire company was on the stage, and a clutching hand had appeared round the edge of the curtain, ready to pull at the right moment. It looked like the finale all right. It wasn't long before I realized that it was something more. It was the finish.

I take it you know that Orange number at the Palace? It goes:

> Oh, won't you something something oranges,
>   My something oranges,
>   My something oranges;
> Oh, won't you something something something I forget,
> Something something something tumty tumty yet:
> Oh –

or words to that effect. It's a dashed clever lyric, and the tune's good, too; but the thing that made the number was the business where the girls take oranges out of their baskets, you know, and toss them lightly to the audience. I don't know if you've ever noticed it, but it always seems to tickle an audience to bits when they get things thrown at them from the stage. Every time I've been to the Palace the customers have simply gone wild over this number.

But at the Palace, of course, the oranges are made of yellow wool, and the girls don't so much chuck them as drop them limply into the first and second rows. I began to gather that the business was going to be treated rather differently tonight when a dashed great chunk of pips and mildew sailed past my ear and burst on the wall behind me. Another landed with a squelch on the neck of one of the Nibs in the third row. And then a third took me right on the tip of the nose, and I kind of lost interest in the proceedings for a while.

When I had scrubbed my face and got my eye to stop watering for a moment, I saw that the evening's entertainment had begun to resemble one of Belfast's livelier nights. The air was thick with shrieks and fruit. The kids on the stage, with Bingo buzzing distractedly to and fro in their midst, were having the time of their lives. I suppose they realized that this couldn't go on for ever, and were making the most of their chances. The Tough Eggs had begun to pick up all the oranges that hadn't burst and were shooting them back, so that the audience got it both coming and going. In fact, take it all round, there was a certain amount of confusion; and, just as things had begun really to hot up, out went the lights again.

It seemed to me about my time for leaving, so I slid for the door. I was hardly outside when the audience began to stream out. They surged about me in twos and threes, and I've never seen a public body so dashed unanimous on any point. To a man – and to a woman – they were cursing poor old Bingo; and there was a large and rapidly growing school of thought which held that the best thing to do would be to waylay him as he emerged and splash him about in the village pond a bit.

There were such a dickens of a lot of these enthusiasts and they looked so jolly determined that it seemed to me that the only matey thing to do was to go behind and warn young Bingo to turn his coat-collar up and breeze off snakily by some side exit. I went behind, and found him sitting on a box in the wings, perspiring pretty freely and looking more or less like the spot marked with a cross where the accident happened. His hair was standing up and his ears were hanging down, and one harsh word would undoubtedly have made him burst into tears.

'Bertie,' he said hollowly, as he saw me, 'it was that blighter Steggles! I caught one of the kids before he could get away and got it all out of him. Steggles substituted real oranges for the balls of wool which with infinite sweat and at a cost of nearly a quid I had specially prepared. Well, I will now proceed to tear him limb from limb. It'll be something to do.'

I hated to spoil his day-dreams, but it had to be.

'Good heavens, man,' I said, 'you haven't time for frivolous amusements now. You've got to get out. And quick!'

'Bertie,' said Bingo in a dull voice, 'she was here just now. She said it was all my fault and that she would never speak to me again. She said she had always suspected me of being a heartless practical joker, and now she knew. She said – Oh, well, she ticked me off properly.'

'That's the least of your troubles,' I said. It seemed impossible to rouse the poor zib to a sense of his position. 'Do you realize that about two hundred of Twing's heftiest are waiting for you outside to chuck you into the pond?'

'No!'

'Absolutely!'

For a moment the poor chap seemed crushed. But only for a moment. There has always been something of the good old English bulldog breed about Bingo. A strange, sweet smile flickered for an instant over his face.

'It's all right,' he said. 'I can sneak out through the cellar and climb over the wall at the back. They can't intimidate *me*!'

It couldn't have been more than a week later when Jeeves, after he had brought me my tea, gently steered me away from the sporting page of the *Morning Post* and directed my attention to an announcement in the engagements and marriages column.

It was a brief statement that a marriage had been arranged and would shortly take place between the Hon. and Rev. Hubert Wingham, third son of the Right Hon. the Earl of Sturridge, and Mary, only daughter of the late Matthew Burgess, of Weatherly Court, Hants.

'Of course,' I said, after I had given it the east-to-west, 'I expected this, Jeeves.'

'Yes, sir.'

'She would never forgive him what happened that night.'

'No, sir.'

'Well,' I said, as I took a sip of the fragrant and steaming, 'I don't suppose it will take old Bingo long to get over it. It's about the hundred and eleventh time this sort of thing has happened to him. You're the man I'm sorry for.'

'Me, sir?'

'Well, dash it all, you can't have forgotten what a deuce of a lot of trouble you took to bring the thing off for Bingo. It's too bad that all your work should have been wasted.'

'Not entirely wasted, sir.'

'Eh?'

'It is true that my efforts to bring about the match between Mr Little and the young lady were not successful, but I still look back upon the matter with a certain satisfaction.'

'Because you did your best, you mean?'

'Not entirely, sir, though of course that thought also gives me pleasure. I was alluding more particularly to the fact that I found the affair financially remunerative.'

'Financially remunerative? What do you mean?'

'When I learned that Mr Steggles had interested himself in the contest, sir, I went shares with my friend Brookfield and bought the book which had been made on the issue by the landlord of the Cow and Horses. It had proved a highly profitable investment. Your breakfast will be ready almost immediately, sir. Kidneys on toast and mushrooms. I will bring it when you ring.'

Jeeves and the Greasy Bird

THE shades of night were falling fairly fast as I latch-keyed self and suitcase into the Wooster G.H.Q. Jeeves was in the sitting room messing about with holly, for we would soon be having Christmas at our throats and he is always a stickler for doing the right thing. I gave him a cheery greeting.

'Well, Jeeves, here I am, back again.'

'Good evening, sir. Did you have a pleasant visit?'

'Not too bad. But I'm glad to be home. What was it the fellow said about home?'

'If your allusion is to the American poet John Howard Payne, sir, he compared it to its advantage with pleasures and palaces. He called it sweet and said there was no place like it.'

'And he wasn't so far out. Shrewd chap, John Howard Payne.'

'I believe he gave uniform satisfaction, sir.'

I had just returned from a week end at the Chuffnell Regis clinic of Sir Roderick Glossop, the eminent loony doctor, or nerve specialist as he prefers to call himself – not, I may add, as a patient but as a guest. My Aunt Dahlia's cousin Percy had recently put in there for repairs, and she had asked me to pop down and see how he was making out. He had got the idea, I don't know why, that he was being followed about by little men with black beards, a state of affairs which he naturally wished to have adjusted with all possible speed.

'You know, Jeeves,' I said some moments later, as I sat quaffing the whisky-and-s with which he had supplied me, 'life's odd, you can't say it isn't. You never know where you are with it.'

'There was some particular aspect of it that you had in mind, sir?'

'I was thinking of me and Sir R. Glossop. Who would ever have thought the day would come when he and I would be hobnobbing like a couple of sailors on shore leave? There was a time, you probably remember, when he filled me with a nameless fear and I leaped like a startled grasshopper at the sound of his name. You have not forgotten?'

'No, sir, I recall that you viewed Sir Roderick with concern.'

'And he me with ditto.'

'Yes, sir, a stiffness certainly existed. There was no fusion between your souls.'

'Yet now our relations are as cordial as they can stick. The barriers that separated us have come down with a bump. I beam at him. He beams at me. He calls me Bertie. I call him Roddy. To put the thing in a nutshell, the dove of peace is in a rising market and may quite possibly go to par. Of course, like Shadrach, Meshach and Abednego, if I've got the names right, we passed through the furnace together, and that always forms a bond.'

I was alluding to the time when – from motives I need not go into beyond saying that they were fundamentally sound – we had both blacked our faces, he with burned cork, I with boot polish, and had spent a night of terror wandering through Chuffnell Regis with no place to lay our heads, as the expression is. You don't remain on distant terms with somebody you've shared an experience like that with.

'But I'll tell you something about Roddy Glossop, Jeeves,' I said, having swallowed a rather grave swallow of the strengthening fluid. 'He has something on his mind. Physically I found him in excellent shape – few fiddles could have been fitter – but he was gloomy . . . distrait . . . brooding. Conversing with him, one felt that his thoughts were far away and that those thoughts were stinkers. I could hardly get a word out of him. It made me feel like that fellow in the Bible who tried to charm the deaf adder and didn't get to first base. There was a blighter named Blair Eggleston there, and it may have been this that depressed him, for this Eggleston . . . Ever hear of him? He writes books.'

'Yes, sir. Mr Eggleston is one of our angry young novelists. The critics describe his work as frank, forthright and fearless.'

'Oh, do they? Well, whatever his literary merits he struck me as a fairly noxious specimen. What's he angry about?'

'Life, sir.'

'He disapproves of it?'

'So one would gather from his output, sir.'

'Well, I disapproved of him, which makes us all square. But I don't think it was having him around that caused the Glossop gloom. I am convinced that the thing goes deeper than that. I believe it's something to do with his love life.'

I must mention that while at Chuffnell Regis Pop Glossop, who was a widower with one daughter, had become betrothed to Myrtle, Lady Chuffnell, the aunt of my old crony Marmaduke ('Chuffy') Chuffnell, and that I should have found him still single more than a year later seemed strange to me. One would certainly have expected him by this time to have raised the price of a marriage licence and had the Bishop and assistant clergy getting their noses down to it. A red-blooded loony doctor under the influence of the divine passion ought surely to have put the thing through months ago.

'Do you think they've had a row, Jeeves?'

'Sir?'

'Sir Roderick and Lady Chuffnell.'

'Oh no, sir. I am sure there is no diminution of affection on either side.'

'Then why the snag?'

'Her ladyship refuses to take part in the wedding ceremony while Sir Roderick's daughter remains unmarried, sir. She has stated in set terms that nothing will induce her to share a home with Miss Glossop. This would naturally render Sir Roderick moody and despondent.'

A bright light flashed upon me. I saw all. As usual, Jeeves had got to the very heart of the matter.

A thing that always bothers me when compiling these memoirs of mine is the problem of what steps to take when I bring on the stage a dramatis persona, as I believe the expression is, who has already appeared in some earlier instalment. Will the customers, I ask myself, remember him or her or will they have completely forgotten her or him, in which case they will naturally want a few footnotes to put them abreast. This difficulty arises in regard to Honoria Glossop, who got into the act in what I suppose would be about Chapter Two of the Wooster Story. Some will recall her, but there may be those who will protest that they have never heard of the beazel in their lives, so perhaps better be on the safe side and risk the displeasure of the blokes with good memories.

Here, then, is what I recorded with ref. to this H. Glossop at the time when owing to circumstances over which I had no control we had become engaged.

'Honoria Glossop,' I wrote, 'was one of those large, strenuous, dynamic girls with the physique of a middle-weight catch-as-catch-can wrestler and a laugh resembling the sound made by the Scotch Express going under a bridge. The effect she had on me was to make me slide into a cellar and lie low there till they blew the All Clear.'

One could readily, therefore, understand the reluctance of Myrtle, Lady Chuffnell, to team up with Sir Roderick while the above was still a member of the home circle. The stand she had taken reflected great credit on her sturdy commonsense, I considered.

A thought struck me, the thought I so often have when Jeeves starts dishing the dirt.

'How do you know all this, Jeeves? Did he confer with you?' I said, for I knew how wide his consulting practice was. 'Put it up to Jeeves' is so much the slogan in my circle of acquaintance that it might be that even Sir Roderick Glossop, finding himself on a sticky wicket, had decided to place his affairs in his hands. Jeeves is like Sherlock

Holmes. The highest in the land come to him with their problems. For all I know, they may give him jewelled snuff boxes.

It appeared that I had guessed wrong.

'No, sir, I have not been honoured with Sir Roderick's confidence.'

'Then how did you find out about his spot of trouble? By extra-whatever-it's-called?'

'Extra-sensory perception? No, sir. I happened to be glancing yesterday at the G section of the club book.'

I got the gist. Jeeves belongs to a butlers and valets club in Curzon Street called the Junior Ganymede, and they have a book there in which members are required to enter information about their employers. I remember how stunned I was when he told me one day that there are eleven pages about me in it.

'The data concerning Sir Roderick and the unfortunate situation in which he finds himself were supplied by Mr Dobson.'

'Who?'

'Sir Roderick's butler, sir.'

'Of course, yes,' I said, recalling the dignified figure into whose palm I had pressed a couple of quid on leaving that morning. 'But surely Sir Roderick didn't confide in him?'

'No, sir, but Dobson's hearing is very acute and it enabled him to learn the substance of conversations between Sir Roderick and her ladyship.'

'He listened at the keyhole?'

'So one would be disposed to imagine, sir.'

I mused awhile. So that was how the cookie crumbled. A pang of p for the toad beneath the harrow whose affairs we were discussing passed through me. It would have been plain to a far duller auditor than Bertram Wooster that poor old Roddy was in a spot. I knew how deep was his affection and esteem for Chuffy's Aunt Myrtle. Even when he was liberally coated with burned cork that night at Chuffnell Regis I had been able to detect the lovelight in his eyes as he spoke of her. And when I reflected how improbable it was that anyone would ever be ass enough to marry his daughter Honoria, thus making his path straight and ironing out the bugs in the scenario, my heart bled for him.

I mentioned this to Jeeves.

'Jeeves,' I said, 'my heart bleeds for Sir R. Glossop.'

'Yes, sir.'

'Does your heart bleed for him?'

'Profusely, sir.'

'And nothing to be done about it. We are helpless to assist.'

'One fears so, sir.'

'Life can be very sad, Jeeves.'

'Extremely, sir.'

'I'm not surprised that Blair Eggleston has taken a dislike to it.'

'No, sir.'

'Perhaps you had better bring me another whisky-and-s, to cheer me up. And after that I'll pop off to the Drones for a bite to eat.'

He gave me an apologetic look. He does this by allowing one eyebrow to flicker for a moment.

'I am sorry to say I have been remiss, sir. I inadvertently forgot to mention that Mrs Travers is expecting you to entertain her to dinner here tonight.'

'But isn't she at Brinkley?'

'No, sir, she has temporarily left Brinkley Court and taken up residence at her town house in order to complete her Christmas shopping.'

'And she wants me to give her dinner?'

'That was the substance of her words to me on the telephone this morning, sir.'

My gloom lightened perceptibly. This Mrs Travers is my good and deserving Aunt Dahlia, with whom it is always a privilege and pleasure to chew the fat. I would be seeing her, of course, when I went to Brinkley for Christmas, but getting this preview was an added attraction. If anyone could take my mind off the sad case of Roddy Glossop, it was she. I looked forward to the reunion with bright anticipation. I little knew that she had a bombshell up her sleeve and would be touching it off under my trouser seat while the night was yet young.

On these occasions when she comes to town and I give her dinner at the flat there is always a good deal of gossip from Brinkley Court and neighbourhood to be got through before other subjects are broached, and she tends not to allow a nephew to get a word in edgeways. It wasn't till Jeeves had brought the coffee that any mention of Sir Roderick Glossop was made. Having lit a cigarette and sipped her first sip, she asked me how he was, and I gave her the same reply I had given Jeeves.

'In robust health,' I said, 'but gloomy. Sombre. Moody. Despondent.'

'Just because you were there, or was there some other reason?'

'He didn't tell me,' I said guardedly. I always have to be very careful not to reveal my sources when Jeeves gives me information he has gleaned from the club book. The rules about preserving secrecy concerning its contents are frightfully strict at the Junior Ganymede. I don't know what happens to you if you're caught giving away inside stuff, but I should imagine that you get hauled up in a hollow square of valets and butlers and have your buttons snipped off before being formally bunged out of the institution. And it's a very comforting thought that such precautions are taken, for I should hate to think that there was any chance of those eleven pages about me receiving wide publicity. It's bad enough to know that a book like that – pure dynamite, as you might say – is in existence. 'He didn't let me in on what was eating him. He just sat there being gloomy and despondent.'

The old relative laughed one of those booming laughs of hers which in the days when she hunted with the Quorn and Pytchley probably lifted many a sportsman from the saddle. Her vocal delivery when amused always resembles one of those explosions in London street you read about in the papers.

'Well, Percy had been with him for several weeks. And then you on top of Percy. Enough to blot the sunshine from any man's life. How is Percy, by the way?'

'Quite himself again. A thing I wouldn't care to be, but no doubt it pleases him.'

'Little men no longer following him around?'

'If they are, they've shaved. He hasn't seen a black beard for quite a while, he tells me.'

'That's good. Percy'll be all right if he rids himself of the idea that alcohol is a food. Well, we'll soon buck Glossop up when he comes to Brinkley for Christmas.'

'Will he be there?'

'He certainly will, and joy will be unconfined. We're going to have a real old-fashioned Christmas with all the trimmings.'

'Holly? Mistletoe?'

'Yards of both. And a children's party complete with Santa Claus.'

'With the vicar in the stellar role?'

'No, he's down with flu.'

'The curate?'

'Sprained his ankle.'

'Then who are you going to get?'

'Oh, I'll find someone. Was anyone else at Glossop's?'

'Only a fellow of the name of Eggleston.'

'Blair Eggleston, the writer?'

'Yes, Jeeves tells me he writes books.'

'And articles. He's doing a series for me on the Modern Girl.'

For some years, helped out by doles from old Tom Travers, her husband, Aunt Dahlia had been running a weekly paper for women called *Milady's Boudoir*, to which I once contributed a 'piece', as we journalists call it, on What The Well-Dressed Man Is Wearing. The little sheet has since been sold, but at that time it was still limping along and losing its bit of money each week, a source of considerable spiritual agony to Uncle Tom, who had to foot the bills. He has the stuff in sackfuls, but he hates to part.

'I'm sorry for that boy,' said Aunt Dahlia.

'For Blair Eggleston? Why?'

'He's in love with Honoria Glossop.'

'What!' I cried. She amazed me. I wouldn't have thought it could be done.

'And is too timid to tell her so. It's often that way with these frank, fearless young novelists. They're devils on paper, but put them up against a girl who doesn't come out of their fountain pen and their feet get as cold as a dachshund's nose. You'd think, when you read his novels, that Blair Eggleston was a menace to the sex and ought to be kept on a chain in the interests of pure womanhood, but is he? No, sir. He's just a rabbit. I don't know if he has ever actually found himself in an incense-scented boudoir alone with a girl with sensual lips and dark smouldering eyes, but if he did, I'll bet he would take a chair as far away from her as possible and ask her if she had read any good books lately. Why are you looking like a half-witted fish?'

'I was thinking of something.'

'What?'

'Oh, just something,' I said warily. Her character sketch of Blair Eggleston had given me one of those ideas I do so often get quick as a flash, but I didn't want to spill it till I'd had time to think it over and ponder on it. It never does to expose these brain waves to the public eye before you've examined them from every angle. 'How do you know all this?' I said.

'He told me in a burst of confidence the other day when we were discussing his Modern Girl Series. I suppose I must have one of those sympathetic personalities which invite confidences. You will recall that you have always told me about your various love affairs.'

'That's different.'

'In what way?'

'Use the loaf, old flesh-and-blood. You're my aunt. A nephew naturally bares his soul to a loved aunt.'

'I see what you mean. Yes, that makes sense. You do love me dearly, don't you?'

'Like billy-o. Always have.'

'Well, I'm certainly glad to hear you say that—'

'Well-deserved tribute.'

'—because there's something I want you to do for me.'

'Consider it done.'

'I want you to play Santa Claus at my children's Christmas party.'

Should I have seen it coming? Possibly. But I hadn't, and I tottered where I sat. I was trembling like an aspen. I don't know if you've ever seen an aspen – I haven't myself as far as I can remember – but I knew they were noted for trembling like the dickens. I uttered a sharp cry, and she said if I was going to sing, would I kindly do it elsewhere, as her ear drum was sensitive.

'Don't say such things even in fun,' I begged her.

'I'm not joking.'

I gazed at her incredulously.

'You seriously expect me to put on white whiskers and a padded stomach and go about saying 'Ho, ho, ho' to a bunch of kids as tough as those residing near your rural seat?'

'They aren't tough.'

'Pardon me. I've seen them in action. You will recollect that I was present at the recent school treat.'

'You can't go by that. Naturally they wouldn't have the Christmas spirit at a school treat in the middle of summer. You'll find them as mild as newborn lambs on Christmas Eve.'

I laughed a sharp, barking laugh.

'*I* shan't.'

'Are you trying to tell me you won't do it?'

'I am.'

She snorted emotionally and expressed the opinion that I was a worm.

'But a prudent, level-headed worm,' I assured her. 'A worm who knows enough not to stick its neck out.'

'You really won't do it?'

'Not for all the rice in China.'

'Not to oblige a loved aunt?'

'Not to oblige a posse of loved aunts.'

'Now listen, young Bertie, you abysmal young blot . . .'

As I closed the front door behind her some twenty minutes later, I had rather the feeling you get when parting company with a tigress of the jungle or one of those fiends with hatchet who are always going about slaying six. Normally the old relative is as genial a soul as ever downed a veal cutlet, but she's apt to get hot under the collar when thwarted, and in the course of the recent meal, as we have seen, I had been compelled to thwart her like a ton of bricks. It was with quite a few beads of persp bedewing the brow that I went back to the dining room, where Jeeves was cleaning up the debris.

'Jeeves,' I said, brushing away the b of p with my cambric handkerchief, 'you were off stage towards the end of dinner, but did you happen to drink in any of the conversation that was taking place?'

'Oh yes, sir.'

'Your hearing, like Dobson's, is acute?'

'Extremely, sir. And Mrs Travers has a robust voice. I received the impression that she was incensed.'

'She was as sore as a gumboil. And why? Because I stoutly refused to portray Santa Claus at the Christmas orgy she is giving down at Brinkley for the children of the local yokels.'

'So I gathered from her obiter dicta, sir.'

'I suppose most of the things she called me were picked up on the hunting field in her hunting days.'

'No doubt, sir.'

'Members of the Quorn and Pytchley are not guarded in their speech.'

'Very seldom, sir, I understand.'

'Well, her efforts were . . . what's that word I've heard you use?'

'Bootless, sir?'

'Or fruitless?'

'Whichever you prefer, sir.'

'I was not to be moved. I remained firm. I am not a disobliging man, Jeeves. If somebody wanted me to play Hamlet, I would do my best to give satisfaction. But at dressing up in white whiskers and a synthetic stomach I draw the line and draw it sharply. She huffed and puffed, as you heard, but she might have known that argument would be bootless. As the wise old saying has it, you can take a horse to the water, but you can't make it play Santa Claus.'

'Very true, sir.'

'You think I was justified in being adamant?'

'Fully justified, sir.'

'Thank you, Jeeves.'

I must say I thought it pretty decent of him to give the young master the weight of his support like this, for though I haven't mentioned it before it was only a day or two since I had been compelled to thwart him as inflexibly as I had thwarted the recent aunt. He had been trying to get me to go to Florida after Christmas, handing out a lot of talk about how pleasant it would be for my many American friends, most of whom make a bee line for Hobe Sound in the winter months, to have me with them again, but I recognized this, though specious, as merely the old oil. I knew what was the thought behind his words. He likes the fishing in Florida and yearns some day to catch a tarpon.

Well, I sympathized with his sporting aspirations and would have pushed them along if I could have managed it, but I particularly wanted to be in London for the Drones Club Darts Tournament, which takes place in February and which I confidently expected to win this year, so I said Florida was out and he said 'Very good, sir', and that was that. The point I'm making is that there was no dudgeon or umbrage or anything of that sort on his part, as there would have been if he had been a lesser man, which of course he isn't.

'And yet, Jeeves,' I said, continuing to touch on the affair of the stricken aunt, 'though my firmness and resolution enabled me to emerge victorious from the battle of wills, I can't help feeling a pang.'

'Sir?'

'Of remorse. It's always apt to gnaw you when you've crushed someone beneath the iron heel. You can't help thinking that you ought to do something to bind up the wounds and bring the sunshine back into the poor slob's life. I don't like the thought of Aunt Dahlia biting her pillow tonight and trying to choke back the rising sobs because I couldn't see my way to fulfilling her hopes and dreams. I think I should extend something in the way of an olive branch or *amende honorable*.'

'It would be a graceful act, sir.'

'So I'll blow a few bob on flowers for her. Would you mind nipping out tomorrow morning and purchasing say two dozen long-stemmed roses?'

'Certainly, sir.'

'I think they'll make her face light up, don't you?'

'Unquestionably, sir. I will attend to the matter immediately after breakfast.'

'Thank you, Jeeves.'

I was smiling one of my subtle smiles as he left the room, for in the recent exchanges I had not been altogether frank, and it tickled me to think that he thought that I was merely trying to apply a soothing poultice to my conscience.

Mark you, what I had said about wanting to do the square thing by the aged relative and heal the breach and all that sort of thing was perfectly true, but there was a lot more than that behind the gesture. It was imperative that I get her off the boil, because her co-operation was essential to the success of a scheme or plan or plot which had been fizzing in the Wooster brain ever since the moment after dinner when she had asked me why I was looking like a half-witted fish. It was a plan designed to bring about the happy ending for Sir R. Glossop, and now that I had had time to give it the once-over it seemed to me that it couldn't miss.

Jeeves brought the blooms while I was in my bath, and having dried the frame and donned the upholstery and breakfasted and smoked a cigarette to put heart into me I started out with them.

I wasn't expecting a warm welcome from the old flesh-and-blood, which was lucky, because I didn't get one. She was at her haughtiest, and the look she gave me was the sort of look which in her Quorn and Pytchley days she would have given some fellow-sportsman whom she had observed riding over hounds.

'Oh, it's you?' she said.

Well, it was, of course, no argument about that, so I endorsed her view with a civil good morning and a smile – rather a weak smile, probably, for her aspect was formidable. She was plainly sizzling.

'I hope you thoroughly understand,' she said, 'that after your craven exhibition last night I'm not speaking to you.'

'Oh, aren't you?'

'Certainly not. I'm treating you with silent contempt. What's that you've got there?'

'Some long-stemmed roses. For you.'

She sneered visibly.

'You and your long-stemmed roses! It would take more than long-stemmed roses to change my view that you're a despicable cowardy custard and a disgrace to a proud family. Your ancestors fought in the Crusades and were often mentioned in despatches, and you cringe like a salted snail at the thought of appearing as Santa Claus before an audience of charming children who wouldn't hurt a fly. It's enough to make an aunt turn her face to the wall and give up the struggle. But perhaps,' she said, her manner softening for a moment, 'you've come to tell me you've changed your mind?'

'I fear not, aged relative.'

'Then buzz off, and on your way home try if possible to get run over by a motor bus. And may I be there to hear you go pop.'

I saw that I had better come to the *res* without delay.

'Aunt Dahlia,' I said, 'it is within your power to bring happiness and joy into a human life.'

'If it's yours, I don't want to.'

'Not mine. Roddy Glossop's. Sit in with me in a plan or scheme which I have in mind, and he'll go pirouetting about his clinic like a lamb in Springtime.'

She drew a sharp breath and eyed me keenly.

'What's the time?' she asked.

I consulted the wrist-w.

'A quarter to eleven. Why?'

'I was only thinking that it's very early for anyone, even you, to get pie-eyed.'

'I'm not pie-eyed.'

'Well, you're talking as if you were. Have you got a piece of chalk?'

I tut-tutted impatiently.

'Of course I haven't. Do you think I go about with pieces of chalk on my person? What do you want it for?'

'I would like to draw a line on the carpet and see if you can walk along it, because it's being borne in upon me more emphatically every moment that you're stewed to the gills. Say "Truly rural".'

I did so.

'And "She stood at the door of Burgess's fish sauce shop, welcoming him in".'

Again I passed the test.

'Well,' she said grudgingly, 'you seem as sober as you ever are. What do you mean about bringing happiness and joy into old Glossop's life?'

'The matter is susceptible of a ready explanation. I must begin by saying that Jeeves told me a story yesterday that shocked me to the core. No,' I said in answer to her query, 'it was not the one about the young man of Calcutta. It had to do with Roddy's love life. It's a long story, but I'll condense it into a short-short, and I would like to stress before embarking on my narrative that you can rely on it being accurate, for when Jeeves tells you anything, it's like getting it straight from the mouth of the stable cat. Furthermore, it's substantiated by Mr Dobson, Roddy's butler. You know, Myrtle, Lady Chuffnell?'

'I've met her.'

'She and Roddy are betrothed.'

'So I've heard.'

'They love each other fondly.'

'So what's wrong with that?'

'I'll tell you what's wrong. She stoutly declines to go centre-aisleing with him until his daughter Honoria gets married.'

I had expected this to make her sit up, and it did. For the first time her demeanour conveyed the impression that she wasn't labelling my utterances as just delirious babble from the sick bed. She has always been fond of R. Glossop and it came as a shock to her to learn that he was so firmly established in the soup. I wouldn't say she turned pale, for after years of following the hounds in all weathers she can't, but she snorted and I could see that she was deeply moved.

'For heaven's sake! Is this true?'

'Jeeves has all the facts.'

'Does Jeeves know everything?'

'I believe so. Well, you can understand Ma Chuffnell's attitude. If you were a bride, would you want to have Honoria a permanent resident of your little nest?'

'I wouldn't.'

'Exactly. So obviously steps must be taken by Roddy's friends and well-wishers to get her married. And that brings me to the nub. I have a scheme.'

'I'll bet it's rotten.'

'On the contrary, it's a ball of fire. It flashed on me last night, when you were telling me that Blair Eggleston loves Honoria. That is where hope lies.'

'You mean you're thinking that he will marry her and take her off the strength?'

'Precisely.'

'Not a chance. I told you he was too much of a rabbit to suggest a merger. He'll never have the nerve to propose.'

'Unless helped by a push from behind.'

'And who's going to give him that?'

'I am. With your co-operation.'

She gave me another of those long keen looks, and I could see that she was again asking herself if her favourite nephew wasn't steeped to the tonsils in the juice of the grape. Fearing more tests and further references to pieces of chalk, I hastened to explain.

'Here's the idea. I start giving Honoria the rush of a lifetime. I lush her up at lunch and dinner. I take her to theatres and night clubs. I haunt her like a family spectre and cling to her closer than a porous plaster.'

I thought I heard her mutter 'Poor girl', but I ignored the slur and continued.

'You meanwhile . . . Will you be seeing something of Eggleston?'

'I see him daily. He brings me his latest views on the Modern Girl.'

'Then the thing's in the bag. You say he has already confided in you about his warmer-and-deeper-than-ordinary-friendship feelings concerning Honoria, so it won't be difficult for you to bring the subject up in the course of conversation. You warn him in a motherly way that he's a sap if he goes on not telling his love and letting concealment like a worm in the bud feed on his damask cheek – one of Jeeves's gags, I thought he put it rather well – and stress the fact that he had better heat up his feet and grab the girl while the grabbing's good, because you happen to know that your nephew Bertram is making a heavy play in her direction and may sew up the deal at any moment. Use sufficient eloquence, and I can't see how he can fail to respond. He'll be pouring out his love before you know where you are.'

'And suppose she doesn't feel like getting engaged to him?'

'Absurd. Why, she was once engaged to *me*.'

She was silent for space, plunged in thought, as the expression is.

'I'm not sure,' she said at length, 'that you haven't got something.'

'It's a snip.'

'Yes, I think you're right. Jeeves has a great brain.'

'What's Jeeves got to do with it?'

'Wasn't it his idea?'

I drew myself up rather haughtily – not an easy thing to do when you're sitting in an armchair. I resent this universal tendency to take it for granted that whenever I suggest some particularly ripe scheme, it must be Jeeves's.

'The sequence was entirely mine.'

'Well, it's not at all a bad one. I've often said that you sometimes have lucid intervals.'

'And you'll sit in and do your bit?'

'It will be a pleasure.'

'Fine. Can I use your phone? I want to ask Honoria Glossop to lunch.'

I should imagine that it has often been said of Bertram Wooster that when he sets his hand to the plough he does not readily sheathe the sword. I had told Aunt Dahlia that I was going to give Honoria the rush of a lifetime, and the rush of a lifetime was precisely what I gave her. I lunched, dined and on two occasions nightclubbed her. It ran into money, but you can put up with a few punches in the pocketbook when you're working in a good cause. Even when wincing at the figures at the foot of the bill I was able to console myself with the thought of what all this was in aid of. Nor did I grudge the hours spent in the society of a girl whom in normal circs I would willingly have run a mile in tight shoes to avoid. Pop Glossop's happiness was at stake, and when a pal's happiness is at stake, the undersigned does not count the cost.

Nor were my efforts bootless. Aunt Dahlia was always ringing me up to tell me that Blair Egglestone's temperature was rising steadily day by day and it seemed to her only a question of time before the desired object would be achieved. And came a day when I was able to go to her with the gratifying news that the d.o. had indeed been a.

I found her engrossed in an Erle Stanley Gardner, but she lowered the volume courteously as I entered.

'Well, ugly,' she said, 'what brings you here? Why aren't you off somewhere with Honoria Glossop, doing your South American Joe act? What's the idea of playing hooky like this?'

I smiled one of my quiet smiles.

'Aged relative,' I said, 'I have come to inform you that I think we have reached the end of the long, long trail,' and without further preamble I gave her the low-down. 'Have you been out today?'

'I went for a stroll, yes.'

'The weather probably struck you as extraordinarily mild for the latter part of December. More like spring than winter.'

'You haven't come here to talk about the weather?'

'You will find it is germane to the issue. Because the afternoon was so balmy—'

'Like others I could name.'

'I beg your pardon?'

'I didn't speak. Go on.'

'Well, as it was such a nice day I thought I would take a walk in the Park. I did so, and blowed if the first thing I saw wasn't Honoria. She was sitting on a chair by the Serpentine. I was about to duck, but it was too late. She had seen me, so I had to heave alongside and chat. And suddenly who should come along but Blair Eggleston.'

I had enchained her interest. She uttered a yip.

'He saw you?'

'With the naked eye.'

'Then that was your moment. If you'd had an ounce of sense, you'd have kissed her.'

I smiled another of my quiet ones.

'I did.'

'You *did*?'

'Yes, sir, I folded her in a close embrace and let her have it.'

'And what did Eggleston say?'

'I didn't wait to hear. I pushed off.'

'But you're sure he saw you?'

'He couldn't have missed. He was only a yard or two away, and the visibility was good.'

It isn't often that I get unstinted praise from my late father's sister, she as a rule being my best friend and severest critic, but on this occasion she gave me a rave notice. It was a pleasure to listen to her.

'That should have done it,' she said after handing me some stately compliments on my ingenuity and resource. 'I saw Eggleston yesterday, and when I mentioned what fun you and Honoria were having going about together, he looked like a blond Othello. His hands were clenched, his eyes burning, and if he wasn't grinding his teeth, I don't know a ground tooth when I hear one. That kiss was just what he needed to push him over the edge. He probably proposed to her the moment you were out of the way.'

'That's how I had it figured out.'

'Oh, hell,' said the old ancestor, for at this moment the telephone rang, interrupting us just when we wanted to go on discussing the thing undisturbed. She reached for it, and a long one-sided conversation ensued. I say one-sided because her contribution to it consisted merely of Ohs and Whats. Eventually whoever was at the other end appeared to have said his or her say, for she replaced the receiver and turned a grave face in my direction.

'That was Honoria,' she said.

'Oh, really?'

'And what she had to tell me was fraught with interest.'

'Did matters work out according to plan?'

'Not altogether.'

'How do you mean, not altogether?'

'Well, to begin with, it seems that Blair Eggleston, no doubt inflamed by what I told you I had said to him yesterday, proposed to her last night.'

'He did?'

'And was accepted.'

'That's good.'

'Not so good.'

'Why not?'

'Because when he saw you kiss her, he blew his top and broke the engagement.'

'Oh, my God!'

'Nor is that all. The worst is yet to come. She now says she's going to marry you. She said she quite realized your many defects but is sure she can correct them and mould you, and even though you aren't the mate of her dreams, she feels that your patient love should be rewarded. Obviously what happened was that you made yourself too fascinating. There was always that risk, I suppose.'

Long before she had concluded these remarks I had gone into my aspen act again. I goggled at her, stunned.

'But this is frightful!'

'I told you it wasn't so good.'

'You aren't pulling my leg?'

'No, it's official.'

'Then what shall I do for the best?'

She shrugged a moody shoulder.

'Don't ask me,' she said. 'Consult Jeeves. He may be able to suggest something.'

Well, it was all very well to say consult Jeeves, but it wasn't as simple as she seemed to think. The way I looked at it was that to place him in possession of the facts in what you might call pitiless detail would come under the head of bandying a woman's name, which, as everybody knows, is the sort of thing that gets you kicked out of clubs and cut by the County. On the other hand, to be in a jam like this and not seek his counsel would be a loony proceeding. It was only after profound thought that I saw how the thing could be worked. I gave him a hail, and he presented himself with a courteous 'Sir?'

'Oh, Jeeves,' I said, 'I hope I'm not interrupting you when you were curled up with your Spinoza's *Ethics* or whatever it is, but I wonder if you could spare me a moment of your valuable time?'

'Certainly, sir.'

'A problem has arisen in the life of a friend of mine who shall be nameless, and I want your advice. I must begin by saying that it's one of those delicate problems where not only my friend must be nameless but all the other members of the personnel. In other words, I can't mention names. You see what I mean?'

'I understand you perfectly, sir. You would prefer to term the protagonists A and B.'

'Or North and South?'

'A and B is more customary, sir.'

'Just as you say. Well, A is male, B female. You follow me so far?'

'You have been lucidity itself, sir.'

'And owing to . . . what's that something of circumstances you hear people talking about? Cats enter into it, if I remember rightly.'

'Would concatenation be the word for which you are groping?'

'That's it. Owing to a concatenation of circumstances B has got it into her nut that A's in love with her. But he isn't. Still following?'

'Yes, sir.'

I had to pause here for a moment to marshal my thoughts. Having done so, I proceeded.

'Now until quite recently B was engaged to—'

'Shall we call him C, sir?'

'Caesar's as good a name as any, I suppose. Well, as I was saying, until quite recently B was engaged to Caesar and A hadn't a worry in the world. But now there has been a rift within the lute, the fixture has been scratched, and B is talking freely of teaming up with A, and what I want you to bend your brain to is the problem of how A can oil out of it. Don't get the idea that it's simple, because A is what is known as a *preux chevalier*, and this hampers him. I mean when B comes to him and says "A, I will be yours", he can't just reply "You will, will you? That's what *you* think". He has his code, and the code rules that he must kid her along and accept the situation. And frankly, Jeeves, he would rather be dead in a ditch. So there you are. The facts are before you. Anything stirring?'

'Yes, sir.'

I was astounded. Experience has taught me that he generally knows all the answers, but this was certainly quick service.

'Say on, Jeeves. I'm all agog.'

'Obviously, sir, B's matrimonial plans would be rendered null and void if A were to inform her that his affections were engaged elsewhere.'

'But they aren't.'

'It would be necessary merely to convey the impression that such was the case.'

I began to see what he was driving at.

'You mean if I – or, rather, A – were to produce some female and have her assert that she was betrothed to me – or I should say him – the peril would be averted?'

'Precisely, sir.'

I mused.

'It's a thought,' I agreed, 'but there's the dickens of a snag – viz. how to get hold of the party of the second part. You can't rush about London asking girls to pretend they're engaged to you. At least, I suppose you can, but it would be quite a nervous strain.'

'That, sir, *is* the difficulty.'

'You haven't an alternative plan to suggest?'

'I fear not, sir.'

I confess I was baffled, but it's pretty generally recognized at the Drones and elsewhere that while you can sometimes baffle Bertram Wooster for the nonce, he rarely stays baffled long. I happened to run into Catsmeat Potter-Pirbright at the Drones that night, and I suddenly saw how the snag to which I had alluded could be got around.

Catsmeat is on the stage and now in considerable demand for what are called juvenile roles, but in his early days he had been obliged, like all young hams, to go from agent to agent seeking employment – or trying to get a shop, as I believe the technical term is – and he was telling me anecdotes about them after dinner. And it struck me like a blow in the midriff that if you wanted a girl to exhibit as your fiancée, a theatrical agent was the very man to help you out. Such a bloke would be in an admirable position to supply some resting artiste who would be glad to sit in on an innocent deception in return for a moderate fee.

Catsmeat had told me where these fauna were to be found. The Charing Cross Road is apparently where most of them hang out, and on the following morning I might have been observed entering the premises of Jas Waterbury on the top floor of a building about half way up that thoroughfare.

The reason my choice had fallen on Jas was not that I had heard glowing reports of him from every side, it was simply because all the other places I had tried had been full of guys and dolls standing bumper to bumper and it hadn't seemed worthwhile waiting. Entering *chez* Waterbury I found his outer office completely empty. It was as if he had parted company with the human herd.

It was possible, of course, that he had stepped across the road for a quick one, but it was also possible that he was lurking behind the door labelled Private, so I rapped on it. I hadn't expected anything to start into life, but I was wrong. A head popped out.

I've seen heads that were more of a feast for the eye. It was what I would describe as a greasy head. Its summit was moist with hair oil and the face, too, suggested that its proprietor after the morning shave had thought fit to rub his cheeks with butter. But I'm a broad-minded man and I had no objection to him being greasy, if he liked being greasy. Possibly, I felt, if I had had the privilege of meeting Kenneth Molyneux, Malcolm McCullen, Edmund Ogilvy and Horace Furnival, the other theatrical agents I had visited, I would have found them greasy, too. It may be that all theatrical agents are. I made a mental note to ask Catsmeat Potter-Pirbright about this.

'Oh, hullo, cocky,' said the oleaginous character, speaking thickly for he was making an early lunch on what looked like a ham sandwich. 'Something I can do for you?'

'Jas Waterbury?'

'That's me. You want a shop?'

'I want a girl.'

'Don't we all? What's your line? Are you running a touring company?'

'No, it's more like amateur theatricals.'

'Oh, those? Well, let's have the inside story.'

I had told myself that it would be embarrassing confiding one's intimate private affairs to a theatrical agent, and it was embarrassing, but I stiffened the upper lip and had at it, and as my narrative proceeded it was borne in upon me that I had sized up Jas Waterbury all wrong. Misled by his appearance, I had assumed him to be one of those greasy birds who would be slow on the uptake and unable to get hep to the finer points. He proved to be both quick and intelligent. He punctuated my remarks with understanding nods, and when I had finished said I had come to the right man, for he had a niece called Trixie who would fill the bill to my complete satisfaction. The whole project, he said, was right up Trixie's street. If I placed myself in her hands, he added, the act must infallibly be a smash hit.

It sounded good, but I pursed my lips a bit dubiously. I was asking myself if an uncle's love might not have made him give the above Trixie too enthusiastic a build-up.

'You're sure,' I said, 'that this niece of yours would be equal to this rather testing job? It calls for considerable histrionic skill. Can she make her role convincing?'

'She'll smother you with burning kisses, if that's what you're worrying about.'

'What I had in mind was more the dialogue. We don't want her blowing up in her lines. Don't you think we ought to get a seasoned professional?'

'That's just what Trixie is. Been playing Fairy Queens in panto for years. Never got a shop in London owing to jealousy in high places, but ask them in Leeds and Wigan what they think of her. Ask them in Hull. Ask them in Huddersfield.'

I said I would, always provided I happened to come across them, and he carried on in a sort of ecstasy.

' "This buxom belle" – *Leeds Evening Chronicle*. "A talented bit of all right" – *Hull Daily News*. "Beauty and dignity combined" – *Wigan Intelligencer*. Don't you fret yourself, cocky, Trix'll give you your money's worth. And talking of that, how much does the part pay?'

'I was thinking of a fiver.'

'Make it ten.'

'Right ho.'

'Or, rather, fifteen. That way you'll get every ounce of zest and co-operation.'

I was in no mood to haggle. Aunt Dahlia had rung up while I was breakfasting to tell me that Honoria Glossop had told her that she would be looking in on me at four o'clock, and it was imperative that the reception committee be on hand to greet her. I dished out the fifteen quid and asked how soon he could get hold of his niece, as time was of the essence. He said her services would be at my disposal well ahead of zero hour, and I said Fine.

'Give me a ring when it's all set,' I said. 'I'll be lunching at the Drones Club.'

This seemed to interest him quite a bit.

'Drones Club, eh? You a member there? I've got some good friends at the Drones Club. You know a Mr Widgeon?'

'Freddie Widgeon? Yes, very well.'

'And Mr Prosser?'

'Yes, I know Oofy Prosser.'

'Give them my best, if you see them. Nice lads, both. And now you can trot along and feed your face without a care in the world. I'll have contacted Trixie before you're half-way through your fish and chips.'

And I was called to the phone while having the after-luncheon coffee in the smoking room. It was, as I had anticipated, Jas Waterbury.

'That you, cocky?'

I said it was, and he said everything was under control. Trixie had been contacted and would be up and doing with a heart for any fate in good time for the rise of the curtain. What, he asked, was the address they were to come to, and I told him and he said they would be there at a quarter to four without fail. So that was all fixed, and I was full of kindly feelings towards Jas Waterbury as I made my way back to the smoking room. He was a man whom I would have hesitated to invite to come with me on a long walking tour and I still felt that he would have been well advised to go easier on the grease as regarded both his hair and his person, but there was no getting away from it that if circumstances rendered it necessary for you to plot plots, he was the ideal fellow to plot them with.

During my absence from the smoking room Catsmeat Potter-Pirbright had taken the chair next to mine, and I lost no time in sounding him out on the subject of Jas Waterbury.

'You remember you were telling me about theatrical agents, Catsmeat. Did you ever happen to come across one called Waterbury?'

He pondered awhile.

'The name seems vaguely familiar. What does he look like?'

'Nothing on earth.'

'That doesn't place him. All theatrical agents look like nothing on earth. But it's odd that I seem to know the name. Waterbury? Waterbury? Ha! Is he a greasy bird?'

'Very greasy.'

'And is his first name Jas?'

'That's right.'

'Then I know the chap you mean. I never met him myself – I doubt if he was going at the time when I was hoofing it from agent to agent – but I've heard of him from Freddie Widgeon and Oofy Prosser.'

'Yes, he said they were friends of his.'

'He'd revise that view if he could listen to them talking about him. Oofy in particular. Jas Waterbury once chiselled him out of two thousand pounds.'

I was amazed.

'He chiselled *Oofy* out of two thousand pounds?' I gasped, wondering if I could believe my e. Oofy is the Drones Club millionaire, but it is well known that it's practically impossible to extract as much as five bob from him without using chloroform and a forceps. Dozens have tried it and failed.

'That's what Freddie Widgeon told me. Freddie says that once Jas Waterbury enters your life, you can kiss at least a portion of your holdings goodbye. Has he taken anything off you?'

'Fifteen quid.'

'You're lucky it wasn't fifteen hundred.'

If you're saying to yourself that these words of Catsmeat's must have left me uneasy and apprehensive, you are correct to the last drop. A quarter to four found me pacing the Wooster carpet with furrowed brow. If it had been merely a matter of this grease-coated theatrical agent tapping Freddie Widgeon for a couple of bob, it would have been different. A child can tap Freddie. But when it came to him parting Oofy Prosser, a man in whose wallet moths nest and raise large families, from a colossal sum like two thousand pounds, the brain reeled and one sought in vain for an explanation. Yet so it was. Catsmeat said it was impossible to get the full story, because every time Jas's name was mentioned Oofy just turned purple and spluttered, but the stark fact remained that Jas's bank balance was that amount up and Oofy's that amount down, and it made me feel like a fellow in a novel of suspense who suddenly realizes that he's up against an Octopus of Crime and hasn't the foggiest how he's going to avoid the menacing tentacles.

But it wasn't long before Reason returned to its throne and I saw that I'd been alarming myself unnecessarily. Nothing like that was going to happen to me. It might be that Jas Waterbury would have a shot at luring me into some business venture with the ultimate aim of leaving me holding the baby, but if he did he would find himself stymied by a firm *nolle prosequi*, so to cut a long story s, by the time the front door bell rang Bertram was himself again.

I answered the bell, for it was Jeeves's afternoon off. Once a week he downs tools and goes off to play Bridge at the Junior Ganymede.

I opened the door and Jas and his niece came in, and I stood gaping dumbly. For an instant, you might say I was spellbound.

Not having attended the performance of a pantomime since fairly early childhood, I had forgotten how substantial Fairy Queens were, and the sight of Trixie Waterbury was like a blow from a blunt instrument. A glance was enough to tell me why the dramatic critic of the *Leeds Evening Chronicle* had called her buxom. She stood about five feet nine in her short French vamps and bulged in every direction. Also the flashing eyes and the gleaming teeth. It was some moments before I was able to say Good Afternoon.

'Afternoon,' said Jas Waterbury. He looked about him approvingly. 'Nice little place you've got here. Costs a packet to keep up, I'll bet. This is Mr Wooster, Trixie. You call him Bertie.'

The Fairy Queen said wouldn't 'sweetie-pie' be better, and Jas Waterbury told her with a good deal of enthusiasm that she was quite right.

'Much more box office,' he agreed. 'Didn't I say she would be right for the part, cocky? You can rely on her to give a smooth West End performance. When do you expect your lady friend?'

'Any moment now.'

'Then we'd better be dressing the stage. Discovered, you sitting in that chair there with Trixie on your lap.'

'What!'

He seemed to sense the consternation in my voice, for he frowned a little under the grease.

'We're all working for the good of the show,' he reminded me austerely. 'You want the scene to carry conviction, and there's nothing like a sight gag.'

I could see there was much in what he said. This was not a time for half measures. I sat down. I don't say I sat blithely, but I sat, and Wigan's favourite Fairy Queen descended on my lap with a bump that made the stout chair tremble like an aspen. And scarcely had she started to nestle when the door bell rang.

'Curtain going up,' said Jas Waterbury. 'Let's have that passionate embrace, Trixie, and make it good.'

She made it good, and I felt like a Swiss mountaineer engulfed by an avalanche smelling of patchouli. Jas Waterbury flung wide the gates, and who should come in but Blair Eggleston, the last caller I was expecting.

He stood goggling. I sat goggling. Jas Waterbury goggled, too. One could understand how he was feeling. Anticipating the entrance of the female star and observing coming on left centre a character who wasn't a member of the cast at all, he was pardonably disconcerted. No impresario likes that sort of thing.

I was the first to speak. After all, I was the host and it was for me to get the conversation going.

'Oh, hullo, Eggleston,' I said, 'Come along in. I don't think you've met Mr Waterbury, have you, Mr Eggleston, Mr Jas Waterbury. And his niece Miss Trixie Waterbury, my fiancée.'

'Your *what*?'

'Fiancée. Betrothed. Affianced.'

'Good Lord!'

Jas Waterbury appeared to be feeling that as the act had been shot to pieces like this, there was no sense in hanging around.

'Well, Trix,' he said, 'your Bertie'll be wanting to talk to his gentleman friend, so give him a kiss and we'll be getting along. Pleased to have met you, Mr What-is-it,' and with a greasy smile he led the Fairy Queen from the room.

Blair Eggleston seemed still at a loss. He looked at the door through which they had passed as if asking himself if he had really seen what he thought he had seen, then turned to me with the air of one who intends to demand an explanation.

'What's all this, Wooster?'

'What's all what, Eggleston? Be more explicit.'

'Who on earth is that female?'

'Weren't you listening? My fiancée.'

'You're really engaged to her?'

'That's right.'

'Who is she?'

'She plays Fairy Queens in pantomime. Not in London owing to jealousy in high places, but they think a lot of her in Leeds, Wigan, Hull and Huddersfield. The critic of the *Hull Daily News* describes her as a talented bit of all right.'

He was silent for a space, appearing to be turning this over in his mind. Then he spoke in the frank, forthright and fearless way these modern novelists have.

'She looks like a hippopotamus.'

I conceded this.

'There is a resemblance, perhaps. I suppose Fairy Queens have to be stoutish if they are to keep faith with their public in towns like Leeds and Huddersfield. Those audiences up North want lots for their money.'

'And she exudes a horrible scent which I am unable at the moment to identify.'

'Patchouli. Yes, I noticed that.'

He mused again.

'I can't get over you being engaged to her.'

'Well, I am.'

'It's official?'

'Absolutely.'

'Well, this will be great news for Honoria.'

I didn't get his drift.

'For Honoria?'

'Yes. It will relieve her mind. She was very worried about you, poor child. That's why I'm here. I came to break it to you that she can never be yours. She's going to marry me.'

I stared at him. My first impression was that even though the hour was only about four-thirty he was under the influence of alcoholic stimulants.

'But I learned from a usually reliable source that that was all off.'

'It was, but now it's on again. We have had a complete reconciliation.'

'Well, fancy that!'

'And she shrank from coming and telling you herself. She said she couldn't bear to see the awful dumb agony in your eyes. When I tell her you're engaged, she'll go singing about the West End of London, not only because of the relief of knowing that she hasn't wrecked your life but because she'll be feeling what a merciful escape she's had. Just imagine being married to you! It doesn't bear thinking of. Well, I'll be going along and telling her the good news,' he said, and took his departure.

A moment later the bell rang. I opened the door and found him on the mat.

'What,' he asked, 'was that name again?'

'Name?'

'Your fiancée's.'

'Trixie Waterbury.'

'Good God!' he said, and pushed off. And I returned to the reverie he had interrupted.

There was a time when if somebody had come to me and said 'Mr Wooster, I have been commissioned by a prominent firm of publishers to write your biography and I need some intimate stuff which only you can supply. Looking back, what would you consider the high spot in your career?', I would have had no difficulty in slipping him the info. It occurred, I would have replied, in my fourteenth year when I was a resident pupil at Malvern House, Bramley-on-Sea, the private school conducted by that prince of stinkers, Aubrey Upjohn, M.A. He had told me to present myself in his study on the following morning, which always meant six of the juiciest with a cane that bit like a serpent and stung like an adder, and blowed if when morning came I wasn't all over pink spots. I had contracted measles and the painful interview was of course postponed *sine die*, as the expression is.

That had always been my supreme moment. Only now was I experiencing to an even greater extent the feeling of quiet happiness which comes to you when you've outsmarted the powers of darkness.

I felt as if a great weight had been lifted off me. Well, it had of course in one sense, for the Fairy Queen must have clocked in at fully a hundred and sixty pounds ring-side, but what I mean is that a colossal burden had been removed from the Wooster soul. It was as though the storm clouds had called it a day and the sun come smiling through.

The only thing that kept the moment from being absolutely perfect was that Jeeves was not there to share my hour of triumph. I toyed with the idea of ringing him up at the Junior Ganymede, but I didn't want to interrupt him when he was probably in the act of doubling six no trumps.

The thought of Aunt Dahlia presented itself. She of all people should be the one to hear the good news, for she was very fond of Roddy Glossop and had shown herself deeply concerned when informed of his in-the-soup-ness. Furthermore, she could scarcely not be relieved to learn that a loved nephew had escaped the fate that is worse than death – viz. marrying Honoria. It was true that my firm refusal to play Santa Claus at her children's party must still be rankling, if that's the word, but at our last meeting I had found her far less incandescent than she had been, so there was reason to suppose that if I looked in on her now I should not get a cordial reception. Well, not absolutely cordial, perhaps, but something near enough to it. So I left a note for Jeeves saying where I'd gone and hared off to her address in a swift taxi.

It was as I had anticipated. I don't say her face lit up when she saw me, but she didn't throw her Perry Mason at me and she called me no new names, and after I had told my story she was all joviality and enthusiasm. We were saying what a wonderful Christmas present the latest development would be for Pop Glossop and speculating as to what it would feel like being married to his daughter Honoria and, for the matter of that, being married to Blair Eggleston, and we had just agreed that both Honoria and Blair had it coming to them, when the telephone rang. The instrument was on a table near her chair, and she reached for it.

'Hullo?' she boomed. 'Who?' Or, rather, WHO, for when at the telephone her vocal delivery is always of much the same calibre as it used to be on the hunting field. She handed me the receiver. 'One of your foul friends wants you. Says his name's Waterbury.'

Jas Waterbury, placed in communication with self, seemed perplexed. In rather an awed voice he asked:

'Where are you, cocky? At the Zoo?'

'I don't follow you, Jas Waterbury.'

'A lion just roared at me.'

'Oh, that was my aunt.'

'Sooner yours than mine. I thought the top of my head had come off.'

'She has a robust voice.'

'I'll say she has. Well, cully, I'm sorry I had to disturb her at feeding time, but I thought you'd like to know that Trix and I have been talking it over and we both think a simple wedding at the registrar's would be best. No need for a lot of fuss and expense. And she says she'd like Brighton for the honeymoon. She's always been fond of Brighton.'

I was at something of a loss to know what on earth he was talking about, but reading between the lines I gathered that the Fairy Queen was thinking of getting married. I asked if this was so, and he chuckled greasily.

'Always kidding, Bertie. You will have your joke. If you don't know she's going to get married, who does?'

'I haven't a notion. Who to?'

'Why, you, of course. Didn't you introduce her to your gentleman friend as your fiancée?'

I lost no time in putting him straight.

'But that was just a ruse. Surely you explained it to her?'

'Explained what?'

'That I just wanted her to pretend that we were engaged.'

'What an extraordinary idea. What would I have done that for?'

'Fifteen quid.'

'I don't remember any fifteen quid. As I recall it, you came to me and told me you'd seen Trixie as the Fairy Queen in *Cinderella* at the Wigan Hippodrome and fallen in love with her at first sight, as so many young fellows have done. You had found out somehow that she was my niece and you asked me to bring her to your address. And the moment we came in I could see the love light in your eyes, and the love light was in her eyes, too, and it wasn't five minutes after that that you'd got her on your lap and there you were as snug as two bugs in a rug. Just a case of love at first sight, and I don't mind telling you it touched me. I like to see the young folks getting together in Springtime. Not that it's Springtime now, but the principle's the same.'

At this point Aunt Dahlia, who had been simmering gently, intervened to call me a derogatory name and ask what the hell was going on. I waved her down with an imperious hand. I needed every ounce of concentration to cope with this misunderstanding which seemed to have arisen.

'You're talking through your hat, Jas Waterbury.'

'Who, me?'

'Yes, you. You've got your facts all wrong.'

'You think so do you?'

'I do, and I will trouble you to break it to Miss Waterbury that those wedding bells will not ring out.'

'That's what I was telling you. Trixie wants it to be at the registrar's.'

'Well, that registrar won't ring out, either.'

He said I amazed him.

'You don't want to marry Trixie?'

'I wouldn't marry her with a ten-foot pole.'

An astonished 'Lord love a duck' came over the wire.

'If that isn't the most remarkable coincidence,' he said. 'Those were the very words Mr Prosser used when refusing to marry another niece of mine after announcing his betrothal before witnesses, same as you did. Shows what a small world it is. I asked him if he hadn't ever heard of breach of promise cases, and he shook visibly and swallowed once or twice. Then he looked me in the eye and said "How much?" I didn't get his meaning at first, and then it suddenly flashed on me. "Oh, you mean you want to break the engagement," I said, "and feel it's your duty as a gentleman to see that the poor girl gets her bit of heart balm," I said. "Well, it'll have to be something substantial," I said, "because there's her despair and desolation to be taken into account." So we talked it over and eventually settled on two thousand quid, and that's what I'd advise in your case. I think I can talk Trixie into accepting that. Nothing, mind you, can ever make life anything but a dreary desert for her after losing you, but two thousand quid would help.'

'BERTIE!' said Aunt Dahlia.

'Ah,' said Jas Waterbury, 'there's that lion again. Well, I'll leave you to think it over. I'll come and see you tomorrow and get your decision, and if you feel that you don't like writing that cheque, I'll ask a friend of mine to try what he can do to persuade you. He's an all-in wrestler of the name of Porky Jupp. I used to manage him at one time. He's retired now because he broke a fellow's spine and for some reason that gave him a distaste for the game. But he's still in wonderful condition. You ought to see him crack Brazil nuts with his fingers. He thinks the world of me and there's nothing he wouldn't do for me. Suppose, for instance, somebody had done me down in a business transaction, Porky would spring to the task of plucking him limb from limb like some innocent little child doing She-loves-me she-loves-me-not with a daisy. Good night, good night,' said Jas Waterbury, and rang off.

I would have preferred, of course, after this exceedingly unpleasant conversation to have gone off into a quiet corner somewhere and sat there with my head between my hands, reviewing the situation from every angle, but Aunt Dahlia was now making her desire for explanatory notes so manifest that I had to give her my attention. In a broken voice I supplied her with the facts and was surprised and touched to find her sympathetic and understanding. It's often this way with the female sex. They put you through it in no uncertain manner if you won't see eye to eye with them in the matter – to take an instance at random – of disguising yourself in white whiskers and stomach padding, but if they see you are really up against it, their hearts melt, rancour is forgotten and they do all they can to give you a shot in the arm. It was so with the aged relative. Having expressed the opinion that I was the king of the fat-heads and ought never to be allowed out without a nurse, she continued in gentler strain.

'But after all you are my brother's son whom I frequently dandled on my knee as a baby, and a subhuman baby you were if ever I saw one, though I suppose you were to be pitied rather than censured if you looked like a cross between a poached egg and a ventriloquist's dummy, so I can't let you sink in the soup without a trace. I must rally round and lend a hand.'

'Well, thanks old flesh-and-blood. Awfully decent of you to want to assist. But what can you do?'

'Nothing by myself, perhaps, but I can confer with Jeeves and between us we ought to think of something. Ring him up and tell him to come here at once.'

'He won't be home yet. He's playing Bridge at his club.'

'Give him a buzz, anyway.'

I did so, and was surprised when I heard a measured voice say 'Mr Wooster's residence'.

'Why, hullo, Jeeves,' I said. 'I didn't expect you to be home so early.'

'I left in advance of my usual hour, sir. I did not find my Bridge game enjoyable.'

'Bad cards?'

'No, sir, the hands dealt to me were uniformly satisfactory, but I was twice taken out of business doubles, and I had not the heart to continue.'

'Too bad. So you're at a loose end at the moment?'

'Yes, sir.'

'Then will you hasten to Aunt Dahlia's place? You are sorely needed.'

'Very good, sir.'

'Is he coming?' said Aunt Dahlia.

'Like the wind. Just looking for his bowler hat.'

'Then you pop off.'

'You don't want me for the conference?'

'No.'

'Three heads are better than two,' I argued.

'Not if one of them is solid ivory from the neck up,' said the aged relative, reverting to something more like her customary form.

I slept fitfully that night, my slumbers much disturbed by dreams of being chased across country by a pack of Fairy Queens with Jas Waterbury galloping after them shouting 'Yoicks' and 'Tally ho'. It was past eleven when I presented myself at the breakfast table.

'I take it, Jeeves,' I said as I started to pick at a moody fried egg, 'that Aunt Dahlia has told you all?'

'Yes, sir, Mrs Travers was most informative.'

Well, that was a relief in a way, because all that secrecy and A-and-B stuff is always a strain.

'Disaster looms, wouldn't you say?'

'Certainly your predicament is one of some gravity, sir.'

'I can't face a breach of promise action with a crowded court giving me the horse's laugh and the jury mulcting . . . Is it mulcting?'

'Yes, sir, you are quite correct.'

'And the jury mulcting me in heavy damages. I wouldn't be able to show my face in the Drones again.'

'The publicity would certainly not be agreeable, sir.'

'On the other hand, I thoroughly dislike the idea of paying Jas Waterbury two thousand pounds.'

'I can appreciate your dilemma, sir.'

'But perhaps you have already thought of some terrific scheme for foiling Jas and bringing his greasy hairs in sorrow to the grave. What do you plan to do when he calls?'

'I shall attempt to reason with him, sir.'

The heart turned to lead in the bosom. I suppose I've become so used to having Jeeves wave his magic wand and knock the stuffing out of the stickiest crises that I expect him to produce something brilliant from the hat every time, and though never at my brightest at breakfast I could see that what he was proposing to do was far from being what Jas Waterbury would have called box office. Reason with him, forsooth! To reason successfully with that king of the twisters one would need brass knucks and a stocking full of sand. There was reproach in my voice as I asked him if that was the best he could do.

'You do not think highly of the idea, sir?'

'Well, I don't want to hurt your feelings—'

'Not at all, sir.'

'– but I wouldn't call it one of your top thoughts.'

'I am sorry, sir. Nevertheless—'

I leaped from the table, the fried egg frozen on my lips. The front door bell had given tongue. I don't know if my eyes actually rolled as I gazed at Jeeves, but I should think it extremely likely, for the sound had got in amongst me like the touching off of an ounce or so of trinitrotoluol.

'There he is!'

'Presumably, sir.'

'I can't face him as early in the morning as this.'

'One appreciates your emotion, sir. It might be advisable if you were to conceal yourself while I conduct the negotiations. Behind the piano suggests itself as a suitable locale.'

'How right you are, Jeeves!'

To say that I found it comfortable behind the piano would be to give my public a totally erroneous impression, but I secured privacy, and privacy was just what I was after. The facilities, too, for keeping in touch with what was going on in the great world outside were excellent. I heard the door opening and then Jas Waterbury's voice.

'Morning, cocky.'

'Good morning, sir.'

'Wooster in?'

'No, sir, he has just stepped out.'

'That's odd. He was expecting me.'

'You are Mr Waterbury?'

'That's me. Where's he gone?'

'I think it was Mr Wooster's intention to visit his pawnbroker, sir.'

'What!'

'He mentioned something to me about doing so. He said he hoped to raise, as he expressed it, a few pounds on his watch.'

'You're kidding! What's he want to pop his watch for?'

'His means are extremely straightened.'

There was what I've heard called a pregnant silence. I took it that Jas Waterbury was taking time off to allow this to sink in. I wished I could have joined in the conversation, for I would have liked to say 'Jeeves, you are on the right lines' and offer him an apology for ever having doubted him. I might have known that when he said he was going to reason with Jas he had the ace up his sleeve which makes all the difference.

It was some little time before Jas Waterbury spoke, and when he did his voice had a sort of tremolo in it, as if he'd begun to realize that life wasn't the thing of roses and sunshine he'd been thinking it. I knew how he must be feeling. There is no anguish like that of the man who, supposing that he has found the pot of gold behind the rainbow, suddenly learns from an authoritative source that he hasn't, if you know what I mean. To him until now Bertram Wooster had been a careless scatterer of fifteen quids, a thing you can't do if you haven't a solid bank balance behind you, and to have him presented to him as a popper of watches must have made the iron enter into his soul, if he had one. He spoke as if stunned.

'But what about this place of his?'

'Sir?'

'You don't get a Park Lane flat for nothing.'

'No, indeed, sir.'

'Let alone a vally.'

'Sir?'

'You're a vally, aren't you?'

'No, sir. I was at one time a gentleman's personal gentleman, but at the moment I am not employed in that capacity. I represent Messrs Alsopp and Wilson, wine merchants, goods supplied to the value of three hundred and four pounds, fifteen shillings and eightpence, a bill which Mr Wooster finds it far beyond his fiscal means to settle. I am what is technically known as the man in possession.'

A hoarse 'Gorblimey' burst from Jas's lips. I thought it rather creditable of him that he did not say anything stronger.

'You mean you're a broker's man?'

'Precisely, sir. I am sorry to say I have come down in the world and my present situation was the only one I could secure. But while not what I have been accustomed to, it has its compensations. Mr Wooster is a very agreeable young gentleman and takes my intrusion in an amiable spirit. We have long and interesting conversations, and in the course of these he has confided his financial position to me. It appears that he is entirely dependent on the bounty of his aunt, a Mrs Travers, a lady of uncertain temper who has several times threatened unless he curbs his extravagance to cancel his allowance and send him to Canada to subsist on a small monthly remittance. She is of course under the impression that I am Mr Wooster's personal attendant. Should she learn of my official status, I do not like to envisage the outcome, though if I may venture on a pleasantry, it would be a case of outgo rather than outcome for Mr Wooster.'

There was another pregnant s, occupied, I should imagine, by Jas Waterbury in wiping his brow, which one presumes had by this time become wet with honest sweat.

Finally he once more said 'Gorblimey'.

Whether or not he would have amplified the remark I cannot say, for his words, if he had intended uttering any, were dashed from his lips. There was a sound like a mighty rushing wind and a loud snort informed me that Aunt Dahlia was with us. In letting Jas Waterbury in, Jeeves must have omitted to close the front door.

'Jeeves,' she boomed, 'can you look me in the face?'

'Certainly, madam, if you wish.'

'Well, I'm surprised you can. You must have the gall of an Army mule. I've just found out that you're a broker's man in valet's clothing. Can you deny it?'

'No, madam. I represent Messrs Alsopp and Wilson, wines, spirits and liqueurs supplied to the value of three hundred and four pounds fifteen shillings and eightpence.'

The piano behind which I cowered hummed like a dynamo as the aged relative unshipped a second snort.

'Good God! What does young Bertie do – bathe in the stuff? Three hundred and four pounds fifteen shillings and eightpence! Probably owes as much, too, in a dozen other places. And in the red to that extent he's planning, I hear, to marry the fat woman in a circus.'

'A portrayer of Fairy Queens in pantomime, madam.'

'Just as bad. Blair Eggleston says she looks like a hippopotamus.'

I couldn't see him, of course, but I imagine Jas Waterbury drew himself to his full height at this description of a loved niece, for his voice when he spoke was stiff and offended.

'That's my Trixie you're talking about, and he's going to marry her or else get sued for breach of promise.'

It's just a guess, but I think Aunt Dahlia must have drawn herself to her full height, too.

'Well, she'll have to go to Canada to bring her action,' she thundered, 'because that's where Bertie Wooster'll be off to on the next boat, and when he's there he won't have money to fritter away on breach of promise cases. It'll be as much as he can manage to keep body and soul together on what I'm going to allow him. If he gets a meat meal every third day, he'll be lucky. You tell that Trixie of yours to forget Bertie and go and marry the Demon King.'

Experience has taught me that except in vital matters like playing Santa Claus at children's parties it's impossible to defy Aunt Dahlia, and apparently Jas Waterbury realized this, for a moment later I heard the front door slam. He had gone without a cry.

'So that's that,' said Aunt Dahlia. 'These emotional scenes take it out of one, Jeeves. Can you get me a drop of something?'

'Certainly, madam.'

'How was I? All right?'

'Superb, madam.'

'I think I was in good voice.'

'Very sonorous, madam.'

'Well, it's nice to think our efforts were crowned with success. This will relieve young Bertie's mind. I use the word mind loosely. When do you expect him back?'

'Mr Wooster is in residence, madam. Shrinking from confronting Mr Waterbury, he prudently concealed himself. You will find him behind the piano.'

I was already emerging, and my first act was to pay them both a marked tribute. Jeeves accepted it gracefully, Aunt Dahlia with another of those snorts. Having snorted, she spoke as follows.

'Easy enough for you to hand out the soft soap, but what I'd like to see is less guff and more action. If you were really grateful, you would play Santa Claus at my Christmas party.'

I could see her point. It was well taken. I clenched the hands. I set the jaw. I made the great decision.

'Very well, aged relative.'

'You will?'

'I will.'

'That's my boy. What's there to be afraid of? The worst those kids will do is rub chocolate eclairs on your whiskers.'

'Chocolate eclairs?' I said in a low voice.

'Or strawberry jam. It's a tribal custom. Pay no attention, by the way, to stories you may have heard of them setting fire to the curate's beard last year. It was purely accidental.'

I had begun to go into my aspen act, when Jeeves spoke.

'Pardon me, madam.'

'Yes, Jeeves?'

'If I might offer the suggestion, I think that perhaps a maturer artist than Mr Wooster would give a more convincing performance.'

'Don't tell me you're thinking of volunteering?'

'No, madam. The artist I had in mind was Sir Roderick Glossop. Sir Roderick has a fine presence and a somewhat deeper voice than Mr Wooster. His Ho-ho-ho would be more dramatically effective, and I am sure that if you approached him, you could persuade him to undertake the role.'

'Considering,' I said, putting in my oar, 'that he is always blacking up his face with burned cork.'

'Precisely, sir. This will make a nice change.'

Aunt Dahlia pondered.

'I believe you're right, Jeeves,' she said at length. 'It's tough on those children, for it means robbing them of the biggest laugh they've ever had, but they can't expect life to be one round of pleasure. Well, I don't think I'll have that drink after all. It's a bit early.'

She buzzed off, and I turned to Jeeves, deeply moved. He had saved me from an ordeal at the thought of which the flesh crept, for I hadn't believed for a moment the aged r's story of the blaze in the curate's beard having been an accident. The younger element had probably sat up nights planning it out.

'Jeeves,' I said, 'you were saying something not long ago about going to Florida after Christmas.'

'It was merely a suggestion, sir.'

'You want to catch a tarpon, do you not?'

'I confess that it is my ambition, sir.'

I sighed. It wasn't so much that it pained me to think of some tarpon, perhaps a wife and mother, being jerked from the society of its loved ones on the end of a hook. What gashed me like a knife was the thought of missing the Drones Club Darts Tournament, for which I would have been a snip this year. But what would you? I fought down my regret.

'Then will you be booking the tickets.'

'Very good, sir.'

I struck a graver note.

'Heaven help the tarpon that tries to pit its feeble cunning against you, Jeeves,' I said. 'Its efforts will be bootless.'

Jeeves and the Song of Songs

ANOTHER day had dawned all hot and fresh and, in pursuance of my unswerving policy at that time, I was singing 'Sonny Boy' in my bath, when there was a soft step without and Jeeves's voice came filtering through the woodwork.

'I beg your pardon, sir.'

I had just got to that bit about the Angels being lonely, where you need every ounce of concentration in order to make the spectacular finish, but I signed off courteously.

'Yes, Jeeves? Say on.'

'Mr Glossop, sir.'

'What about him?'

'He is in the sitting-room, sir.'

'Young Tuppy Glossop?'

'Yes, sir.'

'In the sitting-room?'

'Yes, sir.'

'Desiring speech with me?'

'Yes, sir.'

'H'm!'

'Sir?'

'I only said H'm.'

And I'll tell you why I said H'm. It was because the man's story had interested me strangely. The news that Tuppy was visiting me at my flat, at an hour when he must have known that I would be in my bath and consequently in a strong strategic position to heave a wet sponge at him, surprised me considerably.

I hopped out with some briskness and, slipping a couple of towels about the limbs and torso, made for the sitting-room. I found young Tuppy at the piano, playing 'Sonny Boy' with one finger.

'What ho!' I said, not without a certain hauteur.

'Oh, hullo, Bertie,' said young Tuppy. 'I say, Bertie, I want to see you about something important.'

It seemed to me that the bloke was embarrassed. He had moved to the mantelpiece, and now he broke a vase in rather a constrained way.

'The fact is, Bertie, I'm engaged.'

'Engaged?'

'Engaged,' said young Tuppy, coyly dropping a photograph frame into the fender. 'Practically, that is.'

'Practically?'

'Yes. You'll like her. Bertie. Her name is Cora Bellinger. She's studying for Opera. Wonderful voice she has. Also dark, flashing eyes and a great soul.'

'How do you mean, practically?'

'Well, it's this way. Before ordering the trousseau, there is one little point she wants cleared up. You see, what with her great soul and all that, she has a rather serious outlook on life: and the one thing she absolutely bars is anything in the shape of hearty humour. You know, practical joking and so forth. She said if she thought I was a practical joker she would never speak to me again. And unfortunately she appears to have heard about that little affair at the Drones – I expect you have forgotten all about that, Bertie?'

'I have not!'

'No, no, not forgotten exactly. What I mean is, nobody laughs more heartily at the recollection than you. And what I want you to do, old man, is to seize an early opportunity of taking Cora aside and categorically denying that there is any truth in the story. My happiness, Bertie, is in your hands, if you know what I mean.'

Well, of course, if he put it like that, what could I do? We Woosters have our code.

'Oh, all right,' I said, but far from brightly.

'Splendid fellow!'

'When do I meet this blighted female?'

'Don't call her "this blighted female", Bertie, old man. I have planned all that out. I will bring her round here today for a spot of lunch.'

'What!'

'At one-thirty. Right. Good. Fine. Thanks. I knew I could rely on you.'

He pushed off, and I turned to Jeeves, who had shimmered in with the morning meal.

'Lunch for three today, Jeeves,' I said.

'Very good, sir.'

'You know, Jeeves, it's a bit thick. You remember my telling you about what Mr Glossop did to me that night at the Drones?'

'Yes, sir.'

'For months I have been cherishing dreams of getting a bit of my own back. And now, so far from crushing him into the dust, I've got to fill him and fiancée with rich food and generally rally round and be the good angel.'

'Life is like that, sir.'

'True, Jeeves. What have we here?' I asked, inspecting the tray.

'Kippered herrings, sir.'

'And I shouldn't wonder,' I said, for I was in thoughtful mood, 'if even herrings haven't troubles of their own.'

'Quite possibly, sir.'

'I mean, apart from getting kippered.'

'Yes, sir.'

'And so it goes on, Jeeves, so it goes on.'

I can't say I exactly saw eye to eye with young Tuppy in his admiration for the Bellinger female. Delivered on the mat at one-twenty-five, she proved to be an upstanding light-heavyweight of some thirty summers, with a commanding eye and a square chin which I, personally, would have steered clear of. She seemed to me a good deal like what Cleopatra would have been after going in too freely for the starches and cereals. I don't know why it is, but women who have anything to do with Opera, even if they're only studying for it, always appear to run to surplus poundage.

Tuppy, however, was obviously all for her. His whole demeanour, both before and during lunch, was that of one striving to be worthy of a noble soul. When Jeeves offered him a cocktail, he practically recoiled as from a serpent. It was terrible to see the change which love had effected in the man. The spectacle put me off my food.

At half-past two, the Bellinger left to go to a singing lesson. Tuppy trotted after her to the door, bleating and frisking a goodish bit, and then came back and looked at me in a goofy sort of way.

'Well, Bertie?'

'Well, what?'

'I mean, isn't she?'

'Oh, rather,' I said, humouring the poor fish.

'Wonderful eyes?'

'Oh, rather.'

'Wonderful figure?'

'Oh, quite.'

'Wonderful voice?'

Here I was able to intone the response with a little more heartiness. The Bellinger, at Tuppy's request, had sung us a few songs before digging in at the trough, and nobody could have denied that her pipes were in great shape. Plaster was still falling from the ceiling.

'Terrific,' I said.

Tuppy sighed, and, having helped himself to about four inches of whisky and one of soda, took a deep, refreshing draught.

'Ah!' he said. 'I needed that.'

'Why didn't you have it at lunch?'

'Well, it's this way,' said Tuppy. 'I have not actually ascertained what Cora's opinions are on the subject of the taking of slight snorts from time to time, but I thought it more prudent to lay off. The view I took was that laying off would seem to indicate the serious mind. It is touch-and-go, as you might say, at the moment, and the smallest thing may turn the scale.'

'What beats me is how on earth you expect to make her think you've got a mind at all – let alone a serious one.'

'I have my methods.'

'I bet they're rotten.'

'You do, do you?' said Tuppy warmly. 'Well, let me tell you, my lad, that that's exactly what they're anything but. I am handling this affair with consummate generalship. Do you remember Beefy Bingham who was at Oxford with us?'

'I ran into him only the other day. He's a parson now.'

'Yes. Down in the East End. Well, he runs a Lads' Club for the local toughs – you know the sort of thing – cocoa and backgammon in the reading-room and occasional clean, bright entertainments in the Oddfellows' Hall: and I've been helping him. I don't suppose I've passed an evening away from the backgammon board for weeks. Cora is extremely pleased. I've got her to promise to sing on Tuesday at Beefy's next clean, bright entertainment.'

'You have?'

'I absolutely have. And now mark my devilish ingenuity, Bertie. I'm going to sing, too.'

'Why do you suppose that's going to get you anywhere?'

'Because the way I intend to sing the song I intend to sing will prove to her that there are great deeps in my nature, whose existence she has not suspected. She will see that rough, unlettered audience wiping the tears out of its bally eyes and she will say to herself, "What ho! The old egg really has a soul!' For it is not one of your mouldy comic songs, Bertie. No low buffoonery of that sort for me. It is all about Angels being lonely and what not—'

I uttered a sharp cry.

'You don't mean you're going to sing "Sonny Boy"?'

'I jolly well do.'

I was shocked. Yes, dash it, I was shocked. You see, I held strong views on 'Sonny Boy'. I considered it a song only to be attempted by a few of the elect in the privacy of the bathroom. And the thought of it being murdered in open Oddfellows' Hall by a man who could treat a pal as young Tuppy had treated me that night at the Drones sickened me. Yes, sickened me.

I hadn't time, however, to express my horror and disgust, for at this juncture Jeeves came in.

'Mrs Travers has just rung up on the telephone, sir. She desired me to say that she will be calling to see you in a few minutes.'

'Contents noted, Jeeves,' I said. 'Now listen, Tuppy—'

I stopped. The fellow wasn't there.

'What have you done with him, Jeeves?' I asked.

'Mr Glossop has left, sir.'

'Left? How can he have left? He was sitting there—'

'That is the front door closing now, sir.'

'But what made him shoot off like that?'

'Possibly Mr Glossop did not wish to meet Mrs Travers, sir.'

'Why not?'

'I could not say, sir. But undoubtedly at the mention of Mrs Travers' name he rose very swiftly.'

'Strange, Jeeves.'

'Yes, sir.'

I turned to a subject of more moment.

'Jeeves,' I said, 'Mr Glossop proposes to sing "Sonny Boy" at an entertainment down in the East End next Tuesday.'

'Indeed, sir?'

'Before an audience consisting mainly of costermongers, with a sprinkling of whelk-stall owners, purveyors of blood-oranges, and minor pugilists.'

'Indeed, sir?'

'Make a note to remind me to be there. He will infallibly get the bird, and I want to witness his downfall.'

'Very good, sir.'

'And when Mrs Travers arrives, I shall be in the sitting-room.'

Those who know Bertram Wooster best are aware that in his journey through life he is impeded and generally snootered by about as scaly a platoon of aunts as was ever assembled. But there is one exception to the general ghastliness – viz., my Aunt Dahlia. She married old Tom Travers the year Bluebottle won the Cambridgeshire, and is one of the best. It is always a pleasure to me to chat with her, and it was with a courtly geniality that I rose to receive her as she sailed over the threshold at about two fifty-five.

She seemed somewhat perturbed, and snapped into the agenda without delay. Aunt Dahlia is one of those big, hearty women. She used to go in a lot for hunting, and she generally speaks as if she had just sighted a fox on a hillside half a mile away.

'Bertie,' she cried, in the manner of one encouraging a bevy of hounds to renewed efforts. 'I want your help.'

'And you shall have it, Aunt Dahlia,' I replied suavely. 'I can honestly say that there is no one to whom I would more readily do a good turn than yourself; no one to whom I am more delighted to be—'

'Less of it,' she begged, 'less of it. You know that friend of yours, young Glossop?'

'He's just been lunching here.'

'He has, has he? Well, I wish you'd poisoned his soup.'

'We didn't have soup. And, when you describe him as a friend of mine, I wouldn't quite say the term absolutely squared with the facts. Some time ago, one night when we had been dining together at the Drones—'

At this point Aunt Dahlia – a little brusquely, it seemed to me – said that she would rather wait for the story of my life till she could get it in book-form. I could see now that she was definitely not her usual sunny self, so I shelved my personal grievances and asked what was biting her.

'It's that young hound Glossop,' she said.

'What's he been doing?'

'Breaking Angela's heart.' (Angela. Daughter of above. My cousin. Quite a good egg.)

'Breaking Angela's heart?'

'Yes . . . Breaking . . . Angela's HEART!'

'You say he's breaking Angela's heart?'

She begged me in rather a feverish way to suspend the vaudeville cross-talk stuff.

'How's he doing that?' I asked.

'With his neglect. With his low, callous, double-crossing duplicity.'

'Duplicity is the word, Aunt Dahlia,' I said. 'In treating of young Tuppy Glossop, it springs naturally to the lips. Let me just tell you what he did to me one night at the Drones. We had finished dinner—'

'Ever since the beginning of the season, up till about three weeks ago, he was all over Angela. The sort of thing which, when I was a girl, we should have described as courting—'

'Or wooing?'

'Wooing or courting, whichever you like.'

'Whichever *you* like, Aunt Dahlia,' I said courteously.

'Well, anyway, he haunted the house, lapped up daily lunches, danced with her half the night, and so on, till naturally the poor kid, who's quite off her oats about him, took it for granted that it was only a question of time before he suggested that they should feed for life out of the same crib. And now he's gone and dropped her like a hot brick, and I hear he's infatuated with some girl he met at a Chelsea tea-party – a girl named – now, what was it?'

'Cora Bellinger.'

'How do you know?'

'She was lunching here today.'

'He brought her?'

'Yes.'

'What's she like?'

'Pretty massive. In shape, a bit on the lines of the Albert Hall.'

'Did he seem very fond of her?'

'Couldn't take his eyes off the chassis.'

'The modern young man,' said Aunt Dahlia, 'is a congenital idiot and wants a nurse to lead him by the hand and some strong attendant to kick him regularly at intervals of a quarter of an hour.'

I tried to point out the silver lining.

'If you ask me, Aunt Dahlia,' I said, 'I think Angela is well out of it. This Glossop is a tough baby. One of London's toughest. I was trying to tell you just now what he did to me one night at the Drones. First having got me in sporting mood with a bottle of the ripest, he betted I wouldn't swing myself across the swimming-bath by the ropes and rings. I knew I could do it on my head, so I took him on, exulting in the fun, so to speak. And when I'd done half the trip and was going as strong as dammit, I found he had looped the last rope back against the rail, leaving me no alternative but to drop into the depths and swim ashore in correct evening costume.'

'He did?'

'He certainly did. It was months ago, and I haven't got really dry yet. You wouldn't want your daughter to marry a man capable of a thing like that?'

'On the contrary, you restore my faith in the young hound. I see that there must be lots of good in him, after all. And I want this Bellinger business broken up, Bertie.'

'How?'

'I don't care how. Any way you please.'

'But what can I do?'

'Do? Why, put the whole thing before your man Jeeves. Jeeves will find a way. One of the most capable fellers I ever met. Put the thing squarely up to Jeeves and tell him to let his mind play round the topic.'

'There may be something in what you say, Aunt Dahlia,' I said thoughtfully.

'Of course there is,' said Aunt Dahlia. 'A little thing like this will be child's play to Jeeves. Get him working on it, and I'll look in tomorrow to hear the result.'

With which, she biffed off, and I summoned Jeeves to the presence.

'Jeeves,' I said, 'you have heard all?'

'Yes, sir.'

'I thought you would. My Aunt Dahlia has what you might call a carrying voice. Has it ever occurred to you that, if all other sources of income failed, she could make a good living calling the cattle home across the Sands of Dee?'

'I had not considered the point, sir, but no doubt you are right.'

'Well, how do we go? What is your reaction? I think we should do our best to help and assist.'

'Yes, sir.'

'I am fond of my Aunt Dahlia and I am fond of my cousin Angela. Fond of them both, if you get my drift. What the misguided girl finds to attract her in young Tuppy, I cannot say, Jeeves, and you cannot say. But apparently she loves the man – which shows it can be done, a thing I wouldn't have believed myself – and in pining away like—'

'Patience on a monument, sir.'

'Like Patience, as you very shrewdly remark, on a monument. So we must cluster round. Bend your brain to the problem, Jeeves. It is one that will tax you to the uttermost.'

Aunt Dahlia blew in on the morrow, and I rang the bell for Jeeves. He appeared looking brainier than one could have believed possible – sheer intellect shining from every feature – and I could see at once that the engine had been turning over.

'Speak, Jeeves,' I said.

'Very good, sir.'

'You have brooded?'

'Yes, sir.'

'With what success?'

'I have a plan, sir, which I fancy may produce satisfactory results.'

'Let's have it,' said Aunt Dahlia.

'In affairs of this description, madam, the first essential is to study the psychology of the individual.'

'The what of the individual?'

'The psychology, madam.'

'He means the psychology,' I said. 'And by psychology, Jeeves, you imply—?'

'The natures and dispositions of the principals in the matter, sir.'

'You mean, what they're like?'

'Precisely, sir.'

'Does he talk like this to you when you're alone, Bertie?' asked Aunt Dahlia.

'Sometimes. Occasionally. And, on the other hand, sometimes not. Proceed, Jeeves.'

'Well, sir, if I may say so, the thing that struck me most forcibly about Miss Bellinger when she was under my observation was that hers was a somewhat hard and intolerant nature. I could envisage Miss Bellinger applauding success. I could not so easily see her pitying and sympathizing with failure. Possibly you will recall, sir, her attitude when Mr Glossop endeavoured to light her cigarette with his automatic lighter? I thought I detected a certain impatience at his inability to produce the necessary flame.'

'True, Jeeves. She ticked him off.'

'Precisely, sir,'

'Let me get this straight,' said Aunt Dahlia, looking a bit fogged. 'You think that, if he goes on trying to light her cigarettes with his automatic lighter long enough, she will eventually get fed up and hand him the mitten? Is that the idea?'

'I merely mentioned the episode, madam, as an indication of Miss Bellinger's somewhat ruthless nature.'

'Ruthless,' I said, 'is right. The Bellinger is hard-boiled. Those eyes. That chin. I could read them. A woman of blood and iron, if ever there was one.'

'Precisely, sir. I think, therefore, that, should Miss Bellinger be a witness of Mr Glossop appearing to disadvantage in public, she would cease to entertain affection for him. In the event, for instance, of his failing to please the audience on Tuesday with his singing—'

I saw daylight.

'By Jove, Jeeves! You mean if he gets the bird, all will be off?'

'I shall be greatly surprised if such is not the case, sir.'

I shook my head.

'We cannot leave this thing to chance, Jeeves. Young Tuppy, singing "Sonny Boy", is the likeliest prospect for the bird that I can think of – but, no – you must see for yourself that we can't simply trust to luck.'

'We need not trust to luck, sir. I would suggest that you approach your friend, Mr Bingham, and volunteer your services as a performer at his forthcoming entertainment. It could readily be arranged that you sang immediately before Mr Glossop. I fancy, sir, that, if Mr Glossop were to sing "Sonny Boy" directly after you, too, had sung "Sonny Boy", the audience would respond satisfactorily. By the time Mr Glossop began to sing, they would have lost their taste for that particular song and would express their feelings warmly.'

'Jeeves,' said Aunt Dahlia, 'you're a marvel!'

'Thank you, madam.'

'Jeeves,' I said, 'you're an ass!'

'What do you mean, he's an ass?' said Aunt Dahlia hotly. 'I think it's the greatest scheme I ever heard.'

'Me sing "Sonny Boy" at Beefy Bingham's clean, bright entertainment? I can see myself!'

'You sing it daily in your bath, sir. Mr Wooster,' said Jeeves, turning to Aunt Dahlia, 'has a pleasant, light baritone—'

'I bet he has,' said Aunt Dahlia.

I froze the man with a look.

'Between singing "Sonny Boy" in one's bath, Jeeves, and singing it before a hall full of assorted blood-orange merchants and their young, there is a substantial difference.'

'Bertie,' said Aunt Dahlia, 'you'll sing, and like it!'

'I will not.'

'Bertie!'

'Nothing will induce—'

'Bertie,' said Aunt Dahlia firmly, 'you will sing "Sonny Boy" on Tuesday, the third *prox.*, and sing it like a lark at sunrise, or may an aunt's curse—'

'I won't!'

'Think of Angela!'

'Dash Angela!'

'Bertie!'

'No, I mean, hang it all!'

'You won't?'

'No, I won't.'

'That is your last word, is it?'

'It is. Once and for all, Aunt Dahlia, nothing will induce me to let out so much as a single note.'

And so that afternoon I sent a pre-paid wire to Beefy Bingham, offering my services in the cause, and by nightfall the thing was fixed up. I was billed to perform next but one after the intermission. Following me, came Tuppy. And, immediately after him, Miss Cora Bellinger, the well-known operatic soprano.

'Jeeves,' I said that evening – and I said it coldly – 'I shall be obliged if you will pop round to the nearest music-shop and procure me a copy of "Sonny Boy". It will now be necessary for me to learn both verse and refrain. Of the trouble and nervous strain which this will involve, I say nothing.'

'Very good, sir.'

'But this I do say—'

'I had better be starting immediately, sir, or the shop will be closed.'

'Ha!' I said.

And I meant it to sting.

Although I had steeled myself to the ordeal before me and had set out full of the calm, quiet courage which makes men do desperate deeds with careless smiles, I must admit that there was a moment, just after I had entered the Oddfellows' Hall at Bermondsey East and run an eye over the assembled pleasure-seekers, when it needed all the bulldog pluck of the Woosters to keep me from calling it a day and taking a cab back to civilization. The clean, bright entertainment was in full swing when I arrived, and somebody who looked as if he might be the local undertaker was reciting 'Gunga Din'. And the audience, though not actually chi-yiking in the full technical sense of the term, had a grim look which I didn't like at all. The mere sight of them gave me the sort of feeling Shadrach, Meshach and Abednego must have had when preparing to enter the burning, fiery furnace.

Scanning the multitude, it seemed to me that they were for the nonce suspending judgment. Did you ever tap on the door of one of those New York speakeasy places and see the grille snap back and a Face appear? There is one long, silent moment when its eyes are fixed on yours and all your past life seems to rise up before you. Then you say that you are a friend of Mr Zinzinheimer and he told you they would treat you right if you mentioned his name, and the strain relaxes. Well, these costermongers and whelk-stallers appeared to me to be looking just like that Face. Start something, they seemed to say, and they would know what to do about it. And I couldn't help feeling that my singing 'Sonny Boy' would come, in their opinion, under the head of starting something.

'A nice, full house, sir,' said a voice at my elbow. It was Jeeves, watching the proceedings with an indulgent eye.

'You here, Jeeves?' I said, coldly.

'Yes, sir. I have been present since the commencement.'

'Oh?' I said. 'Any casualties yet?'

'Sir?'

'You know what I mean, Jeeves,' I said sternly, 'and don't pretend you don't. Anybody got the bird yet?'

'Oh, no, sir.'

'I shall be the first, you think?'

'No, sir. I see no reason to expect such a misfortune. I anticipate that you will be well received.'

A sudden thought struck me.

'And you think everything will go according to plan?'

'Yes, sir.'

'Well, I don't,' I said. 'and I'll tell you why I don't. I've spotted a flaw in your beastly scheme.'

'A flaw, sir?'

'Yes. Do you suppose for a moment that, if when Mr Glossop hears me singing that dashed song, he'll come calmly on a minute after me and sing it too? Use your intelligence, Jeeves. He will perceive the chasm in his path and pause in time. He will back out and refuse to go on at all.'

'Mr Glossop will not hear you sing, sir. At my advice, he has stepped across the road to the Jug and Bottle, an establishment immediately opposite the hall, and he intends to remain there until it is time for him to appear on the platform.'

'Oh?' I said.

'If I might suggest it, sir, there is another house named the Goat and Grapes only a short distance down the street. I think it might be a judicious move—'

'If I were to put a bit of custom in their way.'

'It would ease the nervous strain of waiting, sir.'

I had not been feeling any too pleased with the man for having let me in for this ghastly binge, but at these words, I'm bound to say, my austerity softened a trifle. He was undoubtedly right. He had studied the psychology of the individual, and it had not led him astray. A quiet ten minutes at the Goat and Grapes was exactly what my system required. To buzz off there and inhale a couple of swift whisky-and-sodas was with Bertram Wooster the work of a moment.

The treatment worked like magic. What they had put into the stuff, besides vitriol, I could not have said; but it completely altered my outlook on life. That curious, gulpy feeling passed. I was no longer conscious of the sagging sensation at the knees. The limbs ceased to quiver gently, the tongue became loosened in its socket, and the backbone stiffened. Pausing merely to order and swallow another of the same, I bade the barmaid a cheery good night, nodded affably to one or two fellows in the bar whose faces I liked, and came prancing back to the hall, ready for anything.

And shortly afterwards I was on the platform with about a million bulging eyes goggling up at me. There was a rummy sort of buzzing in my ears, and then through the buzzing I heard the sound of a piano starting to tinkle: and, commending my soul to God, I took a good, long breath and charged in.

Well, it was a close thing. The whole incident is a bit blurred, but I seem to recollect a kind of murmur as I hit the refrain. I thought at the time it was an attempt on the part of the many-headed to join in the chorus, and at the moment it rather encouraged me. I passed the thing over the larynx with all the vim at my disposal, hit the high note, and off gracefully into the wings. I didn't come on again to take a bow. I just receded and oiled round to where Jeeves awaited me among the standees at the back.

'Well, Jeeves,' I said, anchoring myself at his side and brushing the honest sweat from the brow, 'they didn't rush the platform.'

'No, sir.'

'But you can spread it about that that's the last time I perform outside my bath. My swan-song, Jeeves. Anybody who wants to hear me in future must present himself at the bathroom door and shove his ear against the keyhole. I maybe wrong, but it seemed to me that towards the end they were hotting up a trifle. The bird was hovering in the air. I could hear the beating of its wings.'

'I did detect a certain restlessness, sir, in the audience. I fancy they has lost their taste for that particular melody.'

'Eh?'

'I should have informed you earlier, sir, that the song had already been sung twice before you arrived.'

'What!'

'Yes, sir. Once by a lady and once by a gentleman. It is a very popular song, sir.'

I gaped at the man. That, with this knowledge, he could calmly have allowed the young master to step straight into the jaws of death, so to speak, paralysed me. It seemed to show that the old feudal spirit had passed away altogether. I was about to give him my views on the matter in no uncertain fashion, when I was stopped by the spectacle of young Tuppy lurching on to the platform.

Young Tuppy had the unmistakable air of a man who has recently been round to the Jug and Bottle. A few cheery cries of welcome, presumably from some of his backgammon-playing pals who felt that blood was thicker than water, had the effect of causing the genial smile on his face to widen till it nearly met at the back. He was plainly feeling about as good as a man can feel and still remain on his feet. He waved a kindly hand to his supporters, and bowed in a regal sort of manner, rather like an Eastern monarch acknowledging the plaudits of the mob.

Then the female at the piano struck up the opening bars of 'Sonny Boy', and Tuppy swelled like a balloon, clasped his hands together, rolled his eyes up at the ceiling in a manner denoting Soul, and began.

I think the populace was too stunned for the moment to take immediate steps. It may seem incredible, but I give you my word that young Tuppy got right through the verse without so much as a murmur. Then they all seemed to pull themselves together.

A costermonger, roused, is a terrible thing. I had never seen the proletariat really stirred before, and I'm bound to say it rather awed me. I mean, it gave you some idea of what it must have been like during the French Revolution. From every corner of the hall there proceeded simultaneously the sort of noise which you hear, they tell me, at one of those East End boxing places when the referee disqualifies the popular favourite and makes the quick dash for life. And then they passed beyond mere words and began to introduce the vegetable motive.

I don't know why, but somehow I had got it into my head that the first thing thrown at Tuppy would be a potato. One gets these fancies. It was, however, as a matter of fact, a banana, and I saw in an instant that the choice had been made by wiser heads than mine. These blokes who have grown up from childhood in the knowledge of how to treat a dramatic entertainment that doesn't please them are aware by a sort of instinct just what to do for the best, and the moment I saw the banana splash on Tuppy's shirt-front I realized how infinitely more effective and artistic it was than any potato could have been.

Not that the potato school of thought had not also its supporters.

As the proceedings warmed up, I noticed several intelligent-looking fellows who threw nothing else.

The effect on young Tuppy was rather remarkable. His eyes bulged and his hair seemed to stand up, and yet his mouth went on opening and shutting, and you could see that in a dazed, automatic way he was still singing 'Sonny Boy'. Then, coming out of his trance, he began to pull for the shore with some rapidity. The last seen of him, he was beating a tomato to the exit by a short head.

Presently the tumult and the shouting died. I turned to Jeeves.

'Painful, Jeeves,' I said. 'But what would you?'

'Yes, sir.'

'The surgeon's knife, what?'

'Precisely, sir.'

'Well, with this happening beneath her eyes, I think we may definitely consider the Glossop-Bellinger romance off.'

'Yes, sir.'

At this point old Beefy Bingham came out on to the platform.

'Ladies and gentlemen,' said old Beefy.

I supposed that he was about to rebuke his flock for the recent expression of feeling. But such was not the case. No doubt he was accustomed by now to the wholesome give-and-take of these clean, bright entertainments and had ceased to think it worthwhile to make any comment when there was a certain liveliness.

'Ladies and gentlemen,' said old Beefy, 'the next item on the programme was to have been Songs by Miss Cora Bellinger, the well-known operatic soprano. I have just received a telephone-message from Miss Bellinger, saying that her car has broken down. She is, however, on her way here in a cab and will arrive shortly. Meanwhile, our friend Mr Enoch Simpson will recite "Dangerous Dan McGrew".'

I clutched at Jeeves.

'Jeeves! You heard?'

'Yes, sir.'

'She wasn't there!'

'No, sir.'

'She saw nothing of Tuppy's Waterloo.'

'No, sir.'

'The whole bally scheme has blown a fuse.'

'Yes, sir.'

'Come, Jeeves,' I said, and those standing by wondered, no doubt, what had caused that clean-cut face to grow so pale and set. 'I have been subjected to a nervous strain unparalleled since the days of the early Martyrs. I have lost pounds in weight and permanently injured my entire system. I have gone through an ordeal, the recollection of which will make me wake up screaming in the night for months to come. And all for nothing. Let us go.'

'If you have no objection, sir, I would like to witness the remainder of the entertainment.'

'Suit yourself, Jeeves,' I said moodily. 'Personally, my heart is dead and I am going to look in at the Goat and Grapes for another of their cyanide specials and then home.'

It must have been about half-past ten, and I was in the old sitting-room sombrely sucking down a more or less final restorative, when the front door bell rang, and there on the mat was young Tuppy. He looked like a man who has passed through some great experience and stood face to face with his soul. He had the beginnings of a black eye.

'Oh, hullo, Bertie,' said young Tuppy.

He came in, and hovered about the mantelpiece as if he were looking for things to fiddle with and break.

'I've just been singing at Beefy Bingham's entertainment,' he said after a pause.

'Oh?' I said. 'How did you go?'

'Like a breeze,' said young Tuppy. 'Held them spell-bound.'

'Knocked 'em, eh?'

'Cold,' said young Tuppy. 'Not a dry eye.'

And this, mark you, a man who had had a good upbringing and had, no doubt, spent years at his mother's knee being taught to tell the truth.

'I suppose Miss Bellinger is pleased?'

'Oh, yes. Delighted.'

'So now everything's all right?'

'Oh, quite.'

Tuppy paused.

'On the other hand, Bertie—'

'Yes?'

'Well, I've been thinking things over. Somehow I don't believe Miss Bellinger is the mate for me after all.'

'You don't?'

'No, I don't.'

'Why don't you?'

'Oh, I don't know. These things sort of flash on you. I respect Miss Bellinger, Bertie. I admire her. But – er – well, I can't help feeling now that a sweet, gentle girl – er – like your cousin Angela, for instance, Bertie – would – er – in fact – well, what I came round for was to ask if you would phone Angela and find out how she reacts to the idea of coming out with me tonight to the Berkeley for a segment of supper and a spot of dancing.'

'Go ahead. There's the phone.'

'No, I'd rather you asked her, Bertie. What with one thing and another, if you paved the way – You see, there's just a chance that she may be – I mean, you know how misunderstandings occur – and – well, what I'm driving at, Bertie, old man, is that I'd rather you surged round and did a bit of paving, if you don't mind.'

I went to the phone and called up Aunt Dahlia's.

'She says come right along,' I said.

'Tell her,' said Tuppy in a devout sort of voice, 'that I will be with her in something under a couple of ticks.'

He had barely biffed, when I heard a click in the keyhole and a soft padding in the passage without.

'Jeeves,' I called.

'Sir?' said Jeeves, manifesting himself.

'Jeeves, a remarkably rummy thing has happened. Mr Glossop has just been here. He tells me that it is all off between him and Miss Bellinger.'

'Yes, sir.'

'You don't seem surprised.'

'No, sir. I confess I had anticipated some such eventuality.'

'Eh? What gave you that idea?'

'It came to me, sir, when I observed Miss Bellinger strike Mr Glossop in the eye.'

'Strike him!'

'Yes, sir.'

'In the eye?'

'The right eye, sir.'

I clutched the brow.

'What on earth made her do that?'

'I fancy she was a little upset, sir, at the reception accorded to her singing.'

'Great Scott! Don't tell me she got the bird, too?'

'Yes, sir.'

'But why? She's got a red-hot voice.'

'Yes, sir. But I think the audience resented her choice of a song.'

'Jeeves!' Reason was beginning to do a bit of tottering on its throne. 'You aren't going to stand there and tell me that Miss Bellinger sang "Sonny Boy", too!'

'Yes, sir. And – rashly, in my opinion – brought a large doll on to the platform to sing it to. The audience affected to mistake it for a ventriloquist's dummy, and there was some little disturbance.'

'But, Jeeves, what a coincidence!'

'Not altogether, sir. I ventured to take the liberty of accosting Miss Bellinger on her arrival at the hall and recalling myself to her recollection. I then said that Mr Glossop had asked me to request her that as a particular favour to him – the song being a favourite of his – she would sing "Sonny Boy". And when she found that you and Mr Glossop had also sung the song immediately before her, I rather fancy that she supposed that she had been made the victim of a practical pleasantry by Mr Glossop. Will there be anything further, sir?'

'No, thanks.'

'Good night, sir.'

'Good night, Jeeves,' I said reverently.

BRIEF EXTRACTS

From A Gentleman of Leisure

THE main smoking-room of the Strollers' Club had been filling for the last half-hour, and was now nearly full. In many ways the Strollers', though not the most magnificent, is the pleasantest club in New York. Its ideals are those of the Savage Club – comfort without pomp – and it is given over after eleven o'clock at night mainly to the Stage. Everybody is young, clean-shaven, and full of conversation – and the conversation strikes a purely professional note.

Everybody in the room on this July night had come from the theatre. Most of those present had been acting, but a certain number had been to the opening performance of the latest better-than-'Raffles' play. There had been something of a boom that season in dramas whose heroes appealed to the public more pleasantly across the footlights than they might have done in real life. In the play which had opened tonight Arthur Mifflin, an exemplary young man off the stage, had been warmly applauded for a series of actions which, performed anywhere except in the theatre, would certainly have debarred him from remaining a member of the Strollers' or any other club. In faultless evening dress, with a debonair smile on his face, he had broken open a safe, stolen bonds and jewellery to a large amount, and escaped without a blush of shame via the window. He had foiled a detective through four acts and held up a band of pursuers with a revolver. A large audience had intimated complete approval throughout.

'It's a hit all right,' said somebody through the smoke.

'These imitation "Raffles" plays always are,' grumbled Willett, who played bluff fathers in musical comedy. 'A few years ago they would have been scared to death of putting on a show with a criminal hero. Now, it seems to me, the public doesn't want anything else. Not that they know what they do want,' he concluded mournfully.

The Belle of Boulogne, in which Willett sustained the role of Cyrus K. Higgs, a Chicago millionaire, was slowly fading away on a diet of free passes, and this possibly prejudiced him.

Raikes, the character-actor, changed the subject. If Willett once got started on the wrongs of the ill-fated *Belle*, general conversation would become impossible. Willett, denouncing the stupidity of the public, was purely a monologue artiste.

From The Girl in Blue

A girl who has brought a strange man home to meet her mother, rather in the tentative spirit of a dog bringing a bone into a drawing-room, naturally seeks the earliest opportunity of learning the latter's opinion of him. Vera, having seen Homer out at the end of his visit, returned to where Dame Flora Faye reclined in her armchair, and Dame Flora looked up at her from its depths with an enquiring, 'Well?'

'Just what I was going to say to you,' said Vera.

'Meaning what did I think of Mr Pyle?'

'Exactly.'

'Well, I'll tell you, my poppet.'

Surprisingly in a woman who in the course of a long career had spread more nervous breakdown among directors, leading men, supporting players and assistant stage managers than any other female star of her weight and age, Dame Flora's vocal delivery was soft and gentle. She had never been one of those empresses of stormy emotion so popular at one time on the silent screen who raged and bellowed; she got her effects more subtly. One of her playwrights, speaking from the nursing home where he was recovering from mental exhaustion, had once described her as the vulture who cooed like a dove.

'It depends,' she continued, 'on what aspect of him you have in mind. If you refer to his looks, I doubt if he will ever win a beauty contest, even a seaside one. On the other hand, he is an American corporation lawyer, and one of the first lessons we learn in life is that there is no such thing as an American corporation lawyer who does not wear hundred-dollar bills next his skin summer and winter. I should imagine that when Mr Pyle is called upon to act for a company in its suit against another company, his clients consider themselves lucky if they come out of it after paying his fee with enough to buy a frugal lunch next day. Give me another cup of tea, dearie, and pass me those little cakes with pink sugar on top.'

'They're fattening.'

'Everything in life that's any fun, as somebody wisely observed, is either immoral, illegal or fattening. Returning to your question, I think

I know why you asked it. You did not fail to notice that you had made a marked impression on this hand across the sea. He couldn't take his eyes off you, and I'm not surprised, because you're the most beautiful thing on earth, my lamb. So you're saying to yourself "Where do I go from here?", and you naturally come to mother for advice. I could give it to you better if I knew how matters are between you and this ginger-headed pavement artist you've got engaged to. As I understand it, he has money coming to him, but it's in trust and his trustee won't give it up and you very prudently refuse to marry him till the deadlock melts, if that's what deadlocks do. I may be thinking of ice packs. You're in the position of a manager who has a show that's a turkey at the box office, and he thinks "Shall I put up the fortnight's notice or shall I carry on on the chance of business improving?" If he knows what's good for him, he puts up the notice, and I advise you to do the same, my dream child.'

'It isn't quite like that, mother. Gerald is getting his money today.'

'How do you know?'

'I told him what to do. I've been studying up the legal end of the thing. It's too long to explain, but it all turns on the trust being terminable. It is terminable, so Mr Scrope won't have a leg to stand on. Gerald was lunching with him today, so by now everything must be settled.'

'I see. But even so, what on earth do you want with him when you can have this excellent corporation lawyer with about a hundred times as much? I wouldn't call Mrs Homer Pyle a euphonious name, but I strongly urge you to take it on. I'm not asking you to love him, mind you. I nearly married for love when I was young and foolish, but I came out of the ether in time and saw there was nothing in it. Mutual respect is what matters in marriage. Pyle respects you, doesn't he? Of course he does. And don't tell me you don't respect someone who makes his sort of money. And you'll be together in Brussels for I don't know how long. And you get lovelier every day. And a man who writes little poems can't have any sales resistance. Why, the thing's in the bag. The scenario couldn't read better if it had been turned out in Hollywood with six supervisors and fifteen writers working on it. Don't wait, honeychile. Get on the phone and tell your French polisher it's all off. I never could see what you saw in him in the first place.'

No daughter could have failed to be stirred by such admirable counsel coming from mother who knew best, and Vera was plainly swayed. Nevertheless, she was dubious.

'But how can I? I wouldn't know what to say.'

Dame Flora smiled a gentle smile. Rising from her chair, she put an arm round her little girl and gave her a kiss, as she had done to a dozen daughters in a dozen productions since the march of time had forced her to play mothers.

'Don't worry your pretty head about that, my pet. I'll do the ringing up. You say that you would be at a loss for words. I won't. Words are the last thing I'm ever at a loss for. I know exactly how the scene should go. I tell him you think he's weak, and you must have a strong man for a husband, because you need someone to guide you and make decisions for you. So-and-so I'll say and so-and-so and so-and-so, and I'll wind up by telling him you will always look on him as a dear, dear friend and will follow his career with considerable interest. Any questions?'

'Oh, mother!' said Vera.

Reaching home, Gerald sat down and continued to ponder. He recalled a musical comedy in which the comedian, reminded by the soubrette that they were engaged to be married, had said, 'I forgot to tell you about that, it's off', and he was thinking wistfully that they managed these things better in musical comedy, when the telephone rang and over the wire came floating the lovely voice of the Dame of the British Empire who, he greatly feared, was about to become his mother-in-law. It surprised him a good deal, for she was not in the habit of chatting with him over the telephone. Indeed, she had always given him the impression that it revolted her to talk to him at all.

'Gerald? Oh, good afternoon, Gerald. I hope I am not interrupting your work?'

'No, I never work on Wednesday.'

'How I envy you. I am resting at the moment, but as a rule the Wednesday matinée is the curse of my life. Did you ever hear the story of the actress who was walking past the fish shop and saw all those fishy eyes staring at her? "That reminds me," she said, "I have a Wednesday matinée." But I didn't ring you up to tell you funny stories. My mission is a serious one. I have just been seeing Vera off to Brussels and she gave me a most unpleasant task to perform.'

'Oh, I'm sorry.'

'I'm afraid you will be even sorrier when you hear what it is,' said Dame Flora, cooing like a turtledove in springtime.

Dame Flora was a woman of her word. She had promised her ewe lamb that she would get her betrothed on the telephone and make it clear to him that his idea that wedding bells were going to ring out was a mistaken one, and this she proceeded to do. It was a masterly performance, for which she would have been justified in charging him the price of an orchestra stall.

'I know you will understand, Gerald,' she concluded. 'And Vera wants me to tell you that she will always look on you as a dear, dear friend. Goodbye, Gerald, goodbye, goodbye.'

The receiver shook in Jerry's hand as he replaced it. In the course of her remarks Dame Flora had stressed the fact that the ewe lamb considered him weak, and weak was what he was feeling, if weak is not too weak a word. Boneless is more the one a stylist like Gustave Flaubert would have chosen, though being French he would have used whatever the French is for boneless – *étourdit* perhaps, or something like that.